IG Macdonald

1972

ALGEBRAIC NUMBER THEORY

SERGE LANG
Columbia University, New York, New York

ADDISON-WESLEY PUBLISHING COMPANY, INC.
Reading, Massachusetts · Menlo Park, California · London · Don Mills, Ontario

This book is in the

ADDISON-WESLEY SERIES IN MATHEMATICS

LYNN H. LOOMIS
Consulting Editor

AMS 1968 Subject Classifications 1065, 1250

Printed in the United States of America. Published simultaneously in Canada. Library of Congress Catalog Card No. 73-111952.

Foreword

The present book gives an exposition of the classical basic algebraic and analytic number theory and supersedes my *Algebraic Numbers*, including much more material, e.g. the class field theory on which I make further comments at the appropriate place later.

For different points of view, the reader is encouraged to read the collection of papers from the Brighton Symposium (edited by Cassels-Frohlich), the Artin-Tate notes on class field theory, Weil's book on *Basic Number Theory*, Borevich-Shafarevich's *Number Theory*, and also older books like those of Weber, Hasse, Hecke, and Hilbert's *Zahlbericht*. It seems that over the years, everything that has been done has proved useful, theoretically or as examples, for the further development of the theory. Old, and seemingly isolated special cases have continuously acquired renewed significance, often after half a century or more.

The point of view taken here is principally global, and we deal with local fields only incidentally. For a more complete treatment of these, cf. Serre's book *Corps Locaux*. There is much to be said for a direct global approach to number fields. Stylistically, I have intermingled the ideal and idelic approaches without prejudice for either. I also include two proofs of the functional equation for the zeta function, to acquaint the reader with different techniques (in some sense equivalent, but in another sense, suggestive of very different moods). Even though a reader will prefer some techniques over alternative ones, it is important at least that he should be aware of all the possibilities.

New York
June 1970

SERGE LANG

Prerequisites

Chapters I through VII are self-contained, assuming only elementary algebra, say at the level of Galois theory.

Some of the chapters on analytic number theory assume some analysis. Chapter XIV assumes Fourier analysis on locally compact groups. Chapters XV through XVII assume only standard analytical facts (we even prove some of them), except for one allusion to the Plancherel formula in Chapter XVII.

In the course of the Brauer-Siegel theorem, we use the conductor-discriminant formula, for which we refer to Artin-Tate where a detailed proof is given. At that point, the use of this theorem is highly technical, and is due to the fact that one does not know that the zeros of the zeta function don't occur in a small interval to the left of 1. If one knew this, the proof would become only a page long, and the L-series would not be needed at all. We give Siegel's original proof for that in Chapter XIII.

My *Algebra* gives more than enough background for the present book. In fact, *Algebra* already contains a good part of the theory of integral extensions, and valuation theory, redone here in Chapters I and II. Furthermore, *Algebra* also contains whatever will be needed of group representation theory, used in a couple of isolated instances for applications of the class field theory, or to the Brauer-Siegel theorem.

The word **ring** will always mean commutative ring without zero divisors and with unit element (unless otherwise specified).

If K is a field, then K^* denotes its multiplicative group, and $\overline{K}$ its algebraic closure. Occasionally, a bar is also used to denote reduction modulo a prime ideal.

We use the o and O notation. If f, g are two functions of a real variable, and g is always $\geqq 0$, we write $f = O(g)$ if there exists a constant $C > 0$ such that $|f(x)| \leqq Cg(x)$ for all sufficiently large x. We write $f = o(g)$ if $\lim_{x\to\infty} f(x)/g(x) = 0$. We write $f \sim g$ if $\lim_{x\to\infty} f(x)/g(x) = 1$.

Contents

Part One
General Basic Theory

Chapter I

Algebraic Integers

Chapter II

Completions

Chapter III

The Different and Discriminant

CHAPTER IV

Cyclotomic Fields

CHAPTER V

Parallelotopes

CHAPTER VI

The Ideal Function

CHAPTER VII

Ideles and Adeles

CHAPTER VIII

Elementary Properties of the Zeta Function and *L*-series

Part Two
Class Field Theory

Chapter IX

Norm Index Computations

Chapter X

The Artin Symbol, Reciprocity Law, and Class Field Theory

Chapter XI

The Existence Theorem and Local Class Field Theory

Chapter XII

L-series Again

Part Three
Analytic Theory

Chapter XIII

Functional Equation of the Zeta Function, Hecke's Proof

Chapter XIV

Functional Equation, Tate's Thesis

Chapter XV

Density of Primes and Tauberian Theorem

Chapter XVI

The Brauer-Siegel Theorem

CHAPTER XVII

Explicit Formulas

PART ONE

BASIC THEORY

CHAPTER I

Algebraic Integers

This chapter describes the basic aspects of the ring of algebraic integers in a number field (always assumed to be of finite degree over the rational numbers $\mathbf{Q}$). This includes the general prime ideal structure.

Some proofs are given in a more general context, but only when they could not be made shorter by specializing the hypothesis to the concrete situation we have in mind. It is not our intention to write a treatise on commutative algebra.

§1. *Localization*

Let A be a ring. By a **multiplicative subset** of A we mean a subset containing 1 and such that, whenever two elements x, y lie in the subset, then so does the product xy. We shall also assume throughout that 0 does not lie in the subset.

Let K be the quotient field of A, and let S be a multiplicative subset of A. By $S^{-1}A$ we shall denote the set of quotients x/s with x in A and s in S. It is a ring, and A has a canonical inclusion in $S^{-1}A$.

If M is an A-module contained in some field L (containing K), then $S^{-1}M$ denotes the set of elements v/s with $v \in M$ and $s \in S$. Then $S^{-1}M$ is an $S^{-1}A$-module in the obvious way. We shall sometimes consider the case when M is a ring containing A as subring.

Let $\mathfrak{p}$ be a prime ideal of A (by definition, $\mathfrak{p} \neq A$). Then the complement of $\mathfrak{p}$ in A, denoted by $A - \mathfrak{p}$, is a multiplicative subset $S = S_{\mathfrak{p}}$ of A, and we shall denote $S^{-1}A$ by $A_{\mathfrak{p}}$.

A **local ring** is a ring which has a unique maximal ideal. If $\mathfrak{o}$ is such a ring, and $\mathfrak{m}$ its maximal ideal, then any element x of $\mathfrak{o}$ not lying in $\mathfrak{m}$ must be a unit, because otherwise, the principal ideal $x\mathfrak{o}$ would be contained in a maximal ideal unequal to $\mathfrak{m}$. Thus $\mathfrak{m}$ is the set of non-units of $\mathfrak{o}$.

The ring $A_\mathfrak{p}$ defined above is a local ring. As can be verified at once, its maximal ideal $\mathfrak{m}_\mathfrak{p}$ consists of the quotients x/s, with x in $\mathfrak{p}$ and s in A but not in $\mathfrak{p}$.

We observe that $\mathfrak{m}_\mathfrak{p} \cap A = \mathfrak{p}$. The inclusion $\supset$ is clear. Conversely, if an element $y = x/s$ lies in $\mathfrak{m}_\mathfrak{p} \cap A$ with $x \in \mathfrak{p}$ and $s \in S$, then $x = sy \in \mathfrak{p}$ and $s \notin \mathfrak{p}$. Hence $y \in \mathfrak{p}$.

Let A be a ring and S a multiplicative subset. Let $\mathfrak{a}'$ be an ideal of $S^{-1}A$. Then

$$\mathfrak{a}' = S^{-1}(\mathfrak{a}' \cap A).$$

The inclusion $\supset$ is clear. Conversely, let $x \in \mathfrak{a}'$. Write $x = a/s$ with some $a \in A$ and $s \in S$. Then $sx \in \mathfrak{a}' \cap A$, whence $x \in S^{-1}(\mathfrak{a}' \cap A)$.

Under multiplication by S^{-1}, the multiplicative system of ideals of A is mapped homomorphically onto the multiplicative system of ideals of $S^{-1}A$. This is another way of stating what we have just proved. If $\mathfrak{a}$ is an ideal of A and $S^{-1}\mathfrak{a}$ is the unit ideal, then it is clear that $\mathfrak{a} \cap S$ is not empty, or as we shall also say, $\mathfrak{a}$ **meets** S.

§2. *Integral closure*

Let A be a ring and x an element of some field L containing A. We shall say that x is **integral** over A if either one of the following conditions is satisfied.

INT 1. *There exists a finitely generated non-zero A-module $M \subset L$ such that $xM \subset M$.*

INT 2. *The element x satisfies an equation*

$$x^n + a_{n-1}x^{n-1} + \cdots + a_0 = 0$$

with coefficients $a_i \in A$, and an integer $n \geqq 1$. (Such an equation will be called an **integral equation.**)

The two conditions are actually equivalent. Indeed, assume **INT 2.** The module M generated by $1, x, \ldots, x^{n-1}$ is mapped into itself by the element x. Conversely, assume there exists $M = \langle v_1, \ldots, v_n \rangle$ such that $xM \subset M$, and $M \neq 0$. Then

$$\begin{aligned} xv_1 &= a_{11}v_1 + \cdots + a_{1n}v_n \\ &\vdots \\ xv_n &= a_{n1}v_1 + \cdots + a_{nn}v_n \end{aligned}$$

with coefficients a_{ij} in A. Transposing $xv_1, \ldots, xv_n$ to the right-hand side of these equations, we conclude that the determinant

$$\begin{vmatrix} x - a_{11} & & & -a_{ij} \\ & x - a_{22} & & \\ -a_{ij} & & \ddots & \\ & & & x - a_{nn} \end{vmatrix}$$

is equal to 0. In this way we get an integral equation for x over A.

Proposition 1. *Let A be a ring, K its quotient field, and x algebraic over K. Then there exists an element $c \neq 0$ of A such that cx is integral over A.*

Proof. There exists an equation

$$a_n x^n + \cdots + a_0 = 0$$

with $a_i \in A$ and $a_n \neq 0$. Multiply it by a_n^{n-1}. Then

$$(a_n x)^n + \cdots + a_0 a_n^{n-1} = 0$$

is an integral equation for $a_n x$ over A.

Let B be a ring containing A. We shall say that B is **integral** over A if every element of B is integral over A.

Proposition 2. *If B is integral over A and finitely generated as an A-algebra, then B is a finitely generated A-module.*

Proof. We may prove this by induction on the number of ring generators, and thus we may assume that $B = A[x]$ for some element x integral over A. But we have already seen that our assertion is true in that case.

Proposition 3. *Let $A \subset B \subset C$ be three rings. If B is integral over A and C is integral over B, then C is integral over A.*

Proof. Let $x \in C$. Then x satisfies an integral equation

$$x^n + b_{n-1}x^{n-1} + \cdots + b_0 = 0$$

with $b_i \in B$. Let $B_1 = A[b_0, \ldots, b_{n-1}]$. Then B_1 is a finitely generated A-module by Proposition 2, and $B_1[x]$ is a finitely generated B_1-module, whence a finitely generated A-module. Since multiplication by x maps $B_1[x]$ into itself, it follows that x is integral over A.

Proposition 4. *Let $A \subset B$ be two rings, and B integral over A. Let σ be a homomorphism of B. Then $\sigma(B)$ is integral over $\sigma(A)$.*

Proof. Apply σ to an integral equation satisfied by any element x of B. It will be an integral equation for $\sigma(x)$ over $\sigma(A)$.

The above proposition is used frequently when σ is an isomorphism and is particularly useful in Galois theory.

Proposition 5. *Let A be a ring contained in a field L. Let B be the set of elements of L which are integral over A. Then B is a ring, called the* **integral closure** *of A in L.*

Proof. Let x, y lie in B, and let M, N be two finitely generated A-modules such that $xM \subset M$ and $yN \subset N$. Then MN is finitely generated, and is mapped into itself by multiplication with $x \pm y$ and xy.

Corollary. *Let A be a ring, K its quotient field, and L a finite separable extension of K. Let x be an element of L which is integral over A. Then the norm and trace of x from L to K are integral over A, and so are the coefficients of the irreducible polynomial satisfied by x over K.*

Proof. For each isomorphism σ of L over K, σx is integral over A. Since the norm is the product of σx over all such σ, and the trace is the sum of σx over all such σ, it follows that they are integral over A. Similarly, the coefficients of the irreducible polynomial are obtained from the elementary symmetric functions of the σx, and are therefore integral over A.

A ring A is said to be **integrally closed in a field** L if every element of L which is integral over A in fact lies in A. It is said to be **integrally closed** if it is integrally closed in its quotient field.

Proposition 6. *Let A be a Noetherian ring, integrally closed. Let L be a finite separable extension of its quotient field K. Then the integral closure of A in L is finitely generated over A.*

Proof. It will suffice to show that the integral closure of A is contained in a finitely generated A-module, because A is assumed to be Noetherian.

Let $w_1, \ldots, w_n$ be a linear basis of L over K. After multiplying each w_i by a suitable element of A, we may assume without loss of generality that the w_i are integral over A (Proposition 1). The trace Tr from L to K is a K-linear map of L into K, and is non-degenerate (i.e. there exists an element $x \in L$ such that $\mathrm{Tr}(x) \neq 0$). If α is a non-zero element of L, then the function $\mathrm{Tr}(\alpha x)$ on L is an element of the dual space of L (as K-vector space), and induces a homomorphism of L into its dual space. Since the kernel is trivial, it follows that L is isomorphic to its dual under the bilinear form

$$(x, y) \mapsto \mathrm{Tr}(xy).$$

Let $w'_1, \ldots, w'_n$ be the dual basis of $w_1, \ldots, w_n$, so that

$$\operatorname{Tr}(w'_i w_j) = \delta_{ij}.$$

Let $c \neq 0$ be an element of A such that cw'_i is integral over A. Let z be in L, integral over A. Then zcw'_i is integral over A, and so is $\operatorname{Tr}(czw'_i)$ for each i. If we write

$$z = b_1 w_1 + \cdots + b_n w_n$$

with coefficients $b_i \in K$, then

$$\operatorname{Tr}(czw'_i) = cb_i,$$

and $cb_i \in A$ because A is integrally closed. Hence z is contained in

$$Ac^{-1}w_1 + \cdots + Ac^{-1}w_n.$$

Since z was selected arbitrarily in the integral closure of A in L, it follows that this integral closure is contained in a finitely generated A-module, and our proof is finished.

Proposition 7. *If A is a unique factorization domain, then A is integrally closed.*

Proof. Suppose that there exists a quotient a/b with $a, b \in A$ which is integral over A, and a prime element p in A which divides b but not a. We have, for some integer $n \geqq 1$,

$$(a/b)^n + a_{n-1}(a/b)^{n-1} + \cdots + a_0 = 0,$$

whence

$$a^n + a_{n-1}ba^{n-1} + \cdots + a_0 b^n = 0.$$

Since p divides b, it must divide a^n, and hence must divide a, contradiction.

Theorem 1. *Let A be a principal ideal ring, and L a finite separable extension of its quotient field, of degree n. Let B be the integral closure of A in L. Then B is a free module of rank n over A.*

Proof. As a module over A, the integral closure is torsion-free, and by the general theory of principal ideal rings, any torsion-free finitely generated module is in fact a free module. It is obvious that the rank is equal to the degree $[L:K]$.

Theorem 1 is applied to the ring of ordinary integers $\mathbf{Z}$. A finite extension of the rational numbers $\mathbf{Q}$ is called a **number field.** The integral closure of $\mathbf{Z}$ in a number field K is called the ring of **algebraic integers** of that field, and is denoted by $\mathfrak{o}_K$.

Proposition 8. *Let A be a subring of a ring B, integral over A. Let S be a multiplicative subset of A. Then $S^{-1}B$ is integral over $S^{-1}A$. If A is integrally closed, then $S^{-1}A$ is integrally closed.*

Proof. If $x \in B$ and $s \in S$, and if M is a finitely generated A-module such that $xM \subset M$, then $S^{-1}M$ is a finitely generated $S^{-1}A$-module which is mapped into itself by $s^{-1}x$, so that $s^{-1}x$ is integral over $S^{-1}A$. As to the second assertion, let x be integral over $S^{-1}A$, with x in the quotient field of A. We have an equation

$$x^n + \frac{b_{n-1}}{s_{n-1}} x^{n-1} + \cdots + \frac{b_0}{s_0} = 0,$$

$b_i \in A$ and $s_i \in S$. Thus there exists an element $s \in S$ such that sx is integral over A, hence lies in A. This proves that x lies in $S^{-1}A$.

Corollary. *If B is the integral closure of A in some field extension L of the quotient field of A, then $S^{-1}B$ is the integral closure of $S^{-1}A$ in L.*

§3. *Prime ideals*

Let $\mathfrak{p}$ be a prime ideal of a ring A and let $S = A - \mathfrak{p}$. If B is a ring containing A, we denote by $B_{\mathfrak{p}}$ the ring $S^{-1}B$.

Let B be a ring containing a ring A. Let $\mathfrak{p}$ be a prime ideal of A and $\mathfrak{P}$ be a prime ideal of B. We say that $\mathfrak{P}$ **lies above** $\mathfrak{p}$ if $\mathfrak{P} \cap A = \mathfrak{p}$ and we then write $\mathfrak{P}|\mathfrak{p}$. If that is the case, then the injection

$$A \to B$$

induces an injection of the factor rings

$$A/\mathfrak{p} \to B/\mathfrak{P},$$

and in fact we have a commutative diagram:

$$\begin{array}{ccc} B & \to & B/\mathfrak{P} \\ \uparrow & & \uparrow \\ A & \to & A/\mathfrak{p} \end{array}$$

the horizontal arrows being the canonical homomorphisms, and the vertical arrows being inclusions.

If B is integral over A, then $B/\mathfrak{P}$ is integral over $A/\mathfrak{p}$ (by Proposition 4).

Nakayama's Lemma. *Let A be a ring, $\mathfrak{a}$ an ideal contained in all maximal ideals of A, and M a finitely generated A-module. If $\mathfrak{a}M = M$, then $M = 0$.*

Proof. Induction on the number of generators of M. Say M is generated by $w_1, \ldots, w_m$. There exists an expression

$$w_1 = a_1 w_1 + \cdots + a_m w_m$$

with $a_i \in \mathfrak{a}$. Hence

$$(1 - a_1) w_1 = a_2 w_2 + \cdots + a_m w_m.$$

If $1 - a_1$ is not a unit in A, then it is contained in a maximal ideal $\mathfrak{p}$. Since $a_1 \in \mathfrak{p}$ by hypothesis, we have a contradiction. Hence $1 - a_1$ is a unit, and dividing by it shows that M can be generated by $m - 1$ elements, thereby concluding the proof.

Proposition 9. *Let A be a ring, $\mathfrak{p}$ a prime ideal, and B a ring containing A and integral over A. Then $\mathfrak{p}B \neq B$, and there exists a prime ideal $\mathfrak{P}$ of B lying above $\mathfrak{p}$.*

Proof. We know that $B_{\mathfrak{p}}$ is integral over $A_{\mathfrak{p}}$, and that $A_{\mathfrak{p}}$ is a local ring with maximal ideal $\mathfrak{m}_{\mathfrak{p}}$. Since we obviously have

$$\mathfrak{p}B_{\mathfrak{p}} = \mathfrak{p}A_{\mathfrak{p}}B = \mathfrak{p}A_{\mathfrak{p}}B_{\mathfrak{p}} = \mathfrak{m}_{\mathfrak{p}}B_{\mathfrak{p}},$$

it will suffice to prove our first assertion when A is a local ring. In that case, if $\mathfrak{p}B = B$, then 1 has an expression as a finite linear combination of elements of B with coefficients in $\mathfrak{p}$,

$$1 = a_1 b_1 + \cdots + a_n b_n$$

with $a_i \in \mathfrak{p}$ and $b_i \in B$. Let $B_0 = A[b_1, \ldots, b_n]$. Then $\mathfrak{p}B_0 = B_0$ and B_0 is a finite A-module by Proposition 2. Hence $B_0 = 0$, contradiction.

To prove our second assertion, we go back to the original notation, and note the following commutative diagram:

$$\begin{array}{ccc} B & \rightarrow & B_{\mathfrak{p}} \\ \uparrow & & \uparrow \\ A & \rightarrow & A_{\mathfrak{p}} \end{array} \qquad \text{(all arrows inclusions).}$$

We have just proved that $\mathfrak{m}_{\mathfrak{p}}B_{\mathfrak{p}} \neq B_{\mathfrak{p}}$. Hence $\mathfrak{m}_{\mathfrak{p}}B_{\mathfrak{p}}$ is contained in a maximal ideal $\mathfrak{M}$ of $B_{\mathfrak{p}}$, and $\mathfrak{M} \cap A_{\mathfrak{p}}$ therefore contains $\mathfrak{m}_{\mathfrak{p}}$. Since $\mathfrak{m}_{\mathfrak{p}}$ is maximal, it follows that

$$\mathfrak{m}_{\mathfrak{p}} = \mathfrak{M} \cap A_{\mathfrak{p}}.$$

Let $\mathfrak{P} = \mathfrak{M} \cap B$. Then $\mathfrak{P}$ is a prime ideal of B, and taking intersections with A going both ways around our diagram shows that $\mathfrak{M} \cap A = \mathfrak{p}$, so that

$$\mathfrak{P} \cap A = \mathfrak{p},$$

as was to be shown.

Remark. Let B be integral over A, and let $\mathfrak{b}$ be an ideal of B, $\mathfrak{b} \neq 0$. Then $\mathfrak{b} \cap A \neq 0$.

To prove this, let $b \in \mathfrak{b}$, $b \neq 0$. Then b satisfies an equation

$$b^n + a_{n-1}b^{n-1} + \cdots + a_0 = 0$$

with $a_i \in A$, and $a_0 \neq 0$. But a_0 lies in $\mathfrak{b} \cap A$.

Proposition 10. *Let A be a subring of B, and assume B integral over A. Let $\mathfrak{P}$ be a prime ideal of B lying over a prime ideal $\mathfrak{p}$ of A. Then $\mathfrak{P}$ is maximal if and only if $\mathfrak{p}$ is maximal.*

Proof. Assume $\mathfrak{p}$ maximal in A. Then $A/\mathfrak{p}$ is a field. We are reduced to proving that a ring which is integral over a field is a field. If k is a field and x is integral over k, then it is standard from elementary field theory that the ring $k[x]$ is itself a field, so x is invertible in the ring. Conversely, assume that $\mathfrak{P}$ is maximal in B. Then $B/\mathfrak{P}$ is a field, which is integral over the ring $A/\mathfrak{p}$. If $A/\mathfrak{p}$ is not a field, it has a non-zero maximal ideal $\mathfrak{m}$. By Proposition 9, there exists a maximal ideal $\mathfrak{M}$ of $B/\mathfrak{P}$ lying above $\mathfrak{m}$, contradiction.

When an extension is given explicitly by a generating element, then we can describe the primes lying above a given prime more explicitly.

Let A be integrally closed in its quotient field K, and let E be a finite extension of K. Let B be the integral closure of A in E. Assume that $B = A[\alpha]$ for some element α, and let $f(X)$ be the irreducible polynomial of α over K. Let $\mathfrak{p}$ be a maximal ideal of A. We have a canonical homomorphism

$$A \to A/\mathfrak{p} = \bar{A},$$

which extends to the polynomial ring, namely

$$g(X) = \sum_{i=1}^{m} c_i X^i \mapsto \sum_{i=1}^{m} \bar{c}_i X^i = \bar{g}(X),$$

where $\bar{c}$ denotes the residue class mod $\mathfrak{p}$ of an element $c \in A$.

We contend that there is a natural bijection between the prime ideals $\mathfrak{P}$ of B lying above $\mathfrak{p}$ and the irreducible factors $\bar{P}(X)$ of $\bar{f}(X)$ (having leading *coefficient* 1). *This bijection is such that a prime* $\mathfrak{P}$ *of* B *lying above* $\mathfrak{p}$ *corresponds to* $\overline{P}$ *if and only if* $\mathfrak{P}$ *is the kernel of the homomorphism*

$$A[\alpha] \to \overline{A}[\bar{\alpha}]$$

where $\bar{\alpha}$ *is a root of* $\overline{P}$.

To see this, let $\mathfrak{P}$ lie above $\mathfrak{p}$. Then the canonical homomorphism $B \to B/\mathfrak{P}$ sends α on a root of $\bar{f}$ which is conjugate to a root of some irreducible factor of $\bar{f}$. Furthermore two roots of $\bar{f}$ are conjugate over $\overline{A}$ if and only if they are roots of the same irreducible factor of $\bar{f}$. Finally, let z be a root of $\overline{P}$ in some algebraic closure of $\overline{A}$. The map

$$g(\alpha) \mapsto \bar{g}(z)$$

for $g(X) \in A[X]$ is a well-defined map, because if $g(\alpha) = 0$ then

$$g(X) = f(X)h(X)$$

for some $h(X) \in A[X]$, whence $\bar{g}(z) = 0$ also. Being well-defined, our map is obviously a homomorphism, and since z is a root of an irreducible polynomial over $\overline{A}$, it follows that its kernel is a prime ideal in B, thus proving our contention.

Remark 1. As usual, the assumption that $\mathfrak{p}$ is maximal can be weakened to $\mathfrak{p}$ prime by localizing.

Remark 2. In dealing with extensions of number fields, the assumption $B = A[\alpha]$ is not always satisfied, but it is true that $B_{\mathfrak{p}} = A_{\mathfrak{p}}[\alpha]$ for all but a finite number of $\mathfrak{p}$, so that the previous discussion holds almost always locally. Cf. Proposition 16 of Chapter III, §3.

§4. Chinese remainder theorem

Chinese Remainder Theorem. *Let* A *be a ring, and* $\mathfrak{a}_1, \dots, \mathfrak{a}_n$ *ideals such that* $\mathfrak{a}_i + \mathfrak{a}_j = A$ *for all* $i \neq j$. *Given elements* $x_1, \dots, x_n \in A$, *there exists* $x \in A$ *such that* $x \equiv x_i \pmod{\mathfrak{a}_i}$ *for all* i.

Proof. If $n = 2$, we have an expression

$$1 = a_1 + a_2$$

for some elements $a_i \in \mathfrak{a}_i$, and we let $x = x_2 a_1 + x_1 a_2$.

For each i we can find elements $a_i \in \mathfrak{a}_1$ and $b_i \in \mathfrak{a}_i$ such that

$$a_i + b_i = 1, \qquad i \geqq 2.$$

The product $\prod_{i=2}^{n} (a_i + b_i)$ is equal to 1, and lies in $\mathfrak{a}_1 + \prod_{i=2}^{n} \mathfrak{a}_i$. Hence

$$\mathfrak{a}_1 + \prod_{i=2}^{n} \mathfrak{a}_i = A.$$

By the theorem for $n = 2$, we can find an element $y_1 \in A$ such that

$$y_1 \equiv 1 \pmod{\mathfrak{a}_1}$$
$$y_1 \equiv 0 \left(\operatorname{mod} \prod_{i=2}^{n} \mathfrak{a}_i\right).$$

We find similarly elements $y_2, \ldots, y_n$ such that

$$y_j \equiv 1 \ (\operatorname{mod} \mathfrak{a}_j); \qquad y_j \equiv 0 \ (\operatorname{mod} \mathfrak{a}_i), \quad i \neq j.$$

Then $x = x_1y_1 + \cdots + x_ny_n$ satisfies our requirements.

In the same vein as above, we observe that if $\mathfrak{a}_1, \ldots, \mathfrak{a}_n$ are ideals of a ring A such that

$$\mathfrak{a}_1 + \cdots + \mathfrak{a}_n = A,$$

and if $\nu_1, \ldots, \nu_n$ are positive integers, then

$$\mathfrak{a}_1^{\nu_1} + \cdots + \mathfrak{a}_n^{\nu_n} = A.$$

The proof is trivial, and is left as an exercise.

§5. *Galois extensions*

Proposition 11. *Let A be a ring, integrally closed in its quotient field K. Let L be a finite Galois extension of K with group G. Let $\mathfrak{p}$ be a maximal ideal of A, and let $\mathfrak{P}$, $\mathfrak{Q}$ be prime ideals of the integral closure of A in L lying above $\mathfrak{p}$. Then there exists $\sigma \in G$ such that $\sigma\mathfrak{P} = \mathfrak{Q}$.*

Proof. Suppose that $\mathfrak{P} \neq \sigma\mathfrak{Q}$ for any $\sigma \in G$. There exists an element $x \in B$ such that

$$x \equiv 0 \ (\operatorname{mod} \mathfrak{P})$$
$$x \equiv 1 \ (\operatorname{mod} \sigma\mathfrak{Q}), \qquad \text{all } \sigma \in G$$

(use the Chinese remainder theorem). The norm

$$N_K^L(x) = \prod_{\sigma \in G} \sigma x$$

lies in $B \cap K = A$ (because A is integrally closed), and lies in $\mathfrak{P} \cap A = \mathfrak{p}$.

But $x \notin \sigma\mathfrak{Q}$ for all $\sigma \in G$, so that $\sigma x \notin \mathfrak{Q}$ for all $\sigma \in G$. This contradicts the fact that the norm of x lies in $\mathfrak{p} = \mathfrak{Q} \cap A$.

If one localizes, one can eliminate the hypothesis that $\mathfrak{p}$ is maximal; just assume that $\mathfrak{p}$ is prime.

Corollary. *Let A be a ring, integrally closed in its quotient field K. Let E be a finite separable extension of K, and B the integral closure of A in E. Let $\mathfrak{p}$ be a maximal ideal of A. Then there exists only a finite number of prime ideals of B lying above $\mathfrak{p}$.*

Proof. Let L be the smallest Galois extension of K containing E. If $\mathfrak{Q}_1$, $\mathfrak{Q}_2$ are two distinct prime ideals of B lying above $\mathfrak{p}$, and $\mathfrak{P}_1$, $\mathfrak{P}_2$ are two prime ideals of the integral closure of A in L lying above $\mathfrak{Q}_1$ and $\mathfrak{Q}_2$ respectively, then $\mathfrak{P}_1 \neq \mathfrak{P}_2$. This argument reduces our assertion to the case that E is Galois over K, and it then becomes an immediate consequence of the proposition.

Let A be integrally closed in its quotient field K, and let B be its integral closure in a finite Galois extension L, with group G. Then $\sigma B = B$ for every $\sigma \in G$. Let $\mathfrak{p}$ be a maximal ideal of A, and $\mathfrak{P}$ a maximal ideal of B lying above $\mathfrak{p}$. We denote by $G_{\mathfrak{P}}$ the subgroup of G consisting of those automorphisms such that $\sigma\mathfrak{P} = \mathfrak{P}$. Then $G_{\mathfrak{P}}$ operates in a natural way on the residue class field $B/\mathfrak{P}$, and leaves $A/\mathfrak{p}$ fixed. To each $\sigma \in G_{\mathfrak{P}}$ we can associate an automorphism $\bar{\sigma}$ of $B/\mathfrak{P}$ over $A/\mathfrak{p}$, and the map given by

$$\sigma \mapsto \bar{\sigma}$$

induces a homomorphism of $G_{\mathfrak{P}}$ into the group of automorphisms of $B/\mathfrak{P}$ over $A/\mathfrak{p}$.

The group $G_{\mathfrak{P}}$ will be called the **decomposition group** of $\mathfrak{P}$. Its fixed field will be denoted by L^d, and will be called the **decomposition field** of $\mathfrak{P}$. Let B^d be the integral closure of A in L^d, and let $\mathfrak{Q} = \mathfrak{P} \cap B^d$. By Proposition 11, we know that $\mathfrak{P}$ is the only prime of B lying above $\mathfrak{Q}$.

Let $G = \bigcup \sigma_j G_{\mathfrak{P}}$ be a coset decomposition of $G_{\mathfrak{P}}$ in G. Then the prime ideals $\sigma_j\mathfrak{P}$ are precisely the distinct primes of B lying above $\mathfrak{p}$. Indeed, for two elements σ, $\tau \in G$ we have $\sigma\mathfrak{P} = \tau\mathfrak{P}$ if and only if $\tau^{-1}\sigma\mathfrak{P} = \mathfrak{P}$, i.e. $\tau^{-1}\sigma$ lies in $G_{\mathfrak{P}}$. Thus τ, σ lie in the same coset mod $G_{\mathfrak{P}}$.

It is then immediately clear that the decomposition group of a prime $\sigma\mathfrak{P}$ is $\sigma G_{\mathfrak{P}} \sigma^{-1}$.

Proposition 12. *The field L^d is the smallest subfield E of L containing K such that $\mathfrak{P}$ is the only prime of B lying above $\mathfrak{P} \cap E$ (which is prime in $B \cap E$).*

Proof. Let E be as above, and let H be the Galois group of L over E. Let $\mathfrak{q} = \mathfrak{P} \cap E$. By Proposition 11, all primes of B lying above $\mathfrak{q}$ are conjugate by elements of H. Since there is only one prime, namely $\mathfrak{P}$, it means that H leaves $\mathfrak{P}$ invariant. Hence $H \subset G_{\mathfrak{P}}$ and $E \supset L^d$. We have already observed that L^d has the required property.

Proposition 13. *Notation being as above, we have $A/\mathfrak{p} = B^d/\mathfrak{Q}$ (under the canonical injection $A/\mathfrak{p} \to B^d/\mathfrak{Q}$).*

Proof. If σ is an element of G, not in $G_{\mathfrak{P}}$, then $\sigma\mathfrak{P} \neq \mathfrak{P}$ and $\sigma^{-1}\mathfrak{P} \neq \mathfrak{P}$. Let

$$\mathfrak{Q}_\sigma = \sigma^{-1}\mathfrak{P} \cap B^d.$$

Then $\mathfrak{Q}_\sigma \neq \mathfrak{Q}$. Let x be an element of B^d. There exists an element y of B^d such that

$$y \equiv x \pmod{\mathfrak{Q}}$$
$$y \equiv 1 \pmod{\mathfrak{Q}_\sigma}$$

for each σ in G, but not in $G_{\mathfrak{P}}$. Hence in particular,

$$y \equiv x \pmod{\mathfrak{P}}$$
$$y \equiv 1 \pmod{\sigma^{-1}\mathfrak{P}}$$

for each σ not in $G_{\mathfrak{P}}$. This second congruence yields

$$\sigma y \equiv 1 \pmod{\mathfrak{P}}$$

for all $\sigma \notin G_{\mathfrak{P}}$. The norm of y from L^d to K is a product of y and other factors σy with $\sigma \notin G_{\mathfrak{P}}$. Thus we obtain

$$N_K^{L^d}(y) \equiv x \pmod{\mathfrak{P}}.$$

But the norm lies in K, and even in A, since it is a product of elements integral over A. This last congruence holds mod $\mathfrak{Q}$, since both x and the norm lie in B^d. This is precisely the meaning of the assertion in our proposition.

If x is an element of B, we shall denote by $\bar{x}$ its image under the homomorphism $B \to B/\mathfrak{P}$. Then $\bar{\sigma}$ is the automorphism of $B/\mathfrak{P}$ satisfying the relation

$$\bar{\sigma}\bar{x} = \overline{\sigma x}.$$

If $f(X)$ is a polynomial with coefficients in B, we denote by $\bar{f}(X)$ its natural image under the above homomorphism. Thus, if

$$f(X) = b_n X^n + \cdots + b_0,$$

then

$$\bar{f}(X) = \bar{b}_n X^n + \cdots + \bar{b}_0.$$

Proposition 14. *Let A be integrally closed in its quotient field K, and let B be its integral closure in a finite Galois extension L of K, with group G. Let $\mathfrak{p}$ be a maximal ideal of A, and $\mathfrak{P}$ a maximal ideal of B lying above $\mathfrak{p}$. Then $B/\mathfrak{P}$ is a normal extension of $A/\mathfrak{p}$, and the map $\sigma \mapsto \bar{\sigma}$ induces a homomorphism of $G_{\mathfrak{P}}$ onto the Galois group of $B/\mathfrak{P}$ over $A/\mathfrak{p}$.*

Proof. Let $\bar{B} = B/\mathfrak{P}$ and $\bar{A} = A/\mathfrak{p}$. Any element of $\bar{B}$ can be written as $\bar{x}$ for some $x \in B$. Let $\bar{x}$ generate a separable subextension of $\bar{B}$ over $\bar{A}$, and let f be the irreducible polynomial for x over K. The coefficients of f lie in A because x is integral over A, and all the roots of f are integral over A. Thus

$$f(X) = \prod_{i=1}^{m} (X - x_i)$$

splits into linear factors in B. Since

$$\bar{f}(X) = \prod (X - \bar{x}_i)$$

and all the $\bar{x}_i$ lie in $\bar{B}$, it follows that $\bar{f}$ splits into linear factors in $\bar{B}$. We observe that $f(x) = 0$ implies $\bar{f}(\bar{x}) = 0$. Hence $\bar{B}$ is normal over $\bar{A}$, and

$$[\bar{A}(\bar{x}) : \bar{A}] \leqq [K(x) : K] \leqq [L : K].$$

This implies that the maximal separable subextension of $\bar{A}$ in $\bar{B}$ is of finite degree over $\bar{A}$ (using the primitive element theorem of elementary field theory). This degree is in fact bounded by $[L : K]$.

There remains to prove that the map $\sigma \mapsto \bar{\sigma}$ gives a surjective homomorphism of $G_{\mathfrak{P}}$ onto the Galois group of $\bar{B}$ over $\bar{A}$. To do this, we shall give an argument which reduces our problem to the case when $\mathfrak{P}$ is the only prime ideal of B lying above $\mathfrak{p}$. Indeed, by Proposition 13, the residue class fields of the ground ring and the ring B^d in the decomposition field are the same. This means that to prove our surjectivity, we may take L^d as ground field. This is the desired reduction, and we can assume $K = L^d$, $G = G_{\mathfrak{P}}$.

This being the case, take a generator of the maximal separable subextension of $\bar{B}$ over $\bar{A}$, and let it be $\bar{x}$, for some element x in B. Let f be the irreducible polynomial of x over K. Any automorphism of $\bar{B}$ is determined by its effect on $\bar{x}$, and maps $\bar{x}$ on some root of $\bar{f}$. Suppose that $x = x_1$. Given any root x_i of f, there exists an element σ of $G = G_{\mathfrak{P}}$ such that $\sigma x = x_i$. Hence $\bar{\sigma}\bar{x} = \bar{x}_i$. Hence the automorphism of $\bar{B}$ over $\bar{A}$

induced by elements of G operate transitively on the roots of $\bar{f}$. Hence they give us all automorphisms of the residue class field, as was to be shown.

Corollary 1. *Let A be a ring integrally closed in its quotient field K. Let L be a finite Galois extension of K, and B the integral closure of A in L. Let $\mathfrak{p}$ be a maximal ideal of A. Let $\varphi : A \to A/\mathfrak{p}$ be the canonical homomorphism, and let ψ_1, ψ_2 be two homomorphisms of B extending φ in a given algebraic closure of $A/\mathfrak{p}$. Then there exists an automorphism σ of L over K such that*

$$\psi_1 = \psi_2 \circ \sigma.$$

Proof. The kernels of ψ_1, ψ_2 are prime ideals of B which are conjugate by Proposition 11. Hence there exists an element τ of the Galois group G such that ψ_1, $\psi_2 \circ \tau$ have the same kernel. Without loss of generality, we may therefore assume that ψ_1, ψ_2 have the same kernel $\mathfrak{P}$. Hence there exists an automorphism ω of $\psi_1(B)$ onto $\psi_2(B)$ such that $\omega \circ \psi_1 = \psi_2$. There exists an element σ of $G_{\mathfrak{P}}$ such that $\omega \circ \psi_1 = \psi_1 \circ \sigma$, by the preceding proposition. This proves what we wanted.

Remark. In all the above propositions, we could assume $\mathfrak{p}$ prime instead of maximal. In that case, one has to localize at $\mathfrak{p}$ to be able to apply our proofs. In the application to number fields, this is unnecessary, since every prime is maximal.

In the above discussions, the kernel of the map

$$G_{\mathfrak{P}} \to \bar{G}_{\mathfrak{P}}$$

is called the **inertia group** $T_{\mathfrak{P}}$ of $\mathfrak{P}$. It consists of those automorphisms of $G_{\mathfrak{P}}$ which induce the trivial automorphism on the residue class field. Its fixed field is called the **inertia field,** and is denoted by L^t.

Corollary 2. *Let the assumptions be as in Corollary* 1, *and assume that $\mathfrak{P}$ is the only prime of B lying above $\mathfrak{p}$. Let $f(X)$ be a polynomial in $A[X]$ with leading coefficient* 1. *Assume that f is irreducible in $K[X]$, and has a root α in B. Then the reduced polynomial $\bar{f}$ is a power of an irreducible polynomial in $\bar{A}[X]$.*

Proof. By Corollary 1, we know that any two roots of $\bar{f}$ are conjugate under some isomorphism of $\bar{B}$ over $\bar{A}$, and hence that $\bar{f}$ cannot split into relative prime polynomials. Therefore, $\bar{f}$ is a power of an irreducible polynomial.

Let k be a number field and E a finite extension of degree N. A non-zero prime ideal of the ring of algebraic integers $\mathfrak{o}_k$ will usually be called a **prime** of k. We say that such a prime $\mathfrak{p}$ **splits completely** in E if there are exactly N different primes of E lying above $\mathfrak{p}$. If K/k is Galois, then $\mathfrak{p}$ splits completely in K if and only if $G_{\mathfrak{P}} = 1$ because G permutes the primes $\mathfrak{P}|\mathfrak{p}$ transitively.

When K/k is abelian, then we have the following characterization of the fixed field of the decomposition group.

Corollary 3. *Let K/k be abelian with group G. Let $\mathfrak{p}$ be a prime of k, let $\mathfrak{P}$ be a prime of K lying above $\mathfrak{p}$ and let $G_{\mathfrak{P}}$ be its decomposition group. Let E be the fixed field of $G_{\mathfrak{P}}$. Then E is the maximal subfield of K containing k in which $\mathfrak{p}$ splits completely*

Proof. Let

$$G = \bigcup_{i=1}^{r} \sigma_i G_{\mathfrak{P}}$$

be a coset decomposition. Let $\mathfrak{q} = \mathfrak{P} \cap E$. Since a Galois group permutes the primes lying above a given prime transitively, we know that $\mathfrak{P}$ is the only prime of K lying above $\mathfrak{q}$. For each i, the prime $\sigma_i\mathfrak{P}$ is the only prime lying above $\sigma_i\mathfrak{q}$, and since $\sigma_1\mathfrak{P}, \ldots, \sigma_r\mathfrak{P}$ are distinct, it follows that the primes $\sigma_1\mathfrak{q}, \ldots, \sigma_r\mathfrak{q}$ are distinct. Since G is abelian, the primes $\sigma_i\mathfrak{q}$ are primes of E, and $[E:k] = r$, so that $\mathfrak{p}$ splits completely in E. Conversely, let F be an intermediate field between k and K in which $\mathfrak{p}$ splits completely, and let H be the Galois group of K/F. If $\sigma \in G_{\mathfrak{P}}$ and $\mathfrak{P} \cap F = \mathfrak{P}_F$, then σ leaves $\mathfrak{P}_F$ fixed. However, the decomposition group of $\mathfrak{P}_F$ over $\mathfrak{p}$ must be trivial since $\mathfrak{p}$ splits completely in F. Hence the restriction of σ to F is the identity, and therefore $G_{\mathfrak{P}} \subset H$. This proves that $F \subset E$, and concludes the proof of our corollary.

Let k be a number field and let K be a Galois extension with group G Let $\mathfrak{p}$ be a prime of $\mathfrak{o}_k$ and $\mathfrak{P}$ a prime of $\mathfrak{o}_K$ lying above $\mathfrak{p}$. The residue class field $\mathfrak{o}_k/\mathfrak{p}$ is finite, and we shall denote the number of its elements by $\mathbf{N}\mathfrak{p}$. It is a power of the prime number p lying in $\mathfrak{p}$. By the theory of finite fields, there exists a unique automorphism of $\mathfrak{o}_K/\mathfrak{P}$ over $\mathfrak{o}_k/\mathfrak{p}$ which generates the Galois group of the residue class field extension and has the effect

$$x \mapsto x^{\mathbf{N}\mathfrak{p}}.$$

In terms of congruences, we can write this automorphism $\bar{\sigma}$ as

$$\sigma\alpha \equiv \alpha^{\mathbf{N}\mathfrak{p}} \pmod{\mathfrak{P}}, \qquad \alpha \in \mathfrak{o}_K.$$

By what we have just seen, there exists a coset $\sigma T_{\mathfrak{P}}$ of $T_{\mathfrak{P}}$ in $G_{\mathfrak{P}}$ which induces $\bar{\sigma}$ on the residue class field extension. Any element of this coset will be called a **Frobenius automorphism** of $\mathfrak{P}$, and will be denoted by $(\mathfrak{P}, K/k)$. If the inertia group $T_{\mathfrak{P}}$ is trivial, then $(\mathfrak{P}, K/k)$ is uniquely determined as an element of the decomposition group $G_{\mathfrak{P}}$.

If $\mathfrak{Q}$ is another prime lying above $\mathfrak{p}$, and $\eta \in G$ is such that $\eta\mathfrak{P} = \mathfrak{Q}$, then the decomposition group of $\mathfrak{Q}$ is given by

$$G_{\mathfrak{Q}} = G_{\eta\mathfrak{P}} = \eta G_{\mathfrak{P}} \eta^{-1},$$

and similarly for the inertia group, and a Frobenius automorphism.

$$(\eta\mathfrak{P}, K/k) = \eta(\mathfrak{P}, K/k)\eta^{-1}.$$

This is immediately verified from the definitions. Furthermore, if $T_{\mathfrak{P}}$ is trivial, we see that $(\mathfrak{P}, K/k) = 1$ if and only if $\mathfrak{p}$ splits completely, meaning that $G_{\mathfrak{P}} = 1$.

If K/k is abelian, and if the inertia group $T_{\mathfrak{P}}$ is trivial for one of the $\mathfrak{P}|\mathfrak{p}$ (and hence for all $\mathfrak{P}|\mathfrak{p}$), it follows that to each $\mathfrak{p}$ in k we are able to associate a uniquely determined element of G, lying in $G_{\mathfrak{P}}$ (the same for all $\mathfrak{P}|\mathfrak{p}$), which we denote by

$$\sigma = (\mathfrak{p}, K/k),$$

and call the **Artin automorphism** of $\mathfrak{p}$ in G. It is characterized by the congruence

$$\sigma\alpha \equiv \alpha^{\mathbf{N}\mathfrak{p}} \pmod{\mathfrak{P}}, \qquad \alpha \in \mathfrak{o}_K.$$

We shall study this automorphism at length in the class field theory.

§6. *Dedekind rings*

Let $\mathfrak{o}$ be a ring and K its quotient field. A **fractional ideal** of $\mathfrak{o}$ in K is an $\mathfrak{o}$-module $\mathfrak{a}$ contained in K such that there exists an element $c \neq 0$ in $\mathfrak{o}$ for which $c\mathfrak{a} \subset \mathfrak{o}$. If $\mathfrak{o}$ is Noetherian, it follows that $c\mathfrak{a}$, and hence $\mathfrak{a}$, is finitely generated.

Theorem 2. *Let $\mathfrak{o}$ be a ring which is Noetherian, integrally closed, and such that every non-zero prime ideal is maximal. Then every ideal of $\mathfrak{o}$ can be uniquely factored into prime ideals, and the non-zero fractional ideals form a group under multiplication.*

Proof. We shall first prove the second assertion, following Van der Waerden.

(i) Let $\mathfrak{a} \neq 0$ be an ideal in $\mathfrak{o}$. Then there exists a product of prime ideals $\mathfrak{p}_1\mathfrak{p}_2 \cdots \mathfrak{p}_r \subset \mathfrak{a}$.

Suppose the assertion false. Since $\mathfrak{o}$ is Noetherian, there exists an ideal $\mathfrak{a} \neq 0$ and maximal with respect to the stated property. This ideal cannot be prime. Hence there exist $b_1, b_2 \in \mathfrak{o}$ such that $b_1b_2 \in \mathfrak{a}$ but neither b_1 nor b_2 lies in $\mathfrak{a}$. Let $\mathfrak{a}_1 = (\mathfrak{a}, b_1)$ and $\mathfrak{a}_2 = (\mathfrak{a}, b_2)$. Then $\mathfrak{a}_1\mathfrak{a}_2 \subset \mathfrak{a}$, and $\mathfrak{a}_1 \neq \mathfrak{a}$, $\mathfrak{a}_2 \neq \mathfrak{a}$. Since $\mathfrak{a}$ was maximal with respect to the stated property, we can find products of prime ideals contained in $\mathfrak{a}_1$ and $\mathfrak{a}_2$. Taking the product of these gives a contradiction.

(ii) Every maximal ideal $\mathfrak{p}$ is invertible.

Let $\mathfrak{p}^{-1}$ be the set of elements $x \in K$ such that $x\mathfrak{p} \subset \mathfrak{o}$. Then $\mathfrak{p}^{-1} \supset \mathfrak{o}$. We contend that $\mathfrak{p}^{-1} \neq \mathfrak{o}$. Let $a \in \mathfrak{p}$, $a \neq 0$. Choose r minimal such that there exists a product

$$\mathfrak{p}_1 \cdots \mathfrak{p}_r \subset (a) \subset \mathfrak{p}.$$

Then one of the $\mathfrak{p}_i$, say $\mathfrak{p}_1$, is contained in $\mathfrak{p}$, and hence equal to $\mathfrak{p}$, since every prime is maximal. Furthermore,

$$\mathfrak{p}_2 \cdots \mathfrak{p}_r \not\subset (a)$$

and hence there exists an element $b \in \mathfrak{p}_2 \cdots \mathfrak{p}_r$ such that $b \notin (a)$. But $b\mathfrak{p} \subset (a)$ and hence $ba^{-1}\mathfrak{p} \subset \mathfrak{o}$, so that $ba^{-1} \in \mathfrak{p}^{-1}$. But $b \notin a\mathfrak{o}$ and hence $ba^{-1} \notin \mathfrak{o}$, thereby proving our contention.

We obtain $\mathfrak{p} \subset \mathfrak{p}\mathfrak{p}^{-1} \subset \mathfrak{o}$. Since $\mathfrak{p}$ is maximal, either $\mathfrak{p} = \mathfrak{p}\mathfrak{p}^{-1}$ or $\mathfrak{p}\mathfrak{p}^{-1} = \mathfrak{o}$. But $\mathfrak{p}^{-1}\mathfrak{p} = \mathfrak{p}$ would mean that $\mathfrak{p}^{-1}$ leaves a finitely generated $\mathfrak{o}$-module invariant, and hence is integral over $\mathfrak{o}$. This is impossible, since $\mathfrak{o}$ is integrally closed. Hence $\mathfrak{p}\mathfrak{p}^{-1} = \mathfrak{o}$.

(iii) Every non-zero ideal is invertible, by a fractional ideal.

Suppose this is not true. There exists a maximal non-invertible ideal $\mathfrak{a}$. We have just seen that $\mathfrak{a}$ cannot be a maximal ideal. Hence $\mathfrak{a} \subset \mathfrak{p}$ for some maximal ideal $\mathfrak{p}$, and $\mathfrak{a} \neq \mathfrak{p}$. We get

$$\mathfrak{a} \subset \mathfrak{a}\mathfrak{p}^{-1} \subset \mathfrak{a}\mathfrak{a}^{-1} \subset \mathfrak{o}.$$

Since $\mathfrak{a}$ is finitely generated, we cannot have $\mathfrak{a}\mathfrak{p}^{-1} = \mathfrak{a}$ (because $\mathfrak{p}^{-1}$ is not integral over $\mathfrak{o}$). Hence $\mathfrak{a}\mathfrak{p}^{-1}$ is larger than $\mathfrak{a}$, hence has an inverse, which, multiplied by $\mathfrak{p}$, obviously gives an inverse for $\mathfrak{a}$, contradiction.

(iv) Let $\mathfrak{a}$ be an ideal $\neq 0$, and $\mathfrak{c}$ a fractional ideal such that $\mathfrak{a}\mathfrak{c} = \mathfrak{o}$. Then $\mathfrak{c} = \mathfrak{a}^{-1}$ (the set of elements $x \in K$ such that $x\mathfrak{a} \subset \mathfrak{o}$).

It is clear that $\mathfrak{c} \subset \mathfrak{a}^{-1}$. Conversely, if $x\mathfrak{a} \subset \mathfrak{o}$, then $x\mathfrak{a}\mathfrak{c} \subset \mathfrak{c}$ and hence $x \in \mathfrak{c}$, because $\mathfrak{a}\mathfrak{c} = \mathfrak{o}$.

We finally conclude that every fractional ideal $\neq 0$ is invertible. Indeed, if $\mathfrak{a}$ is a fractional ideal $\neq 0$, then there exists an element $c \in \mathfrak{o}$ such that $c\mathfrak{a} \subset \mathfrak{o}$, and $c\mathfrak{a}$ is invertible. If $c\mathfrak{a}\mathfrak{b} = \mathfrak{o}$, then $c\mathfrak{b} = \mathfrak{a}^{-1}$. This proves that the non-zero fractional ideals form a group.

From this, we shall prove unique factorization.

First, we note that every non-zero ideal $\mathfrak{a}$ is equal to a product of prime ideals. Indeed, if this is false, there is a maximal ideal $\mathfrak{a}$ which is not such a product, and $\mathfrak{a}$ cannot be prime. Thus $\mathfrak{a} \subset \mathfrak{p}$ and $\mathfrak{a} \neq \mathfrak{p}$ for some prime $\mathfrak{p}$. Then $\mathfrak{a}\mathfrak{p}^{-1} \subset \mathfrak{o}$ and $\mathfrak{a}\mathfrak{p}^{-1} \neq \mathfrak{a}$ but contains $\mathfrak{a}$. Hence $\mathfrak{a}\mathfrak{p}^{-1}$ has a factorization, which, when multiplied by $\mathfrak{p}$ gives a factorization of $\mathfrak{a}$.

Given two fractional ideals $\mathfrak{a}$, $\mathfrak{b}$ we say that $\mathfrak{a}|\mathfrak{b}$ if and only if there exists an ideal $\mathfrak{c}$ such that $\mathfrak{a}\mathfrak{c} = \mathfrak{b}$. This amounts to saying that $\mathfrak{a} \supset \mathfrak{b}$, because in that case, we take $\mathfrak{c} = \mathfrak{a}^{-1}\mathfrak{b}$.

From the definition of a prime ideal, we see that whenever $\mathfrak{a}$, $\mathfrak{b}$ are two ideals and $\mathfrak{p}|\mathfrak{a}\mathfrak{b}$ then $\mathfrak{p}|\mathfrak{a}$ or $\mathfrak{p}|\mathfrak{b}$. (Namely, $\mathfrak{a}\mathfrak{b} \subset \mathfrak{p}$ implies $\mathfrak{a} \subset \mathfrak{p}$ or $\mathfrak{b} \subset \mathfrak{p}$.) Given two factorizations

$$\mathfrak{p}_1\mathfrak{p}_2 \cdots \mathfrak{p}_r = \mathfrak{q}_1\mathfrak{q}_2 \cdots \mathfrak{q}_s$$

into prime ideals, we conclude that $\mathfrak{p}_1$ divides the product on the right, hence divides some $\mathfrak{q}_i$, hence is equal to some $\mathfrak{q}_i$. Multiplying by $\mathfrak{p}_1^{-1}$ both sides of the equality, we proceed by induction to prove that $r = s$ and that the factors on both sides are equal, up to a permutation.

If $\mathfrak{a}$ is a fractional ideal $\neq 0$, and $c \in \mathfrak{o}$ is such that $c \neq 0$ and $c\mathfrak{a} \subset \mathfrak{o}$, then $(c) = \mathfrak{p}_1 \cdots \mathfrak{p}_r$ and $c\mathfrak{a} = \mathfrak{q}_1 \cdots \mathfrak{q}_s$. Hence $\mathfrak{a}$ has the factorization

$$\mathfrak{a} = \frac{\mathfrak{q}_1 \cdots \mathfrak{q}_s}{\mathfrak{p}_1 \cdots \mathfrak{p}_r}$$

(writing $1/\mathfrak{p}$ instead of $\mathfrak{p}^{-1}$). If we cancel any prime appearing both in the numerator and denominator, then it is clear that the factorization is unique.

A ring satisfying the properties of Theorem 2 is called a **Dedekind ring.** The ring of algebraic integers in a number field K is a Dedekind ring, because it satisfies the three properties stated in Theorem 2. The multiplicative group of non-zero fractional ideals of the ring of algebraic integers $\mathfrak{o}_K$ will be denoted by I_K.

From now on, by fractional ideal we shall mean non-zero fractional ideal, unless otherwise specified.

Let A be a Dedekind ring and $\mathfrak{a}$ a fractional ideal. We have a factorization

$$\mathfrak{a} = \prod_{\mathfrak{p}} \mathfrak{p}^{r_\mathfrak{p}}$$

with integers $r_\mathfrak{p}$ all but a finite number of which are 0. We say that $r_\mathfrak{p}$ is the **order** of $\mathfrak{a}$ at $\mathfrak{p}$. If $r_\mathfrak{p} > 0$, we say that $\mathfrak{a}$ has a **zero** at $\mathfrak{p}$. If $r_\mathfrak{p} < 0$, we say that it has a **pole** at $\mathfrak{p}$.

Let α be a non-zero element of the quotient field of A. Then we can form the fractional ideal $(\alpha) = A\alpha$ and we apply the above notions of order, zero, and pole to α.

If $\mathfrak{a}$ and $\mathfrak{b}$ are two fractional ideals, then it is clear that $\mathfrak{a} \supset \mathfrak{b}$ if and only if $\mathrm{ord}_\mathfrak{p}\, \mathfrak{a} \leqq \mathrm{ord}_\mathfrak{p}\, \mathfrak{b}$ for all primes $\mathfrak{p}$. Thus we have a criterion for an element α to belong to a fractional ideal $\mathfrak{a}$ in terms of orders (taking $\mathfrak{b} = (\alpha)$).

If $\mathrm{ord}_\mathfrak{p}\, \alpha = 0$, then we say that α is a **unit at** $\mathfrak{p}$. If that is the case, then α is a unit in the local ring $A_\mathfrak{p}$.

In what follows, by a prime ideal, we shall mean a non-zero prime ideal, unless otherwise specified, and we call a non-zero prime ideal simply a **prime.**

Proposition 15. *Let $\mathfrak{o}$ be a Dedekind ring with only a finite number of prime ideals. Then $\mathfrak{o}$ is a principal ideal ring.*

Proof. Let $\mathfrak{p}_1, \ldots, \mathfrak{p}_s$ be the prime ideals. Given any ideal

$$\mathfrak{a} = \mathfrak{p}_1^{r_1} \cdots \mathfrak{p}_s^{r_s} \neq 0,$$

select an element π_i in $\mathfrak{p}_i$ but not in $\mathfrak{p}_i^2$ and find an element α of $\mathfrak{o}$ such that

$$\alpha \equiv \pi_i^{r_i} \pmod{\mathfrak{p}_i^{r_i+1}}.$$

If

$$(\alpha) = \mathfrak{p}_1^{e_1} \cdots \mathfrak{p}_s^{e_s}$$

is a factorization of the ideal generated by α, then one sees immediately that $e_i = r_i$ for all i, and hence that $\mathfrak{a} = (\alpha)$.

Proposition 16. *Let A be a Dedekind ring and S a multiplicative subset of A. Then $S^{-1}A$ is a Dedekind ring. The map*

$$\mathfrak{a} \mapsto S^{-1}\mathfrak{a}$$

is a homomorphism of the group of fractional ideals of A onto the group of fractional ideals of $S^{-1}A$, and the kernel consists of those fractional ideals of A which meet S.

Proof. If $\mathfrak{p}$ meets S, then

$$S^{-1}\mathfrak{p} = S^{-1}A$$

because 1 lies in $S^{-1}\mathfrak{p}$. If $\mathfrak{a}$, $\mathfrak{b}$ are two ideals of A, then

$$S^{-1}(\mathfrak{a}\mathfrak{b}) = (S^{-1}\mathfrak{a})(S^{-1}\mathfrak{b}),$$

so multiplication by S^{-1} induces a homomorphism of the group of (fractional) ideals.

If $S^{-1}\mathfrak{a} = S^{-1}A$, then we can write $1 = \alpha/s$ for some $\alpha \in \mathfrak{a}$ and $s \in S$. Thus $\alpha = s$ and $\mathfrak{a}$ meets S. This proves that the kernel of our homomorphism is what we said it is.

Our mapping is surjective since we saw in §1 that every ideal of $S^{-1}A$ is of type $S^{-1}\mathfrak{a}$ for some ideal $\mathfrak{a}$ of A. The same applies of course to fractional ideals. This proves our proposition.

By a **principal fractional ideal** we shall mean a fractional ideal of type αA, generated by a single element α in the quotient field of A, and $\alpha \neq 0$ unless otherwise specified.

Let A be a Dedekind ring. The group of fractional ideals modulo the group of **principal ideals** (i.e. non-zero principal fractional ideals) is called the **ideal class group** of A.

Proposition 17. *Let A be a Dedekind ring, and assume that its group of ideal classes is finite. Let $\mathfrak{a}_1, \ldots, \mathfrak{a}_r$ be representative fractional ideals of the ideal classes, and let b be a non-zero element of A which lies in all the $\mathfrak{a}_i$. Let S be the multiplicative subset of A generated by the powers of b. Then every ideal of $S^{-1}A$ is principal.*

Proof. All the ideals $S^{-1}\mathfrak{a}_1, \ldots, S^{-1}\mathfrak{a}_r$ map on the unit ideal in the homomorphism of Proposition 16. Since every ideal of A is equal to some $\mathfrak{a}_i$ times a principal ideal, our proposition follows from the surjectivity of Proposition 16.

If two fractional ideals $\mathfrak{a}$, $\mathfrak{b}$ lie in the same ideal class, we write

$$\mathfrak{a} \sim \mathfrak{b}$$

and we say that $\mathfrak{a}$, $\mathfrak{b}$ are **linearly equivalent.** It is clear that every fractional ideal is linearly equivalent to an ideal.

The assumptions of Proposition 17 will be proved later to be satisfied by the ring of integers of an algebraic number field.

§7. *Discrete valuation rings*

A **discrete valuation ring** $\mathfrak{o}$ is a principal ideal ring having a unique (non-zero) prime ideal $\mathfrak{m}$. It is therefore a local ring. If π is a generator for $\mathfrak{m}$, then it must be the only irreducible element of $\mathfrak{o}$, i.e. the only prime element (since any prime element generates a prime ideal) up to a unit, of course. Thus the unique factorization in an arbitrary principal ideal ring has a particularly simple form in this case: Every element $\alpha \neq 0$ of $\mathfrak{o}$ has an expression

$$\alpha = \pi^r u$$

with some integer r, and a unit u in $\mathfrak{o}$.

Every discrete valuation ring is a Dedekind ring, and every Dedekind ring having only one maximal ideal is a discrete valuation ring. If A is a Dedekind ring, and $\mathfrak{p}$ a prime ideal of A, then $A_{\mathfrak{p}}$ is a discrete valuation ring, since it is equal to $S^{-1}A$ ($S =$ complement of $\mathfrak{p}$ in A) (cf. Proposition 16).

Since every ideal of a discrete valuation ring is principal, it must be some power of the maximal ideal.

In proving theorems about Dedekind rings, it is frequently useful to localize with respect to one prime ideal, in which case one obtains a discrete valuation ring. For instance we have the following proposition.

Proposition 18. *Let A be a Dedekind ring and M, N two modules over A. If $\mathfrak{p}$ is a prime of A, denote by $S_\mathfrak{p}$ the multiplicative set $A - \mathfrak{p}$. Assume that $S_\mathfrak{p}^{-1}M \subset S_\mathfrak{p}^{-1}N$ for all $\mathfrak{p}$. Then $M \subset N$.*

Proof. Let $a \in M$. For each $\mathfrak{p}$ we can find $x_\mathfrak{p} \in N$ and $s_\mathfrak{p} \in S_\mathfrak{p}$ such that $a = x_\mathfrak{p}/s_\mathfrak{p}$. Let $\mathfrak{b}$ be the ideal generated by the $s_\mathfrak{p}$. Then $\mathfrak{b}$ is the unit ideal, and we can write

$$1 = \sum y_\mathfrak{p} s_\mathfrak{p}$$

with elements $y_\mathfrak{p} \in A$ all but a finite number of which are 0. This yields

$$a = \sum y_\mathfrak{p} s_\mathfrak{p} a = \sum y_\mathfrak{p} x_\mathfrak{p}$$

and shows that a lies in N, as desired.

If A is a discrete valuation ring, then in particular, A is a principal ideal ring, and any finitely generated torsion-free module M over A is free. If its rank is n, and if $\mathfrak{p}$ is the maximal ideal of A, then $M/\mathfrak{p}M$ is a free module of rank n.

Proposition 19. *Let A be a local ring and M a free module of rank n over A. Let $\mathfrak{p}$ be the maximal ideal of A. Then $M/\mathfrak{p}M$ is a vector space of dimension n over $A/\mathfrak{p}$.*

Proof. This is obvious, because if $\{x_1, \ldots, x_n\}$ is a basis for M over A, so

$$M = \sum A x_i \quad \text{(direct sum)},$$

then

$$M/\mathfrak{p}M \approx \sum (A/\mathfrak{p})\bar{x}_i \quad \text{(direct sum)},$$

where $\bar{x}_i$ is the residue class of x_i mod $\mathfrak{p}$.

Let A be a Dedekind ring, K its quotient field, L a finite separable extension of K, and B the integral closure of A in L. If $\mathfrak{p}$ is a prime ideal of A, then $\mathfrak{p}B$ is an ideal of B and has a factorization

$$\mathfrak{p}B = \mathfrak{P}_1^{e_1} \cdots \mathfrak{P}_r^{e_r} \qquad (e_i \geqq 1)$$

into primes of B. It is clear that a prime $\mathfrak{P}$ of B occurs in this factorization if and only if $\mathfrak{P}$ lies above $\mathfrak{p}$.

If S is the complement of $\mathfrak{p}$ in A, then multiplying the above factorization by S gives us the factorization of $S^{-1}\mathfrak{p}$ in $S^{-1}B$. The primes $S^{-1}\mathfrak{P}_i$ remain distinct.

Each e_i is called the **ramification index** of $\mathfrak{P}_i$ over $\mathfrak{p}$, and is also written $e(\mathfrak{P}_i/\mathfrak{p})$. If we assume that A is a local ring, then $\mathfrak{p} = (\pi)$ is principal (Proposition 15). Let S_i be the complement of $\mathfrak{P}_i$ in B and let

$$B_i = S_i^{-1}B = B_{\mathfrak{P}_i}.$$

Then $\mathfrak{P}_i$ is principal, generated by an element π_i, and we have

$$\mathfrak{p}B_i = \pi B_i = (\pi_i^{e_i}).$$

Warning: B_i is not necessarily integral over $A_{\mathfrak{p}}$. It is if and only if there exists only one prime ideal $\mathfrak{P}$ above $\mathfrak{p}$ in B. Prove this as an exercise.

Denote by $I(A)$ the group of fractional ideals of a Dedekind ring A. Let K, L, B be as above. Then we have a natural injection

$$I(A) \to I(B)$$

given by $\mathfrak{a} \mapsto \mathfrak{a}B$. We shall define a homomorphism in the other direction.

If $\mathfrak{P}$ lies above $\mathfrak{p}$ in B, we denote by $f_{\mathfrak{P}}$ or $f(\mathfrak{P}/\mathfrak{p})$ the degree of the residue class field extension $B/\mathfrak{P}$ over $A/\mathfrak{p}$, and call it the **residue class degree.** We define the **norm** $N_K^L(\mathfrak{P})$ to be $\mathfrak{p}^{f_{\mathfrak{P}}}$ and extend our map N_K^L to the group of fractional ideals by multiplicativity.

Proposition 20. *Let A be a Dedekind ring, K its quotient field, $K \subset E \subset L$ two finite separable extensions, and $A \subset B \subset C$ the corresponding tower of integral closures of A in E and L. Let $\mathfrak{p}$ be a prime of A, $\mathfrak{q}$ a prime of B lying above $\mathfrak{p}$, and $\mathfrak{P}$ a prime of C lying above $\mathfrak{q}$. Then*

$$e(\mathfrak{P}/\mathfrak{p}) = e(\mathfrak{P}/\mathfrak{q})e(\mathfrak{q}/\mathfrak{p})$$
$$f(\mathfrak{P}/\mathfrak{p}) = f(\mathfrak{P}/\mathfrak{q})f(\mathfrak{q}/\mathfrak{p}).$$

Proof. Obvious.

From Proposition 20 it is clear that the norm is transitive, i.e. if we have a fractional ideal $\mathfrak{c}$ of C, then

$$N_K^E N_E^L(\mathfrak{c}) = N_K^L(\mathfrak{c}).$$

Proposition 21. *Let A be a Dedekind ring, K its quotient field, L a finite separable extension of K, and B the integral closure of A in L. Let $\mathfrak{p}$ be a prime of A. Then*

$$[L:K] = \sum_{\mathfrak{P}|\mathfrak{p}} e_{\mathfrak{P}} f_{\mathfrak{P}}.$$

Proof. We can localize at $\mathfrak{p}$ (multiplying A and B by $S_{\mathfrak{p}}^{-1}$), and thus may assume that A is a discrete valuation ring. In that case, B is a free module of rank $n = [L:K]$ over A, and $B/\mathfrak{p}B$ is a vector space of dimension n over $A/\mathfrak{p}$.

Let $\mathfrak{p}B = \mathfrak{P}_1^{e_1} \cdots \mathfrak{P}_r^{e_r}$ be the factorization of $\mathfrak{p}$ in B. Since $\mathfrak{P}_i^{e_i} \supset \mathfrak{p}B$ for each i, we have a well-defined homomorphism

$$B \to B/\mathfrak{p}B \to B/\mathfrak{P}_i^{e_i}$$

and therefore a homomorphism into the direct sum

$$B \to B/\mathfrak{p}B \to \prod_{i=1}^{r} B/\mathfrak{P}_i^{e_i}.$$

Each $B/\mathfrak{P}_i^{e_i}$ can be viewed as an $A/\mathfrak{p}$-vector space, and hence so can the direct sum. The kernel of our homomorphism consists of those elements of B lying in all the $\mathfrak{P}_i^{e_i}$, and is therefore $\mathfrak{p}B$. Furthermore, our map is surjective by the Chinese remainder theorem. It is obviously an $A/\mathfrak{p}$-homomorphism, and thus $B/\mathfrak{p}B$ is $A/\mathfrak{p}$-isomorphic to the above direct sum.

We shall now determine the dimension of $B/\mathfrak{P}^e$ (if $\mathfrak{P}$ is some $\mathfrak{P}_i$ and $e = e_i$).

Let Π be a generator of $\mathfrak{P}$ in B. (We know from Proposition 15 that $\mathfrak{P}$ is principal.) Let j be an integer $\geqq 1$. We can view $\mathfrak{P}^j/\mathfrak{P}^{j+1}$ as an $A/\mathfrak{p}$-vector space, since $\mathfrak{p}\mathfrak{P}^j \subset \mathfrak{P}^{j+1}$. We consider the map

$$B/\mathfrak{P} \to \mathfrak{P}^j/\mathfrak{P}^{j+1}$$

induced by multiplying an element of B by Π^j. This map is an $A/\mathfrak{p}$-homomorphism, which is clearly injective and surjective. Hence $B/\mathfrak{P}$ and $\mathfrak{P}^j/\mathfrak{P}^{j+1}$ are $A/\mathfrak{p}$-isomorphic.

The $A/\mathfrak{p}$-vector space $B/\mathfrak{P}^e$ has a composition series induced by the inclusions

$$B \supset \mathfrak{P} \supset \mathfrak{P}^2 \supset \cdots \supset \mathfrak{P}^e.$$

The dimension of $B/\mathfrak{P}$ over $A/\mathfrak{p}$ is $f_{\mathfrak{P}}$, by definition. From this it follows that the dimension of $B/\mathfrak{P}^e$ over $A/\mathfrak{p}$ is $e_{\mathfrak{P}} f_{\mathfrak{P}}$, thereby proving our proposition.

If $e_{\mathfrak{P}} = f_{\mathfrak{P}} = 1$ for all $\mathfrak{P}|\mathfrak{p}$, then one says that $\mathfrak{p}$ **splits completely** in L. In that case, there are exactly $[L:K]$ primes of B lying above $\mathfrak{p}$.

Corollary 1. *Let $\mathfrak{a}$ be a fractional ideal of A. Then*

$$N_K^L(\mathfrak{a}B) = \mathfrak{a}^{[L:K]}.$$

Proof. Immediate.

Corollary 2. *Assume that L is Galois over K. Then all the $e_{\mathfrak{P}}$ are equal to the same number e (for $\mathfrak{P}|\mathfrak{p}$), all the $f_{\mathfrak{P}}$ are equal to the same number f (for $\mathfrak{P}|\mathfrak{p}$), and if*

$$\mathfrak{p}B = (\mathfrak{P}_1 \cdots \mathfrak{P}_r)^e,$$

then

$$efr = [L:K].$$

Proof. All the $\mathfrak{P}$ lying above $\mathfrak{p}$ are conjugate to each other, and hence all the ramification indices and residue class degrees are equal. The last formula is clear.

Corollary 3. *Assume again that L is Galois over K with group G, and let $\mathfrak{P}$ be a prime of B lying above $\mathfrak{p}$ in A. Then*

$$N_K^L\mathfrak{P} \cdot B = \prod_{\sigma \in G} \sigma\mathfrak{P} = (\mathfrak{P}_1 \cdots \mathfrak{P}_r)^{ef}$$

(with e, f, r as in Corollary 2, and the ideal on the left is viewed as embedded in $I(B)$). The number ef is the order of the decomposition group of $\mathfrak{P}$, and e is the order of the inertia group.

Proof. The group G operates transitively on the primes of B lying above $\mathfrak{p}$, and the order of $G_{\mathfrak{P}}$ is the order of the isotropy group. Our assertions are therefore obvious, taking into account Proposition 14 of §5.

Proposition 22. *Let A be a Dedekind ring, K its quotient field, E a finite separable extension of K, and B the integral closure of A in E. Let $\mathfrak{b}$ be a fractional ideal of B, and assume $\mathfrak{b}$ is principal, $\mathfrak{b} = (\beta)$, $\beta \neq 0$. Then*

$$N_K^E\mathfrak{b} = (N_K^E(\beta)),$$

the norm on the left being the norm of a fractional ideal as defined above, and the norm on the right being the usual norm of elements of E.

Proof. Let L be the smallest Galois extension of K containing E. The norm from L to E of $\mathfrak{b}$ and of β simply raises these to the power $[L:E]$. Since our proposition asserts an equality between fractional ideals, it will suffice to prove it when the extension is Galois over K. In that case, it follows at once from Corollary 3 above.

Proposition 23. *Let A be a discrete valuation ring, K its quotient field, L a finite separable extension of K, and B the integral closure of A in L. Assume that there exists only one prime $\mathfrak{P}$ of B lying above the maximal ideal $\mathfrak{p}$ of A. Let β be an element of B such that its residue class* mod $\mathfrak{P}$ *generates $B/\mathfrak{P}$ over $A/\mathfrak{p}$ and Π an element of B which is of order 1 at $\mathfrak{P}$. Then $A[\beta, \Pi] = B$.*

Proof. Let C be the ring $A[\beta, \Pi]$. It can be viewed as a submodule of B over A, and by Nakayama's lemma, applied to the factor module B/C, it will suffice to prove that

$$\mathfrak{p}B + C = B.$$

But $\mathfrak{p}B = \mathfrak{P}^e$, and the products $\beta^i\Pi^j$ generate $B/\mathfrak{P}^e$ over $A/\mathfrak{p}$, as in Proposition 21. Hence every element $x \in B$ is such that

$$x \equiv \sum c_{ij}\beta^i\Pi^j \qquad (\text{mod } \mathfrak{p}B)$$

for some $c_{ij} \in A$. This proves our proposition.

Finally, we prove one more result, generalizing the arguments of Proposition 21.

Proposition 24. *Let A be a Dedekind ring, and $\mathfrak{a}$ a non-zero ideal. Let $n_\mathfrak{p} = \text{ord}_\mathfrak{p}\, \mathfrak{a}$. Then the canonical map*

$$A \to \prod_{\mathfrak{p}} A/\mathfrak{p}^{n_\mathfrak{p}}$$

induces an isomorphism of $A/\mathfrak{a}$ onto the product.

Proof. The map is surjective according to the Chinese remainder theorem, and it is clear that its kernel is exactly $\mathfrak{a}$.

Corollary. *Assume that $A/\mathfrak{p}$ is finite for each prime ideal $\mathfrak{p}$. Denote by $\mathbf{N}\mathfrak{a}$ the number of elements in the residue class ring $A/\mathfrak{a}$. Then*

$$\mathbf{N}\mathfrak{a} = \prod_{\mathfrak{p}} (\mathbf{N}\mathfrak{p})^{n_\mathfrak{p}}.$$

We observe that the function $\mathbf{N}$ can simply be viewed as being extended from the prime ideals to all fractional ideals by multiplicativity.

§8. *Explicit factorization of a prime*

We return to the discussion at the end of §3 and give more precise information concerning the splitting of the prime, due to Dedekind.

Proposition 25. *Let A be a Dedekind ring with quotient field K. Let E be a finite separable extension of K. Let B be the integral closure of A in E and assume that $B = A[\alpha]$ for some element α. Let $f(X)$ be the irreducible polynomial of α over K. Let $\mathfrak{p}$ be a prime of A. Let $\bar{f}$ be the reduction of f and $\mathfrak{p}$, and let*

$$\bar{f}(X) = \bar{P}_1(X)^{e_1} \cdots \bar{P}_r(X)^{e_r}$$

be the factorization of $\bar{f}$ into powers of irreducible factors over $\bar{A} = A/\mathfrak{p}$, with leading coefficients 1. *Then*

$$\mathfrak{p}B = \mathfrak{P}_1^{e_1} \cdots \mathfrak{P}_r^{e_r}$$

is the factorization of $\mathfrak{p}$ in B, so that e_i is the ramification index of $\mathfrak{P}_i$ over $\mathfrak{p}$, and we have

$$\mathfrak{P}_i = \mathfrak{p}B + P_i(\alpha)B,$$

if $P_i(X) \in A[X]$ is a polynomial with leading coefficient 1 *whose reduction* mod $\mathfrak{p}$ *is $\bar{P}_i$.*

Proof. Let $\bar{P}$ be an irreducible factor of $\bar{f}$, let $\bar{\alpha}$ be a root of $\bar{P}$, and let $\mathfrak{P}$ be the prime of B which is the kernel of the map

$$A[\alpha] \to \bar{A}[\bar{\alpha}].$$

It is clear that $\mathfrak{p}B + P(\alpha)B$ is contained in $\mathfrak{P}$. Conversely, let $g(\alpha) \in \mathfrak{P}$ for some $g(X) \in A[X]$. Then $\bar{g} = \overline{Ph}$ with some $\bar{h} \in \bar{A}[X]$, and hence $g - Ph$, which is a polynomial with coefficients in $\mathfrak{o}$, in fact has coefficients in $\mathfrak{p}$. This proves the reverse inclusion, and proves the last formula of our proposition.

Finally, let e_i' be the ramification index of $\mathfrak{P}_i$, so that

$$\mathfrak{p}B = \mathfrak{P}_1^{e_1'} \cdots \mathfrak{P}_r^{e_r'},$$

and let d_i be the residue class degree $[B/\mathfrak{P}_i : A/\mathfrak{p}]$. It is clear that d_i is the degree of $\bar{P}_i$. Since $f(\alpha) = 0$, and since

$$f(X) - P_1(X)^{e_1} \cdots P_r(X)^{e_r} \in \mathfrak{p}A[X],$$

it follows that

$$(*) \qquad P_1(\alpha)^{e_1} \cdots P_r(\alpha)^{e_r} \in \mathfrak{p}B.$$

On the other hand, we see that

$$\mathfrak{P}_i^{e_i} \subset \mathfrak{p}B + P_i(\alpha)^{e_i}B,$$

whence using (*) we find

$$\mathfrak{P}_1^{e_1} \cdots \mathfrak{P}_r^{e_r} \subset \mathfrak{p}B + P_1(\alpha)^{e_1} \cdots \mathfrak{P}_r(\alpha)^{e_r}B \subset \mathfrak{p}B = \mathfrak{P}_1^{e_1'} \cdots \mathfrak{P}_r^{e_r'}.$$

This proves that $e_i \geqq e_i'$ for all i. But we know that

$$\sum e_i d_i = \deg f = [E:F] = \sum e_i' d_i.$$

It follows that $e_i = e_i'$ for all i, thus proving our theorem.

Remark. The hypothesis that $B = A[\alpha]$ for some α is not always satisfied, but if we are interested in the decomposition of a single prime $\mathfrak{p}$, then it suffices to look at the localization $B_{\mathfrak{p}}$ over $A_{\mathfrak{p}}$, and in that case $B_{\mathfrak{p}}$ can be generated by a single element except for a finite number of exceptions. See Proposition 16 of Chapter III, §3.

Example. Let $\alpha^3 = 2$, and let $E = \mathbf{Q}(\alpha)$. It can be shown that the ring of algebraic integers $\mathfrak{o}_E$ is precisely $\mathbf{Z}[\alpha]$. Let $p = 5$. Then we have

$$X^3 - 2 \equiv (X - 3)(X^2 + 3X - 1) \pmod 5,$$

and $X^2 + 3X - 1$ is irreducible mod 5. Hence the prime ideal (5) of $\mathbf{Z}$ has the decomposition

$$5\mathfrak{o}_E = \mathfrak{p}_1\mathfrak{p}_2$$

where $\mathfrak{p}_1$ has residue class degree 1, and $\mathfrak{p}_2$ has residue class degree 2 over $\mathbf{Z}/5\mathbf{Z}$.

CHAPTER II

Completions

This chapter introduces the completions of number fields under the $\mathfrak{p}$-adic topologies, and also the completions obtained by embedding the number field into the real or complex numbers.

In §3 we discuss the rough structure of complete fields.

In §4 and §5 we cover the basic facts concerning unramified and tamely ramified extensions. For the higher ramification theory, we refer the reader to Artin-Tate [3]. In §4 and §5 we deal with complete Dedekind rings. We define the notions of $\mathfrak{P}$ unramified, tamely ramified, and totally ramified above $\mathfrak{p}$. These can also be defined globally, since they will depend only on the ramification index and residue class degree. However, in the local case, we can also apply them to the field extension, since to each finite extension of the ground field K there is exactly one $\mathfrak{P}$ above $\mathfrak{p}$.

It is useful to think of finite extensions of a number field as coverings, and of completions as analogous to power-series fields in the theory of functions. Absolute values measure something like the order of a zero or pole of a function.

§1. *Definitions and completions*

Let K be a field. An **absolute value** on K is a real valued function $x \mapsto |x|_v$ on K satisfying the following three properties:

AV 1. *We have* $|x|_v \geqq 0$ *and* $= 0$ *if and only if* $x = 0$.

AV 2. *For all* $x, y \in K$ *we have* $|xy|_v = |x|_v |y|_v$.

AV 3. $|x + y|_v \leqq |x|_v + |y|_v$.

If instead of **AV 3** the absolute value satisfies the stronger condition

AV 4. $|x + y|_v \leqq \max(|x|_v, |y|_v)$,

then we shall say that it is a **valuation** or that it is non-archimedean.

The absolute value which is such that $|x| = 1$ for all $x \neq 0$ is called **trivial.** We shall assume from now on that none of the absolute values we deal with are trivial.

When v is fixed throughout a discussion, we omit it from the notation, and write $|x|$ instead of $|x|_v$.

An absolute value $|\ |$ defines a distance function $(x, y) \mapsto |x - y|$, and thus a topology on the field. Two (non-trivial) absolute values are called **dependent** if they define the same topology. If they do not, they are called **independent.** *It is clear that if* $|\ |_1$ *and* $|\ |_2$ *are absolute values such that there exists some* $\lambda > 0$ *for which*

$$|x|_1 = |x|_2^\lambda, \qquad \text{all } x \in K,$$

then they are dependent. The converse is also true, and thus the weakest notion of dependence implies the strongest. *This is easily seen as follows.* The set of $x \in K$ such that $|x|_1 < 1$ is the same as the set such that $\lim x^n = 0$ for $n \to \infty$. Then if $x \in K$ and $|x|_1 > 1$ we conclude that $|x|_2 > 1$ also, because $|x^{-1}|_1 < 1$. Since the absolute values are assumed to be non-trivial, there exists $y \in K$ such that $|y|_1 > 1$. Let $a = |y|_1$ and let $b = |y|_2$. Let $x \in K$, $x \neq 0$. Say $|x| \geqq 1$. Then $|x|_1 = |y|_1^\alpha$ for some $\alpha \geqq 0$. If m, n are integers > 0 such that $m/n > \alpha$, we have

$$|x|_1 < |y|_1^{m/n},$$

whence $|x^n/y^m|_1 < 1$, and thus $|x^n/y^m|_2 < 1$, so that

$$|x|_2 < |y|_2^{m/n}.$$

Similarly if m, n are integers such that $m/n < \alpha$, then

$$|x|_2 > |y|_2^{m/n}.$$

Hence $|x|_2 = |y|_2^\alpha$. From this it follows immediately that

$$|x|_1 = |x|_2^\lambda,$$

where $\lambda = (\log a)/(\log b)$, thus proving our assertion.

Let v be an absolute value on K. We say that K is **complete** if every Cauchy sequence in K has a limit (i.e. converges). Suppose that K is complete, and let E be a finite extension of K. Assume that we have extended the absolute value to E in some way. Since E is a finite dimensional vector space over K, it is easy to verify that all extensions of v to E are equivalent, and we shall recall the proof below. Since two of them are positive powers of each other, and since they coincide on K, we conclude that they must be equal. Thus we get:

If K is complete under an absolute value, then an extension of this absolute value to a finite extension is uniquely determined. In particular, if E is a *finite extension of* K *and* $\sigma : E \to \sigma E$ *is an isomorphism of* E *over* K, *then*

$$|\sigma\alpha| = |\alpha|$$

for every $\alpha \in E$.

We now recall the result about finite dimensional vector spaces over complete fields.

Let k *be complete with respect to an absolute value. Let* V *be a finite dimensional vector space over* k. *Then all norms on* V *are equivalent.*

By a **norm** on V we mean of course a function which satisfies the same properties as an absolute value, namely its values are real $\geqq 0$, and $|x| > 0$ if $x \neq 0$, the triangle inequality holds, namely

$$|x + y| \leqq |x| + |y|$$

and we have

$$|cx| = |c|\,|x| \qquad c \in k,\ x \in V.$$

We say that two norms are **equivalent** if each one is less than or equal to a positive constant times the other.

The reader can refer to my *Algebra* for a proof in the general case. We give here a slightly simpler argument valid when k is locally compact, which is the only case that matters for this book. Let $\{\alpha_1, \ldots, \alpha_n\}$ be a basis for V over k, and let $\|\ \|$ be the sup norm with respect to this basis. We let $|\ |$ be any other norm. If $x \in V$ and $x_i \in k$ are its coordinates with respect to our basis, then

$$|x| = |x_1\alpha_1 + \cdots + x_n\alpha_n| \leqq C\|x\|,$$

where $C = n \cdot \sup \|\alpha_i\|$. This proves one inequality, and shows that the norm $|\ |$ is continuous with respect to $\|\ \|$. Hence $|\ |$ has a minimum on the unit sphere with respect to $\|\ \|$ (by local compactness), say at the point $v \in V$, so that

$$|v| \leqq |x|, \qquad \text{all } x \in V,\ \|x\| = 1.$$

Let $y \in V$, $y \neq 0$ and write

$$y = y_1\alpha_1 + \cdots + y_n\alpha_n, \qquad y_i \in k.$$

Let j be such that $|y_j| = \max |y_i| = \|y\|$. Then $y = y_j x$ with $\|x\| = 1$, and

$$|v| \leqq |x| = |y/y_j| = |y|/|y_j|.$$

It follows that

$$|v|\,\|y\| \leqq |y|,$$

thus proving the other inequality, and concluding the proof of our assertion.

The vector space V is like n-space over k with respect to the sup norm, and is thus complete with respect to the sup norm, because a sequence in V is Cauchy if and only if the sequences of coordinates with respect to the given basis are Cauchy (in k). From the equivalence of any norm with the sup norm, *we conclude that V is complete with respect to any norm.* All of this applies to a finite extension of k, which may be viewed as a normed vector space over k.

We shall be mostly concerned with the following examples.

Let $K = \mathbf{Q}$ be the rational numbers. Then we have the ordinary absolute value.

For each prime number p we have the p-adic valuation $v_p = |\ |_p$, defined by the formula

$$|p^r m/n|_p = 1/p^r,$$

where r is an integer, and m, n are integers $\neq 0$ and not divisible by p.

Let $\mathfrak{o}$ be a discrete valuation ring with maximal ideal $\mathfrak{m}$, generated by an element π. Every non-zero element α of the quotient field K of $\mathfrak{o}$ can be written in the form $\alpha = \pi^r u$, where r is an integer and u is a unit in $\mathfrak{o}$. We call r the order of α. Let c be a positive real number, $0 < c < 1$. If we define

$$|\alpha| = c^r,$$

then we get an absolute value on K (trivial verification), which is in fact a valuation.

There is of course considerable arbitrariness in the choice of the constant c. In number fields, we shall deal with two possible normalizations of this constant.

Let A be the integral closure of the integers $\mathbf{Z}$ in an algebraic number field K, and let $\mathfrak{p}$ be a prime of A. Let π have order 1 at $\mathfrak{p}$, and let p be the prime number generating $\mathfrak{p} \cap \mathbf{Z}$. Then $p = \pi^e u$ for some integer $e > 0$ and a unit u at $\mathfrak{p}$. Let $f = f_{\mathfrak{p}}$ be the degree of $A/\mathfrak{p}$ over $\mathbf{Z}/p\mathbf{Z}$. The residue class field $A/\mathfrak{p}$ is an extension of degree f over $\mathbf{Z}/p\mathbf{Z}$, and hence has p^f elements. We denote by $\mathbf{N}\mathfrak{p}$ the number of elements in $A/\mathfrak{p}$. We now have two absolute values determined by $\mathfrak{p}$. On the one hand the unique absolute value such that

$$|p|_{\mathfrak{p}} = \frac{1}{p} \qquad \text{and} \qquad |\pi|_{\mathfrak{p}} = \frac{1}{p^{1/e}},$$

and on the other hand the unique absolute value such that

$$\|\pi\|_{\mathfrak{p}} = \frac{1}{\mathbf{N}\mathfrak{p}}.$$

For any $\alpha \in K$, $\alpha \neq 0$, we have

$$\|\alpha\|_{\mathfrak{p}} = |\alpha|_{\mathfrak{p}}^{e_{\mathfrak{p}} f_{\mathfrak{p}}}.$$

Similarly, if L is a finite extension of K, and $\mathfrak{P}$ lies above $\mathfrak{p}$ in the ring of algebraic integers B of L, let Π be an element of order 1 at $\mathfrak{P}$. Then

$$\mathfrak{p}B = \mathfrak{P}^{e(\mathfrak{P}/\mathfrak{p})} \cdots$$

and

$$|\pi|_{\mathfrak{P}} = |\Pi|_{\mathfrak{P}}^{e(\mathfrak{P}/\mathfrak{p})}.$$

The fact that ramification indices and residue class degrees are multiplicative in towers insures the consistency of these definitions when we go to finite extensions.

Given a p-adic valuation on $\mathbf{Q}$, any extension of it to a number field K comes from some prime ideal in the integral closure A of $\mathbf{Z}$ in K. Indeed, if $\mathfrak{o}$ is the given valuation ring in K, and $\mathfrak{m}$ its maximal ideal, then $\mathfrak{m} \cap A$ cannot be 0, and hence is a maximal ideal $\mathfrak{p}$. It is then trivial to verify that $\mathfrak{o} = A_{\mathfrak{p}}$. Thus from our point of view of Dedekind rings and integral closure, we recover all the valuations on K which induce p-adic valuations on $\mathbf{Q}$.

If K is a number field, then every embedding of K into the real or complex numbers will induce an absolute value on K, which will be called **real** or **complex** accordingly.

Let K be a number field. The set of absolute values on K consisting of the $\mathfrak{p}$-adic absolute values $|\ |_{\mathfrak{p}}$ described above, and of the absolute values induced by embedding K in $\mathbf{C}$ or $\mathbf{R}$ will be called the **canonical set,** and will be denoted by M_K. The real or complex absolute values in M_K are also called **archimedean.**

If E is a finite extension of K and $v \in M_K$, then any absolute value w on E extending v lies in M_E, and we write

$$w|v.$$

It is clear that two distinct absolute values in our canonical set are independent, in the sense that they induce distinct topologies on K. We shall prove the approximation theorem, which is the analogue for absolute values of the Chinese remainder theorem, and is due to Artin–Whaples.

Theorem 1. *Let K be a field and $|\ |_1, \ldots, |\ |_s$ non-trivial pairwise independent absolute values on K. Let $x_1, \ldots, x_s$ be elements of K, and $\epsilon > 0$.*

Then there exists $x \in K$ *such that*

$$|x - x_i|_i < \epsilon$$

for all i.

Proof. Consider first two of our absolute values, say v_1 and v_s. By hypothesis we can find $\alpha \in K$ such that $|\alpha|_1 < 1$ and $|\alpha|_s \geqq 1$. Similarly, we can find $\beta \in K$ such that $|\beta|_1 \geqq 1$ and $|\beta|_s < 1$. Let $y = \beta/\alpha$. Then $|y|_1 > 1$ and $|y|_s < 1$.

We shall prove that there exists $z \in K$ such that $|z|_1 > 1$ and $|z|_j < 1$ for $j = 2, \ldots, s$. We prove this by induction, the case $s = 2$ having just been proved. Suppose that we have found $z \in K$ satisfying

$$|z|_1 > 1 \qquad \text{and} \qquad |z|_j < 1 \quad \text{for } j = 2, \ldots, s - 1.$$

If $|z|_s \leqq 1$, then the element $z^n y$ for large n will satisfy our requirements.

If $|z|_s > 1$, then the sequence

$$t_n = z^n/(1 + z^n)$$

tends to 1 at v_1 and v_s, but tends to 0 at v_j ($j = 2, \ldots, s - 1$). For large n, it is then clear that $t_n y$ satisfies our requirements.

Using the element z that we have just constructed, we see that the sequence

$$\frac{z^n}{1 + z^n}$$

tends to 1 at v_1 and to 0 at v_j for $j = 2, \ldots, s$. For each $i = 1, \ldots, s$ we can therefore construct an element z_i which is very close to 1 at v_i and very close to 0 at v_j for $j \neq i$. The element

$$x = z_1 x_1 + \cdots + z_s x_s$$

then satisfies the requirement of the theorem.

Let K be a number field, and v an absolute value (assumed from now on to be always in the canonical set). Then we can form the completion of K in the same way as one constructs the real numbers from the rationals. We consider Cauchy sequences in K. These form a ring. The null sequences form a maximal ideal, and the residue class ring is a field K_v. Our field K is naturally embedded in K_v (by means of the sequences whose elements consist of a fixed element of K), and the absolute value on K can be extended to K_v by continuity. We usually identify K inside K_v, and call K_v the **completion** of K.

If v is archimedean, then K_v is the field of real or complex numbers. In fact, K_v contains the closure of the rational numbers, which is $\mathbf{R}$.

View K as embedded in K_v, as well as $\mathbf{R}$. Then $K\mathbf{R}$ is a finite extension of $\mathbf{R}$, and hence equal to $\mathbf{R}$ or $\mathbf{C}$ (in the latter case, determined up to complex conjugation). But $K\mathbf{R}$ is then complete, hence closed, so that $K\mathbf{R} = K_v$.

If v is non-archimedean, i.e. is a valuation, corresponding to a prime ideal $\mathfrak{p}$ of the ring of algebraic integers of K, then K_v will also be written $K_{\mathfrak{p}}$, and will be called the field of **$\mathfrak{p}$-adic numbers.** We shall now consider in greater detail the situation when $v = v_{\mathfrak{p}}$ is a $\mathfrak{p}$-adic valuation.

Let A be the integral closure of $\mathbf{Z}$ in K, i.e. the ring of algebraic integers of K. Denote by A_v the closure of A in K_v, and let $x \in A_v$. Select $y \in A$ such that

$$|x - y| < |x|$$

($| \; | = | \; |_{\mathfrak{p}}$). Then $|y| = |y - x + x| = |x|$ because of the non-archimedean nature of our valuation. Since all elements of A have a $\mathfrak{p}$-adic absolute value which is $\leqq 1$, it follows that all elements of A_v have a $\mathfrak{p}$-adic absolute value $\leqq 1$. A similar argument shows that the closure of $\mathfrak{p}$ consists of elements of A_v which have absolute value < 1, and that an element $x \in K_v$ which does not lie in A_v has absolute value > 1. In particular, the value group on K_v and K is the same, and is infinite cyclic. If π is an element of order 1 at $\mathfrak{p}$ in A, then $|\pi|$ generates this value group.

Let $\mathfrak{o} = A_{\mathfrak{p}}$ be the local ring at $\mathfrak{p}$. All the elements of $\mathfrak{o}$ have a $\mathfrak{p}$-adic absolute value $\leqq 1$ because their orders at $\mathfrak{p}$ are $\geqq 0$. Hence $\mathfrak{o}$ lies in the closure of A, and hence the closure of $\mathfrak{o}$ in K_v is the same as the closure of A. It is called the ring of **$\mathfrak{p}$-adic integers** in K_v. Let $\mathfrak{m}_{\mathfrak{p}}$ be the maximal ideal of $A_{\mathfrak{p}}$. Then we have canonical isomorphisms

$$A_{\mathfrak{p}}/\mathfrak{m}_{\mathfrak{p}} \leftrightarrow A/\mathfrak{p} \leftrightarrow A_v/\mathfrak{p}_v$$

if we denote by $\mathfrak{p}_v$ the closure of $\mathfrak{p}$ in A_v.

In view of the above remarks, every element $\alpha \neq 0$ in K_v has an expression

$$\alpha = \pi^r u,$$

where $|u|_{\mathfrak{p}} = 1$, and u is therefore a unit in the closure A_v of A. Hence A_v is a unique factorization domain with precisely one prime, and is therefore a discrete valuation ring.

Let E be a finite extension of K, B the integral closure of A in E, and $\mathfrak{P}$ a prime of B lying above $\mathfrak{p}$. Let w be the canonical absolute value corresponding to $\mathfrak{P}$. Then we have a commutative diagram:

$$\begin{array}{ccc} B & \rightarrow & B_w \\ \uparrow & & \uparrow \\ A & \rightarrow & A_v \end{array}$$

the arrows on the top, bottom, and left being inclusions, and the right vertical arrow mapping A_v on the closure of A in B_w. Similarly, we have a commutative diagram of residue class fields:

$$\begin{array}{ccc} B/\mathfrak{P} & \rightarrow & B_w/\mathfrak{P}_w \\ \uparrow & & \uparrow \\ A/\mathfrak{p} & \rightarrow & A_v/\mathfrak{p}_v \end{array}$$

the vertical arrows being injections, and the horizontal arrows being isomorphisms.

Let K_w be the closure of K in E_w. Then the composite field EK_w is a finite extension of K_w contained in E_w. We know that EK_w is complete, hence closed, hence equal to E_w. The same argument of course applies also to the case when v, w are both induced by embeddings into the real or complex numbers.

Theorem 2. *Let K be a number field, v one of its canonical absolute values, E a finite extension of K. Two embeddings σ, $\tau : E \rightarrow \overline{K}_v$ over K give rise to the same absolute value on L if and only if they are conjugate over K_v.*

(By conjugate over K_v we mean that there exists an isomorphism λ of $\sigma E \cdot K_v$ onto $\tau E \cdot K_v$ which is the identity on K_v.)

Proof. Suppose that the two embeddings are conjugate over K_v. Then the uniqueness of the extension of the absolute value from K_v to $\overline{K}_v$ guarantees that the induced absolute values on E are equal. Conversely, suppose that this is the case. Let

$$\lambda : \tau E \rightarrow \sigma E$$

be an isomorphism over K. We shall prove that λ extends to an isomorphism of $\tau E \cdot K_v$ onto $\sigma E \cdot K_v$ over K_v. Since τE is dense in $\tau E \cdot K_v$, an element $x \in \tau E \cdot K_v$ can be written

$$x = \lim \tau x_n$$

with $x_n \in E$. Since the absolute values induced by σ and τ on E coincide, it follows that the sequence

$$\{\lambda \tau x_n\} = \{\sigma x_n\}$$

converges to an element of $\sigma E \cdot K_v$ which we denote by λx. One then verifies immediately that λx is independent of the particular sequence

τx_n used, and that the map

$$\lambda : \tau E \cdot K_v \to \sigma E \cdot K_v$$

is an isomorphism, which clearly leaves K_v fixed. This proves our assertion.

This result gives a clear picture of the nature of the extensions of v to E, including the archimedean absolute values.

Corollary 1. *Let K be a number field and E a finite extension, of degree n. Let $v \in M_K$ and for each absolute value w on E extending v, let n_w be the local degree,*

$$n_w = [E_w : K_v].$$

Then

$$\sum_{w \mid v} n_w = n.$$

Proof. Immediate from Theorem 2 and the fact that for a finite separable extension, the degree is equal to the number of conjugates.

Corollary 2. *Let K be a number field, and v_0 an absolute value in $M_{\mathbf{Q}}$. Let $\alpha \in K$. Then*

$$\prod_{v \mid v_0} |\alpha|_v^{n_v} = |N_{\mathbf{Q}}^K(\alpha)|_{v_0}.$$

Corollary 3. *Let k be a number field and E a finite extension. Let $v \in M_k$ and for each $w|v$ in E, let N_w be the local norm from E_w to k_v, and Tr_w the local trace. Then*

$$N_k^E(\alpha) = \prod_{w \mid v} N_w(\alpha),$$

and

$$\mathrm{Tr}_k^E(\alpha) = \sum_{w \mid v} \mathrm{Tr}_w(\alpha)$$

for all $\alpha \in E$.

Remark. From Corollary 1, viewing a number field as a finite extension of $\mathbf{Q}$, we see immediately that we have an isomorphism

$$K \otimes_{\mathbf{Q}} \mathbf{Q}_{v_0} \approx \prod_{v \mid v_0} K_v$$

if v_0 is a fixed absolute value in $M_{\mathbf{Q}}$.

Let K be a number field and E a finite extension of degree n. Let v be an absolute value in M_K. We shall say that v **splits completely** in E if there exist precisely n extensions of v to E. From Theorem 2, we see at once that v splits completely in E if and only if every embedding σ of E

into $\overline{K}_v$ over K maps E into K_v, i.e. $(\sigma E)K_v = K_v$. From this we immediately obtain some basic properties concerning the case when v splits completely as follows:

SC 1. *Let $E \supset F \supset K$ be finite extensions. An absolute value v in M_K splits completely in E if and only if it splits completely in F, and every $w|v$ in F splits completely in E.*

SC 2. *If v splits completely in E, if K_1/K is finite, and $v_1|v$ in K_1, then v_1 splits completely in EK_1.*

SC 3. *If E_1, E_2 are finite extensions of K, and v splits completely in E_1 and E_2, then v splits completely in the compositum E_1E_2.*

The proofs are immediate.

Let A be a Dedekind ring. Its group of fractional ideals is isomorphic to the free abelian group generated by the prime ideals. If $\mathfrak{p}$ is a prime ideal, and $A_\mathfrak{p}$ the local ring at $\mathfrak{p}$, then the group of fractional ideals of $A_\mathfrak{p}$ is infinite cyclic, generated by the maximal ideal $\mathfrak{m}_\mathfrak{p}$ of $A_\mathfrak{p}$. If v is the absolute value determined by $\mathfrak{p}$ and A_v the completion of A (or $A_\mathfrak{p}$), then A_v is also a Dedekind ring, and its group of fractional ideals is infinite cyclic, generated by $\mathfrak{p}_v$. Thus we have natural maps:

$$I(A_v) \to I(A_\mathfrak{p}) \to I(A),$$

the first arrow being a bijection, and the second an inclusion. It is convenient to make an abuse of language, and occasionally to identify $\mathfrak{p}_v$, $\mathfrak{m}_\mathfrak{p}$, and $\mathfrak{p}$ and just call any one of them $\mathfrak{p}$. A product

$$\mathfrak{d} = \prod_{\mathfrak{p}} \mathfrak{p}^{r_\mathfrak{p}}$$

with integers $r_\mathfrak{p}$ all but a finite number of which are 0 could be called a **formal ideal,** and according to the context can be interpreted as an element of $I(A)$, $I(A_\mathfrak{p})$, or $I(A_v)$. We shall call $\mathfrak{p}^{r_\mathfrak{p}}$ its **$\mathfrak{p}$-component** and denote it by $\mathfrak{d}_\mathfrak{p}$. We say that $r_\mathfrak{p}$ is the **order of $\mathfrak{d}$ at $\mathfrak{p}$** and write

$$r_\mathfrak{p} = \mathrm{ord}_\mathfrak{p}\mathfrak{d}.$$

If $\alpha \neq 0$ is an element of the quotient field of A or of A_v, then we can form the principal fractional ideals αA, $\alpha A_\mathfrak{p}$, or αA_v and the orders of these at $\mathfrak{p}$ are all equal to the same integer, $\mathrm{ord}_\mathfrak{p}\, \alpha$.

If α, β are two such elements, we write

$$\alpha \equiv \beta \pmod{\mathfrak{d}}$$

if $\mathrm{ord}_\mathfrak{p}(\alpha - \beta) \geqq \mathrm{ord}_\mathfrak{p}\, \mathfrak{d}$. If α, β lie in the quotient field of A and we view $\mathfrak{d}$ as being a fractional ideal, then this means that $\alpha - \beta$ lies in $\mathfrak{d}$ and is a congruence in the usual sense. It is convenient to visualize it as applying simultaneously to any one of the three above rings if $\mathfrak{d} = \mathfrak{p}^r$ is the power of a single $\mathfrak{p}$.

Suppose that A is a Dedekind ring and $\mathfrak{p}$ a prime of A, with a corresponding valuation v. Let A_v be the closure of A in the completion K_v of the quotient field, and $\mathfrak{p}_v$ the closure of $\mathfrak{p}$ in A_v. Then A_v is a discrete valuation ring. If $\mathfrak{a}$ is a fractional ideal of A, then we have trivially:

$$\mathfrak{a}A_v = \mathfrak{p}_v^{r_\mathfrak{p}}$$

if $r_\mathfrak{p} = \text{ord}_\mathfrak{p}\, \mathfrak{a}$. Conversely, given a fractional ideal $\mathfrak{p}_v^r$ of A_v, we have

$$\mathfrak{p}_v^r \cap A = \mathfrak{p}^r.$$

The closure of the fractional ideal $\mathfrak{a}$ in A_v is $\mathfrak{a}A_v$. All these statements are trivial to verify, and we leave the details to the reader.

§2. *Polynomials in complete fields*

Throughout this section, we assume that K is a field complete under a valuation, and we let $\mathfrak{o}$ be the ring of integers, i.e. the set of elements of absolute value $\leqq 1$. We don't need to assume that the valuation is discrete. We let $\mathfrak{p}$ be the maximal ideal of $\mathfrak{o}$. We observe that a series

$$\sum_{n=1}^{\infty} a_n$$

with $a_n \in K$ converges if and only if

$$\lim_{n\to\infty} a_n = 0.$$

Thus convergence is easier to deal with than in the archimedean case.

We now discuss the possibility of finding roots to certain polynomials in complete fields.

Proposition 1. *Let m be a positive integer such that*

$$m \not\equiv 0 \pmod{\mathfrak{p}}.$$

Then for any $x \in \mathfrak{p}$ the binomial series of $(1 + x)^{1/m}$ converges to an m-th root of $1 + x$ in U.

Proof. Obvious, because the binomial coefficients have no p in the denominators.

It is frequently necessary to have a more refined criterion for the existence of a root.

Proposition 2. *Let $f(X)$ be a polynomial with coefficients in $\mathfrak{o}$. Let α_0 be an element of $\mathfrak{o}$ such that*

$$|f(\alpha_0)| < |f'(\alpha_0)^2|$$

(here f' denotes the formal derivative of f). Then the sequence

$$\alpha_{i+1} = \alpha_i - \frac{f(\alpha_i)}{f'(\alpha_i)}$$

converges to a root α of $f(X)$ in $\mathfrak{o}$. Furthermore,

$$|\alpha - \alpha_0| \leqq \left|\frac{f(\alpha_0)}{f'(\alpha_0)^2}\right| < 1.$$

Proof. Let $c = |f(\alpha_0)/f'(\alpha_0)^2| < 1$. We show inductively that

(i) $|\alpha_i| \leqq 1$,
(ii) $|\alpha_i - \alpha_0| \leqq c$,
(iii) $\left|\dfrac{f(\alpha_i)}{f'(\alpha_i)^2}\right| \leqq c^{2^i}$.

These three conditions obviously imply our proposition. If $i = 0$, they are hypotheses. By induction, assume them for i. Then:

(i) $\left|\dfrac{f(\alpha_i)}{f'(\alpha_i)^2}\right| \leqq c^{2^i}$ gives $|\alpha_{i+1} - \alpha_i| \leqq c^{2^i} < 1$,

whence $|\alpha_{i+1}| \leqq 1$.

(ii) $|\alpha_{i+1} - \alpha_0| \leqq \max\{|\alpha_{i+1} - \alpha_i|, |\alpha_i - \alpha_0|\} = c$.
(iii) By Taylor's expansion, we have

$$f(\alpha_{i+1}) = f(\alpha_i) - f'(\alpha_i)\frac{f(\alpha_i)}{f'(\alpha_i)} + \beta\left(\frac{f(\alpha_i)}{f'(\alpha_i)}\right)^2$$

for some $\beta \in \mathfrak{o}$, and this is less than or equal to

$$\left|\frac{f(\alpha_i)}{f'(\alpha_i)}\right|^2$$

in absolute value.

Using Taylor's expansion on $f'(\alpha_{i+1})$ we conclude that

$$|f'(\alpha_{i+1})| = |f'(\alpha_i)|.$$

From this we get

$$\left|\frac{f(\alpha_{i+1})}{f('\alpha_{i+1})^2}\right| \leqq c^{2^{i+1}}$$

as desired.

(The interested reader can refer to Bourbaki [4] to see a more general formulation of the preceding proposition.)

As an application, we observe that in the 2-adic field $\mathbf{Q}_2$, the equation $x^2 + 7 = 0$ has a root. In fact, for any element $\gamma \equiv 1 \pmod 8$ in $\mathbf{Q}_2$ the equation $x^2 = \gamma$ has a root. We take $\alpha_0 = 1$ in Proposition 2.

Proposition 2 applies also in the trivial case when

$$f(\alpha_0) \equiv 0 \pmod{\mathfrak{p}} \text{ but } f'(\alpha_0) \not\equiv 0 \pmod{\mathfrak{p}}.$$

The solution of the recursive linear equation needed to refine α_0 to a root of f is then more trivial. Another way of characterizing this situation is to say that α_0 is a root of multiplicity 1 of the polynomial f reduced mod $\mathfrak{p}$. We shall call this the **trivial case** of **Hensel's lemma.**

Proposition 2 also shows that every unit of $\mathfrak{o}$ sufficiently close to 1 has an m-th root if m is not divisible by the characteristic of K. Indeed, we need but consider the equation

$$X^m - u = 0$$

and take $\alpha_0 = 1$, provided $|u - 1| < |m|^2$.

We prove next a useful approximation lemma in finite extensions.

Proposition 3. *Let α, β be two elements of the algebraic closure of K, and assume that α is separable over $K(\beta)$. Assume that for all isomorphisms σ of $K(\alpha)$ over K, $\sigma \neq id$, we have*

$$|\beta - \alpha| < |\sigma\alpha - \alpha|.$$

Then $K(\alpha) \subset K(\beta)$.

Proof. It suffices to show that for all isomorphisms of $K(\beta, \alpha)$ over $K(\beta)$ the element α remains fixed. Let τ be such an isomorphism. By the uniqueness of extensions of absolute values over complete fields, applying τ to $\beta - \alpha$ yields for all $\sigma \neq id$:

$$|\beta - \tau\alpha| < |\sigma\alpha - \alpha|.$$

Using the hypothesis, we obtain

$$|\tau\alpha - \alpha| = |\tau\alpha - \beta + \beta - \alpha| < |\sigma\alpha - \alpha|.$$

This implies that τ is the identity, hence $K(\beta, \alpha) = K(\beta)$, as desired.

Proposition 3 is known as **Krasner's lemma.** It is useful in determining extensions of K.

Next, we note the continuity of the roots of a polynomial.

Let $f(X)$ be a polynomial in $K[X]$ having leading coefficient 1 and admitting a factorization

$$f(X) = \prod (X - \alpha_i)^{r_i}$$

in the algebraic closure of K. Say f has degree n, and the α_i are distinct. Let g also have degree n and leading coefficient 1. As usual, we denote by $|g|$ the maximum of the absolute values of the coefficients of g. One sees immediately that if $|g|$ is bounded, then the absolute values of the roots of g are also bounded.

Suppose that g comes close to f, in the sense that $|f - g|$ is small. If β is any root of g, then

$$|f(\beta) - g(\beta)| = |f(\beta)|$$

is small, and hence β must come close to some root of f. As β comes close to say $\alpha = \alpha_1$, its distance from the other roots of f approaches the distance of α_1 from the other roots and is therefore bounded from below. We may say in that case that β **belongs to** α.

If g comes sufficiently close to f, and say $\beta_1, \ldots, \beta_s$ are the roots of g which belong to α (counting multiplicities), then we contend that $s = r$ (the multiplicity of α in f).

If this is not so, then we can find a sequence g_ν as above, approaching f, with precisely s roots $\beta_1^{(\nu)}, \ldots, \beta_s^{(\nu)}$ belonging to α and $s \neq r$. Thus each $\beta_1^{(\nu)}, \ldots, \beta_s^{(\nu)}$ approaches α. But $\lim_\nu g_\nu = f$ and hence α must have multiplicity s in f, contradiction.

As an application, we have:

Proposition 4. *If f is irreducible and separable, then any polynomial g sufficiently close to f is also irreducible. (Both f and g are still assumed to have leading coefficient* 1, *and the same degree.) Furthermore, given a root α of f, there exists a root β of g belonging to α, and $K(\alpha) = K(\beta)$.*

Proof. If g is sufficiently close to f, then its roots have multiplicity 1, and belong to the distinct roots of f. If β is a root of g very close to the root α of f, then Krasner's lemma immediately shows that $K(\alpha) = K(\beta)$. Hence g is irreducible, since it has the same degree as f.

Corollary. *Let K be a finite extension of $\mathbf{Q}_p$. Then there exists a finite extension E of $\mathbf{Q}$ contained in K such that $[E:\mathbf{Q}] = [K:\mathbf{Q}_p]$ and E is dense in K, so that $K = E\mathbf{Q}_p$.*

Proof. Let $K = \mathbf{Q}_p(\alpha)$, let f be the irreducible polynomial of α over $\mathbf{Q}_p$, and take for g a polynomial very close to f as before, but with coefficients in $\mathbf{Q}$. Then let $E = \mathbf{Q}(\beta)$.

In view of this corollary, we call any finite extension of $\mathbf{Q}_p$ also a **$\mathfrak{p}$-adic field.** The integral closure of the p-adic integers in K has a unique maximal ideal which is denoted by $\mathfrak{p}$.

§3. *Some filtrations*

Let $\mathfrak{o}$ be a discrete valuation ring with maximal ideal $\mathfrak{p}$, let K be its quotient field, and assume that K is complete under the valuation induced by $\mathfrak{o}$. Let π be a generator for $\mathfrak{p}$. This notation will stay fixed throughout the section. We also fix a valuation corresponding to $\mathfrak{o}$.

We know that in the topology given by the valuation, we have subgroups $\mathfrak{p}^r$ ($r = 1, 2, \ldots$) which are **open** in the topology. Indeed, given $x \in K$, if y is an element of K such that $|x - y| < |x|$, then $|y| = |x|$. Thus the $\mathfrak{p}^r$ are open subgroups whose intersection is 0. Consequently, they form a fundamental system of neighborhoods of 0 in K. (We let $\mathfrak{p}^0 = \mathfrak{o}$ by definition.)

As an additive group, each factor group $\mathfrak{p}^r/\mathfrak{p}^{r+1}$ is isomorphic to $\mathfrak{o}/\mathfrak{p}$ under multiplication by π^r.

The units of $\mathfrak{o}$ form a group under multiplication, which will be denoted by U. For each integer $i \geqq 1$ we let

$$U_i = 1 + \mathfrak{p}^i$$

and define $U_0 = U$. Then U_i is a group, because whenever $x, y \in \mathfrak{p}^i$ we see that

$$\begin{aligned}(1 + x)(1 + y) &= 1 + x + y + xy \in 1 + \mathfrak{p}^i \quad (i \geqq 1)\\ &\equiv 1 + x + y \mod(1 + \mathfrak{p}^{i+1})\end{aligned}$$

and

$$(1 - x)^{-1} = 1 + x + x^2 + \cdots$$

is a convergent series.

The units are an open subset of $\mathfrak{o}$.

If π has order 1 at $\mathfrak{p}$, then it is clear that K^* is topologically and algebraically isomorphic to the product $\{\pi\} \times U$ (letting $\{\pi\}$ be the cyclic group generated by π).

Under the canonical map

$$\mathfrak{o} \to \mathfrak{o}/\mathfrak{p}$$

the units map on the non-zero elements of $\mathfrak{o}/\mathfrak{p}$, and the kernel of the induced homomorphism

$$U \to (\mathfrak{o}/\mathfrak{p})^*$$

is precisely U_1. Thus $U/U_1 \approx (\mathfrak{o}/\mathfrak{p})^*$.

Furthermore, for $i \geqq 1$, we have an isomorphism

$$\mathfrak{p}^i/\mathfrak{p}^{i+1} \to U_i/U_{i+1}$$

induced by the map on $\mathfrak{p}^i$ given by

$$x \mapsto (1 + x) \mod U_{i+1}$$

which is immediately verified to be a homomorphism, whose kernel is $\mathfrak{p}^{i+1}$. This map is a truncated exponential map.

If $\mathfrak{o}/\mathfrak{p}$ is a finite field, with q elements, then the number of elements in $\mathfrak{p}^i/\mathfrak{p}^{i+1}$ is also equal to q. The number of elements in U/U_1 is then $q - 1$.

Proposition 5. *If $\mathfrak{o}/\mathfrak{p}$ is finite, then $\mathfrak{o}$ and U are compact.*

Proof. We observe that $\mathfrak{o}$ is the projective limit of the finite groups $\mathfrak{o}/\mathfrak{p}^i$ and hence is compact. (It can be viewed as a closed subgroup of the Cartesian product of the $\mathfrak{o}/\mathfrak{p}^i$.) The same argument applies to U as a projective limit of U/U_i.

The U_i form a fundamental system of neighborhoods of 1 in U.

In view of Proposition 5, we conclude that a $\mathfrak{p}$-adic field is locally compact.

As we remarked in the preceding section, every unit of a $\mathfrak{p}$-adic field sufficiently close to 1 is an m-th power. Thus given a positive integer m, the index $(U : U^m)$ is finite. We shall now determine this index.

We need a group theoretic lemma.

Lemma. *Let f be a homomorphism of a commutative group A into some other group. We denote the image of f by A^f and its kernel by A_f. Let B be a subgroup of A. Then*

$$(A : B) = (A^f : B^f)(A_f : B_f)$$

in the sense that if two of the indices are finite, so is the third and the equality holds.

Proof. Consider the composite homomorphism of f and the canonical map

$$A \to A^f \to A^f/B^f.$$

Its kernel in A is $B + A_f$, and hence we have an isomorphism

$$A/(B + A_f) \approx A^f/B^f.$$

But $A \supset B + A_f \supset B$, and

$$(B + A_f)/B \approx A_f/(A_f \cap B) = A_f/B_f.$$

Our lemma follows at once.

Proposition 6. *Let K be a $\mathfrak{p}$-adic field and U the units of its ring of integers. Let m be a positive integer. Then*

$$(U : U^m) = \frac{1}{\|m\|_{\mathfrak{p}}} (K_m^* : 1)$$

and

$$(K^* : K^{*m}) = \frac{m}{\|m\|_{\mathfrak{p}}} (K_m^* : 1)$$

(where K_m^* is the group of m-th roots of unity contained in K).

Proof. The second formula follows from the first by recalling that $K^* \approx \mathbf{Z} \times U$.

We now consider the unit index, and the proof is taken from Artin [1].

Take r so large that $|m\pi^{r+1}| \geqq |\pi^{2r}|$ and consider the group U_r. Then for any integral x,

$$(1 + x\pi^r)^m \equiv 1 + mx\pi^r \pmod{m\pi^{r+1}}.$$

Thus if $\mathrm{ord}_{\mathfrak{p}}\, m = s$, we have

$$U_r^m = U_{r+s}.$$

Take r sufficiently large that no m-th root of unity except 1 lies in U_r. We apply the lemma to the homomorphism $f(a) = a^m$, applied to the units. We obtain

$$\begin{aligned}(U\colon U_r) &= (U^m : U_{r+s})(K_m^* : 1) \\ &= \frac{(U : U_{r+s})}{(U : U^m)} (K_m^* : 1).\end{aligned}$$

Hence

$$(U : U^m) = \frac{(U : U_{r+s})}{(U : U_r)} (K_m^* : 1) = (U_r : U_{r+s})(K_m^* : 1).$$

But $(U_r : U_{r+s}) = (\mathbf{N}\mathfrak{p})^s$ and our assertion follows.

Corollary. *If K contains the m-th roots of unity, then*

$$(U:U^m) = \frac{m}{\|m\|_{\mathfrak{p}}} \quad \text{and} \quad (K^*:K^{*m}) = \frac{m^2}{\|m\|_{\mathfrak{p}}}\cdot$$

§4. *Unramified extensions*

We continue to assume that K is complete under a discrete valuation, with ring A and maximal ideal $\mathfrak{p}$.

If E is a finite extension of K and B the integral closure of A in E, then there is a unique prime ideal $\mathfrak{P}$ of B lying above $\mathfrak{p}$, and B is a discrete valuation ring. If e is the ramification index and f the residue class degree, then

$$ef = [E:K].$$

(In this book, we have proved this only when E is separable over K. As we are primarily interested in number fields, we don't give the proof in general. The reader may assume that K has characteristic 0 if he wishes.)

We see that $e = 1$ if and only if

$$[E:K] = [B/\mathfrak{P}:\mathfrak{o}/\mathfrak{p}].$$

If this equality holds and the residue class field extension $B/\mathfrak{P}$ over $A/\mathfrak{p}$ is separable, then we shall say that $\mathfrak{P}$ is **unramified** over $\mathfrak{p}$, or that E is unramified over K.

Let $\varphi: B \to B/\mathfrak{P}$ be the canonical homomorphism. If

$$g = \beta_n X^n + \cdots + \beta_0$$

is a polynomial with coefficients in B, then we denote by g^φ the polynomial $\varphi(\beta_n)X^n + \cdots + \varphi(\beta_0)$, obtained by applying the map φ to the coefficients of g.

Proposition 7. *Let E be finite over K, and assume that $\mathfrak{P}$ is unramified over $\mathfrak{p}$. Let $\bar{\alpha} \in B^\varphi$ be such that $B^\varphi = A^\varphi(\bar{\alpha})$ and let α be an element of B such that $\varphi\alpha = \bar{\alpha}$. Then $E = K(\alpha)$, and the irreducible polynomial $g(X)$ of α over K is such that g^φ is irreducible. Conversely, if $E = K(\alpha)$ for some $\alpha \in B$ satisfying a polynomial $g(X)$ in $A(X)$ having leading coefficient 1 and such that g^φ has no multiple root, then $\mathfrak{P}$ is unramified over $\mathfrak{p}$ and $B^\varphi = A^\varphi(\varphi\alpha)$.*

Proof. First assume $\mathfrak{P}$ unramified. Let $\bar{g}(X)$ be the irreducible polynomial of $\bar{\alpha}$ over A^φ. Let α be an element of B such that $\varphi\alpha = \bar{\alpha}$, and let $g(X)$ be its irreducible polynomial over K. Then α is integral over A, and $\bar{\alpha}$ is a root of g^{φ}, whence $\bar{g}$ divides g^{φ}. On the other hand

$$\deg \bar{g} = [B^{\varphi} : A^{\varphi}] = [E : K] \geqq \deg g$$

and so $\bar{g} = g^{\varphi}$. This proves the first statement.

Conversely, if α satisfies the stated condition, then we may assume without loss of generality that its irreducible polynomial $g(X)$ is such that g^{φ} has no multiple roots. We can now apply Corollary 2 of Proposition 14, Chapter I, §5 (to the smallest Galois extension of K containing E) to conclude that g^{φ} is a power of an irreducible polynomial, and hence is irreducible. Using the inequalities

$$[A^{\varphi}(\varphi\alpha) : A^{\varphi}] \leqq [B^{\varphi} : A^{\varphi}] \leqq [E : K]$$

we now conclude that we must have an equality everywhere, and that

$$B^{\varphi} = A^{\varphi}(\varphi\alpha).$$

This proves our proposition.

Proposition 8. *Let E be a finite extension of K.*

(i) *If $E \supset F \supset K$, then E is unramified over K if and only if E is unramified over F and F is unramified over K.*
(ii) *If E is unramified over K, and K_1 is a finite extension of K, then EK_1 is unramified over K_1.*
(iii) *If E_1 and E_2 are finite unramified over K, then so is E_1E_2.*

Proof. The first assertion comes from the fact that the degrees of residue class field extensions are bounded by the degrees of the field extensions, and their multiplicativity property in towers. One must also use the fact that assertion (i) holds when "unramified" is replaced by "a finite separable extension". The second assertion is an immediate consequence of our criterion in Proposition 7. The third comes formally from the first and second.

Proposition 9. *For each finite extension E of K in a given algebraic closure, let B_E be the integral closure of A in E. Let $\bar{A}$ be the integral closure of A in the algebraic closure $\bar{K}$ of K. Let φ be a homomorphism of $\bar{A}$ such that its restriction to B_E has the maximal ideal $\mathfrak{P}_E$ as kernel. Then the map*

$$B_E \mapsto B_E^{\varphi}$$

induces a bijection between unramified extensions E of K and separable extensions of A^{φ}.

Proof. We have shown in Proposition 7 that every finite separable extension of A^{φ} is obtainable as an image B_E^{φ} for some finite extension E

of K, unramified over K. We now must prove the uniqueness. If $E_1 \subset E_2$ are unramified, then clearly $\varphi B_{E_1} \subset \varphi B_{E_2}$. Let $E_1 = K(\alpha_1)$ and $E_2 = K(\alpha_2)$ be unramified extensions, generated by elements α_1, α_2 respectively satisfying polynomials over A having leading coefficient 1, and whose reductions mod $\mathfrak{p}$ have no multiple roots. Then $E_1E_2 = E_2(\alpha_1)$, and α_1 satisfies with respect to E_2 a similar condition (with the same polynomial as over K). Let $E = E_1E_2$. Using Proposition 7 once more, we conclude that

$$\varphi B_E = \varphi B_{E_2}(\varphi\alpha_1) = A^{\varphi}(\varphi\alpha_1, \varphi\alpha_2) = (\varphi B_{E_1})(\varphi B_{E_2}).$$

If $\varphi B_{E_1} = \varphi B_{E_2}$, we conclude that $E_1 = E_2$, thus proving our proposition.

If we assume that A^{φ} is a finite field, as is the case in number theory, then its algebraic extensions are all separable, and in fact are cyclic. The Galois group is generated by a canonical automorphism, the Frobenius automorphism σ (Chapter I, §5) such that

$$\sigma x = x^q$$

if q is the number of elements in the residue class field $A/\mathfrak{p}$. Thus each finite unramified extension of K is in fact cyclic, and has a uniquely determined automorphism corresponding to σ. In fact, we see that in Proposition 14 of Chapter I, §5 the Galois group G of an unramified extension is equal to $G_{\mathfrak{P}}$ because there is only one $\mathfrak{P}$ above $\mathfrak{p}$, and $G_{\mathfrak{P}}$ is isomorphic to the Galois group of the residue class field extension.

Corollary. *Let K be a $\mathfrak{p}$-adic field (i.e. completion of a number field under a $\mathfrak{p}$-adic valuation). Let E be an unramified extension of K. Then every unit of K is a norm of a unit in E.*

Proof. Let u be a unit in K. We identify the Galois group of E over K with the Galois group of the residue class field extension. It is a simple consequence of Hilbert's Theorem 90 (or anything else you can think of) that both the trace and norm from a finite extension of a finite field are surjective. Hence there exists a unit α_0 in E such that

$$u \equiv N_K^E\alpha_0 \pmod{\mathfrak{p}}.$$

Then

$$uN_K^E\alpha_0^{-1} \equiv 1 + c_1\pi \pmod{\mathfrak{p}^2}.$$

for some $c_1 \in A$. Let

$$\alpha_1 = 1 + \pi x_1$$

with x_1 in B_E. Then

$$N_K^E\alpha_1 \equiv 1 + \mathrm{Tr}(x_1)\pi \pmod{\mathfrak{p}^2}$$

where Tr is the trace, and it is again an easy matter to verify that the trace is surjective in the residue class field extension. Hence we can select x_1 such that

$$\mathrm{Tr}(x_1) \equiv c_1 \pmod{\mathfrak{p}},$$

whence we can find α_1 such that

$$uN_K^E\alpha_0^{-1} \equiv N_K^E\alpha_1 \pmod{\mathfrak{p}^2}.$$

Proceeding inductively, we can find $\alpha_0, \alpha_1, \ldots, \alpha_n$ such that

$$\alpha_n \equiv 1 \pmod{\mathfrak{p}^n}$$

and such that

$$uN_K^E(\alpha_0 \cdots \alpha_n)^{-1} \equiv 1 \pmod{\mathfrak{p}^{n+1}}.$$

The infinite product

$$\prod_{i=0}^{\infty} \alpha_i$$

is convergent to an element α such that

$$N_K^E\alpha = u,$$

thus proving our corollary.

§5. *Tamely ramified extensions*

We still assume that K is complete, under a discrete valuation, with Dedekind ring A and maximal ideal $\mathfrak{p}$, and we assume that $A/\mathfrak{p}$ is perfect.

If E is a finite extension, we denote by $B = B_E$ the integral closure of A in E, and $\mathfrak{P} = \mathfrak{P}_E$ its maximal ideal.

We shall say that $\mathfrak{P}$ is **totally ramified** above $\mathfrak{p}$ if $[E : K] = e$. In that case, the residue class degree is equal to 1 (because $ef = n$). Since $\mathfrak{P}$ is the only prime of B lying above $\mathfrak{p}$, we say that E is totally ramified over K.

Proposition 10. *Let E be a finite extension of K. Let E_u be the compositum of all unramified subfields over K. Then E_u is unramified over K, and E is totally ramified over E_u.*

Proof. The first statement comes from Proposition 8 of the preceding section. As to the second, we consider the towers

$$\begin{array}{ccc} E & & B/\mathfrak{P} \\ | & & | \\ E_u & & B_u/\mathfrak{P}_u \\ | & & | \\ K & & A/\mathfrak{p} \end{array}$$

If the residue class field extension in the upper level of the tower had degree > 1, then it could be lifted back to an unramified subfield of E over E_u, of the same degree, contradicting the maximality of E_u. Hence the degree must be equal to 1, and therefore E is totally ramified over E_u.

Let E be a finite extension of K. We shall say that $\mathfrak{P}$ is **tamely ramified** over $\mathfrak{p}$ (or E tamely ramified over K) if the characteristic p of the residue class field $A/\mathfrak{p}$ does not divide e. If it does, we say that $\mathfrak{P}$ is **strongly ramified.** We shall now describe totally and tamely ramified extensions.

Proposition 11. *Assume that E is totally ramified over K. Let Π be an element of order 1 at $\mathfrak{P}$. Then Π satisfies an Eisenstein equation*

$$X^e + a_{e-1}X^{e-1} + \cdots + a_0 = 0,$$

where $a_i \in \mathfrak{p}$ for all i and $a_0 \not\equiv 0 \pmod{\mathfrak{p}^2}$. Conversely, such an equation is irreducible, and a root generates a totally ramified extension of degree e.

Proof. All conjugates of Π over K have the same absolute value (by the uniqueness of the extension of $\mathfrak{p}$ to any finite extension), and hence the coefficients of its irreducible equation, which are polynomial functions of the roots, lie in $\mathfrak{P} \cap A = \mathfrak{p}$. The last coefficient a_0 is the product of Π and its conjugates, and there are e of those. Hence

$$|a_0| = |\Pi|^e,$$

so $a_0 = \pi$ is an element of order 1 at $\mathfrak{p}$. As to the converse, an Eisenstein equation is irreducible. If β is a root, then the same argument we applied to Π before now applies to β and shows that $|\beta|^e = |\pi|$. Hence $e = [K(\beta) : K]$.

We observe that if $p \nmid e$, then the extension is tamely ramified.

Proposition 12. *Let E be totally and tamely ramified over K. Then there exists an element Π of order 1 at $\mathfrak{P}$ in E satisfying an equation*

$$X^e - \pi = 0$$

with π of order 1 at $\mathfrak{p}$ in K. Conversely, let a be an element of A, and e a positive integer not divisible by p. Then any root of an equation

$$X^e - a = 0$$

generates a tamely ramified extension of K, and this extension is totally ramified if the order at $\mathfrak{p}$ of a is relatively prime to e.

Proof. Let $f(X) = X^e - a$ with $a \in A$ and e not divisible by p. Let α be any root of f. Write $a = \pi^r u$ with some integer r and a unit u of A.

Then $K(\alpha)$ is contained in $K(\zeta, u^{1/e}, \pi^{1/e})$, where ζ is a primitive e-th root of unity. The extension $F = K(\zeta, u^{1/e})$ is unramified over K, and hence π is still a prime element in $\mathfrak{P}_F$. The extension $F(\pi^{1/e})$ is totally and tamely ramified, and hence the ramification index of $K(\alpha)$ over K divides that of $K(\zeta, u^{1/e}, \pi^{1/e})$ over K. This proves that $K(\alpha)$ is tamely ramified over K. If the order of a at $\mathfrak{p}$ is relatively prime to e, then we can find two integers s, t such that

$$se + tr = 1.$$

Let $\beta = \alpha^t\pi^s$. Then β^e and π have the same order at $\mathfrak{P}$, whence the ramification index is at least equal to e. It must therefore be equal to e (because $[K(\alpha) : K] \leqq e$), and our extension is totally tamely ramified.

There remains to prove that any totally and tamely ramified extension is generated by the root of an equation

$$X^e - \pi = 0$$

for some prime element π of $\mathfrak{p}$. For this we shall need a lemma.

Lemma. *Let e be a positive integer not divisible by p. Let E be a finite extension of K, π_0 a prime element in $\mathfrak{p}$, and β an element of E such that $|\beta|^e = |\pi_0|$. Then there exists an element π of order 1 in $\mathfrak{p}$ such that one of the roots of the equation $X^e - \pi = 0$ is contained in $K(\beta)$.*

Proof. We can write $\beta^e = \pi_0 u$ with a unit u in B. Since the extension is totally ramified, the residue class degree is equal to 1, and hence there exists a unit u_0 in A such that $u \equiv u_0 \pmod{\mathfrak{P}}$. Letting $\pi = \pi_0 u_0$ we get

$$\beta^e = \pi + \pi x$$

with some element $x \equiv 0 \pmod{\mathfrak{P}}$. Thus

$$|\beta^e - \pi| < |\pi|.$$

Let $f(X) = X^e - \pi$, and let $\alpha_1, \ldots, \alpha_e$ be its roots. Then

$$|f(\beta)| = |\beta - \alpha_1| \cdots |\beta - \alpha_e|.$$

But $|\alpha_i| = |\beta|$ for each i. Hence for at least one value of i, say $i = 1$, we have

$$|\beta - \alpha_1| < |\alpha_1|.$$

On the other hand,

$$|f'(\alpha_1)| = |\alpha_1|^{e-1} = |\alpha_1 - \alpha_2| \cdots |\alpha_2 - \alpha_e|$$

and $|\alpha_i - \alpha_j| \leqq |\alpha_1|$. This proves that for all pairs i, j with $i \neq j$, we have $|\alpha_i - \alpha_j| = |\alpha_1|$. By Krasner's lemma, it follows that $K(\alpha_1) \subset K(\beta)$ thereby proving our assertion.

Proposition 12 follows at once by taking $\beta = \Pi$.

Proposition 13. *Let E be a finite extension of K. Then all statements of Proposition 8 hold if the word "unramified" is replaced throughout by the words "tamely ramified".*

Proof. Routine, using the multiplicativity of the ramification index, and Proposition 12.

Corollary. *Let E be a finite extension of K, and let E_t be the compositum of all tamely ramified subextensions. Then E_t is tamely ramified over K, and E is totally ramified over E_t. Furthermore, if p is the characteristic of the residue class field, then the degree $[E:E_t]$ is a power of p.*

Proof. Let e be the ramification index and write

$$e = e_0 p^r,$$

where e_0 is prime to p. Let Π be an element of order 1 at $\mathfrak{P}$, and let

$$\beta = \Pi^{p^r}.$$

By the lemma, $K(\beta)$ contains a tamely ramified subextension of ramification index e_0. The composite of this extension with the maximal unramified subfield of E gives us a tamely ramified extension F of K, and from the definition of β, it follows that the ramification index of E over F is p^r. On the other hand, E is totally ramified over F (because F contains E_u), and hence $[E:F] = p^r$. Any tamely ramified subextension of E must be contained in F, otherwise its compositum with F would be tamely ramified over F. This proves the corollary.

Lastly, we specialize to p-adic fields and prove a useful finiteness statement.

Proposition 14. *Let K be a $\mathfrak{p}$-adic field (finite extension of $\mathbf{Q}_p$). Given an integer n, there exists only a finite number of extensions of degree $\leqq n$.*

Proof. Since there is exactly one unramified extension of a given degree, corresponding to an extension of the residue class field, and since every extension is a tower of an unramified and totally ramified extension, it will suffice to prove that there is only a finite number of totally ramified extensions of a given degree e. But such extensions are obtained by Eisenstein equations

$$X^e + a_{e-1}X^{e-1} + \cdots + u_0\pi = 0,$$

where the coefficients a_i belong to $\mathfrak{p}$ and u_0 is a unit (π being a fixed prime element of $\mathfrak{p}$). The Cartesian product

$$\mathfrak{p} \times \cdots \times \mathfrak{p} \times U$$

of the units and of $\mathfrak{p}$ taken $e - 1$ times is compact. Any point in it can be viewed as determining a finite number of extensions of degree e (corresponding to the distinct roots of the equation). By Krasner's lemma, it follows that a neighborhood of such a point determines the same extensions (Proposition 4 of §2), and by compactness the finiteness follows.

CHAPTER III

The Different and Discriminant

The study of the different and discriminant provides some information on ramified primes, and also gives a sort of duality which plays a role both in the algebraic study of ramification and the later chapters on analytic duality. It also gives a good method for computing the ring of algebraic integers in a number field, as in Proposition 10.

§1. Complementary modules

Throughout this section, A is a Dedekind ring, K its quotient field, E a finite separable extension of K, and B the integral closure of A in E. Let L be an additive subgroup of E. We define its **complementary set** (relative to the trace) to be the set of $x \in E$ such that

$$\mathrm{Tr}_K^E(xL) \subset A,$$

and denote it by L'. Then L' is an additive group. If $AL = L$, then $AL' = L'$.

If L, M are two additive subgroups of E, and $L \subset M$, then $M' \subset L'$. We also have the following properties.

Proposition 1. *If $w_1, \ldots, w_n$ is a basis of E over K and*

$$L = Aw_1 + \cdots + Aw_n,$$

then

$$L' = Aw_1' + \cdots + Aw_n',$$

where $\{w_i'\}$ is the dual basis relative to the trace.

Proof. Let $\alpha \in L'$ and write

$$\alpha = a_1w_1' + \cdots + a_nw_n'$$

with $a_i \in K$. Then $\mathrm{Tr}(\alpha w_i) = a_i$, whence $a_i \in A$ for all i. This proves the inclusion $\subset$. Conversely,

$$\mathrm{Tr}(Aw_i'L) = A \cdot \mathrm{Tr}(w_i'L) \subset A$$

so the inclusion $\supset$ is equally trivial.

Since every fractional ideal of B is squeezed between two A-modules of type $Aw_1 + \cdots + Aw_n$ for suitable bases $\{w_i\}$ of E over K, and since A is Noetherian, we obtain:

Corollary. *If $\mathfrak{b}$ is a fractional ideal of B, then $\mathfrak{b}'$ is also a fractional ideal. Furthermore $B \subset B'$.*

Proposition 2. *Let $E = K(\alpha)$ be a finite separable extension, of degree n. Let f be the irreducible polynomial of α over K, f' its derivative, and*

$$\frac{f(X)}{X - \alpha} = b_0 + b_1 X + \cdots + b_{n-1}X^{n-1}.$$

Then the dual basis of $1, \alpha, \ldots, \alpha^{n-1}$ is

$$\frac{b_0}{f'(\alpha)}, \ldots, \frac{b_{n-1}}{f'(\alpha)}.$$

Proof. Let $\alpha_1, \ldots, \alpha_n$ be the distinct roots of f. Then

$$\sum_{i=1}^{n} \frac{f(X)}{(X - \alpha_i)} \frac{\alpha_i^r}{f'(\alpha_i)} = X^r, \qquad 0 \leqq r \leqq n - 1.$$

To see this, let $g(X)$ be the difference of the left- and right-hand side of this equality. Then g has degree $\leqq n - 1$, and has n roots $\alpha_1, \ldots, \alpha_n$; hence g is identically 0.

The polynomials

$$\frac{f(X)}{X - \alpha_i} \frac{\alpha_i^r}{f'(\alpha_i)}$$

are all conjugate to each other. If we define the trace of a polynomial with coefficients in E to be the polynomial obtained by applying the trace to the coefficients, then

$$\mathrm{Tr}\left[\frac{f(X)}{X - \alpha} \frac{\alpha^r}{f'(\alpha)}\right] = X^r.$$

Looking at the coefficient of each power of X in this equation, we see that

$$\mathrm{Tr}\left(\alpha^i \frac{b_j}{f'(\alpha)}\right) = \delta_{ij}$$

thereby proving our assertion.

Corollary. *Assume that* $B = A[\alpha]$. *Then* $B' = B/f'(\alpha)$.

Proof. Using the recurring formulas

$$\begin{aligned} b_{n-1} &= 1 \\ b_{n-2} - \alpha b_{n-1} &= a_{n-1} \\ &\vdots \end{aligned}$$

we see that the module generated by $1, \alpha, \ldots, \alpha^{n-1}$ over A is the same as that generated by $b_0, \ldots, b_{n-1}$. Our corollary follows immediately.

Proposition 3. *Assume that* A *is a discrete valuation ring, that there is only one prime* $\mathfrak{P}$ *of* B *above* A, *and that* $B/\mathfrak{P}$ *is separable over* $A/\mathfrak{p}$. *Then there exists* $\alpha \in B$ *such that* $B = A[\alpha]$.

Proof. Let β be an element of B whose residue class mod $\mathfrak{P}$ generates $B/\mathfrak{P}$ over $A/\mathfrak{p}$. Let f be a polynomial with leading coefficient 1 and coefficients in A such that its reduced polynomial mod $\mathfrak{p}$ is an irreducible polynomial for β mod $\mathfrak{P}$. Let Π be an element of order one at $\mathfrak{P}$ in B. Then

$$f(\beta + \Pi) \equiv f(\beta) + f'(\beta)\Pi \pmod{\mathfrak{P}^2},$$

and $f'(\beta) \not\equiv 0 \pmod{\mathfrak{P}}$. Hence taking either β or $\beta + \Pi$ yields an element α such that its residue class generates $B/\mathfrak{P}$ over $A/\mathfrak{p}$ and such that there exists an element of order 1 at $\mathfrak{P}$ in the ring $A[\alpha]$. We conclude by Proposition 23 of Chapter I, §7 that $B = A[\alpha]$.

The preceding proposition gives us a criterion when we can apply Proposition 2. It applies in particular in the local case, when our Dedekind ring is complete.

Proposition 4. *Let* $\mathfrak{b}$ *be a fractional ideal of* B. *Then*

$$\mathfrak{b}' = B'\mathfrak{b}^{-1}.$$

Proof. We have

$$\mathrm{Tr}(B'\mathfrak{b}^{-1}\mathfrak{b}) = \mathrm{Tr}(B'B) \subset A$$

whence $B'\mathfrak{b}^{-1} \subset \mathfrak{b}'$. The converse is equally clear.

For purposes of the following proposition, we denote by $B'_{E/K}$ the complementary module of B. We need some index, since we shall deal with more than two fields.

Proposition 5. *Let* $E \supset F \supset K$ *be two separable extensions,* C *the integral closure of* A *in* F, *and* B *the integral closure of* A *in* E. *Then*

$$B'_{E/K} = B'_{E/F}C'_{F/K}.$$

Proof. We prove first the inclusion $\supset$. We have

$$\begin{aligned}\operatorname{Tr}_K^E(B'_{E/F}C'_{F/K}B) &= \operatorname{Tr}_K^F \operatorname{Tr}_F^E(B'_{E/F}C'_{F/K}B) \\ &= \operatorname{Tr}_K^F(C'_{F/K} \operatorname{Tr}_F^E(B'_{E/F}B)) \\ &\subset A.\end{aligned}$$

This proves the desired inclusion.

Conversely, let $\beta \in B'_{E/K}$. Then

$$\operatorname{Tr}_K^E(\beta B) = \operatorname{Tr}_K^F(C \operatorname{Tr}_F^E(\beta B)) \subset A$$

(we can insert C since $CB = B$). Thus

$$\operatorname{Tr}_F^E(\beta B) \subset C'_{F/K},$$

and

$$C'^{-1}_{F/K} \operatorname{Tr}_F^E(\beta B) \subset C.$$

The C-fractional ideal $C'^{-1}_{F/K}$ can be taken inside the trace Tr_F^E because it is contained in F. Hence

$$\beta C'^{-1}_{F/K} \subset B'_{E/F}.$$

Multiplying by $C'_{F/K}$ shows that $\beta \in C'_{F/K}B'_{E/F}$ and concludes the proof of the reverse inclusion.

Notation being as above, we define the **different** $\mathfrak{D}_{B/A}$ to be $B'^{-1}_{E/K}$. The preceding proposition gives us the rule

$$\mathfrak{D}_{B/C}\mathfrak{D}_{C/A} = \mathfrak{D}_{B/A},$$

which is called the **multiplicativity of the different in towers.**

The different is the inverse of a fractional ideal containing the integers, and therefore is an ideal.

Proposition 6. *Let S be a multiplicative subset of A. Then*

$$\mathfrak{D}_{S^{-1}B/S^{-1}A} = S^{-1}\mathfrak{D}_{B/A}.$$

Proof. Obvious.

Proposition 6 allows us to compute the different by localizing at a prime $\mathfrak{p}$ of A. This has the advantage that $A_\mathfrak{p}$ becomes principal.

We shall now see how the different localizes in the completion, and how it can be computed purely locally.

Using Proposition 6, we may assume that A is a discrete valuation ring.

Proposition 7. *Let A be a discrete valuation ring, v its valuation, and $\mathfrak{P}$ a prime of B lying above the prime $\mathfrak{p}$ of A. Let $w_{\mathfrak{P}}$ be the valuation corresponding to $\mathfrak{P}$ and A_v, $B_{w_{\mathfrak{P}}}$ the respective completions. Then:*

$$\mathfrak{D}_{B/A}B_{w_{\mathfrak{P}}} = \mathfrak{D}_{B_{w_{\mathfrak{P}}}/A_v}.$$

Proof. Since the differents are ideals, it suffices to prove that

$$\operatorname{ord}_{\mathfrak{P}} \mathfrak{D}_{B/A} = \operatorname{ord}_{\mathfrak{P}} \mathfrak{D}_{B_{w_{\mathfrak{P}}}/A_v}.$$

Let Tr denote the trace from E to K and Tr_w the local trace from E_w to K_v for any w extending v in E. Then

$$\mathrm{Tr} = \sum_{w|v} \mathrm{Tr}_w$$

(as an operator on E).

Let $x \in E_{w_{\mathfrak{P}}}$ and assume that $\mathrm{Tr}_{w_{\mathfrak{P}}}(xB_{w_{\mathfrak{P}}}) \subset A_v$. Select an element ξ of E which is very close to x at $w_{\mathfrak{P}}$ and very close to 0 at all other $w|v$. Let $y \in B$. Then $\mathrm{Tr}_w(\xi y)$ is close to 0 if $w \neq w_{\mathfrak{P}}$ and $\mathrm{Tr}_w(\xi y)$ lies in A_v if $w = w_{\mathfrak{P}}$, by assumption and the fact that the local trace is continuous. This implies that $\mathrm{Tr}(\xi y)$ lies in A and hence that ξ lies in the complementary module B'.

Conversely, let x be an element in B' and let $y \in B_{w_{\mathfrak{P}}}$. Find an element ξ of E which is close to x at $w_{\mathfrak{P}}$ and close to 0 at the other $w|v$. Find an element η of B close to y at $w_{\mathfrak{P}}$ and close to 0 at the other $w|v$. Then

$$\mathrm{Tr}(\xi\eta) = \mathrm{Tr}_{w_{\mathfrak{P}}}(\xi\eta) + \sum_{w \neq w_{\mathfrak{P}}} \mathrm{Tr}_w(\xi\eta).$$

The global trace on the left lies in A. Each term in the sum on the right lies in A_v. Hence $\mathrm{Tr}_{w_{\mathfrak{P}}}(\xi\eta)$ lies in A_v. Since ξ and η are close to x, y respectively, it follows that $\mathrm{Tr}_{w_{\mathfrak{P}}}(xy)$ also lies in A_v.

The above arguments show that B' is dense in $B'_{w_{\mathfrak{P}}}$ (= local complementary module with respect to $\mathrm{Tr}_{w_{\mathfrak{P}}}$) and the proposition follows.

Let $\mathfrak{D}$ denote the different of B over A. If we think of formal ideals, then we have the relation

$$\mathfrak{D} = \prod_{\mathfrak{P}} \mathfrak{D}_{\mathfrak{P}}.$$

Each $\mathfrak{D}_{\mathfrak{P}}$ can be interpreted as the $\mathfrak{P}$-component of $\mathfrak{D}_{B/A}$, as the $\mathfrak{P}$-component of $\mathfrak{D}_{B_{\mathfrak{P}}/A_{\mathfrak{P}}}$ (if $\mathfrak{P}|\mathfrak{p}$), or as $\mathfrak{D}_{B_w/A_v}$ if w and v are the valuations corresponding to $\mathfrak{P}$ and $\mathfrak{p}$ respectively.

One usually calls $\mathfrak{D}_{B/A}$ the **global different,** and $\mathfrak{D}_{B_w/A_v}$ the **local different.** We may identify $\mathfrak{D}_{B_w/A_v}$ with $\mathfrak{D}_{\mathfrak{P}}$ as a formal ideal, and in this sense, we may say that the global different is the product of the local differents.

§2. *The different and ramification*

In this section, we let A be a Dedekind ring, K its quotient field, E a finite separable extension of K, and B the integral closure of A in E. We shall also assume that for any prime $\mathfrak{p}$ of A the residue class field $A/\mathfrak{p}$ is perfect.

Proposition 8. *Let $\mathfrak{P}$ be a prime of B lying above $\mathfrak{p}$, and let e be its ramification index. Then $\mathfrak{P}^{e-1}$ divides $\mathfrak{D}_{B/A}$. If $\mathfrak{P}$ is strongly ramified, then $\mathfrak{P}^e$ divides $\mathfrak{D}_{B/A}$. If $\mathfrak{P}$ is unramified, then $\mathfrak{P}$ does not divide $\mathfrak{D}_{B/A}$. There is only a finite number of ramified primes. Finally, $\mathfrak{D}_{B/A}$ is the greatest common divisor of all ideals $(f'(\alpha))$, where α is an integral generator of E over K, and f the irreducible polynomial for α over K.*

Proof. In view of the fact that ramification theory and the theory of the different localize to the completion, we may prove the first assertions under the assumption that K is complete.

Since we work over a complete field, we can apply Proposition 3 of §1, the Corollary of Proposition 2, §1, and Proposition 23 of Chapter I, §7. If $\mathfrak{P}$ is unramified, this yields $\mathfrak{D}_{B/A} = (1)$. Using Proposition 5 of §1 (multiplicativity in towers), we may also assume that $\mathfrak{P}$ is totally ramified. In that case, we can write $B = A[\Pi]$ for some element Π of order 1 at $\mathfrak{P}$, and Π satisfies an Eisenstein equation

$$f(\Pi) = \Pi^e + a_{n-1}\Pi^{e-1} + \cdots + \pi = 0,$$

for $a_i \in \mathfrak{p}$ and $\pi \in A$ of order 1 at $\mathfrak{p}$. Then

$$f'(\Pi) \equiv e\Pi^{e-1} \pmod{\mathfrak{P}^e},$$

and the second assertion of the proposition follows from the definitions.

We now return to the global case. Let α be an integral generator for E over K, and let f be its irreducible polynomial over K. There is only a finite number of primes $\mathfrak{P}$ dividing $(f'(\alpha))$, and hence by Proposition 7 of Chapter II, §4, these primes are the only possible primes which may ramify (we may view α as a generator of the completion $E_{w\mathfrak{P}}$ over $K_{v\mathfrak{P}}$). Since $B \supset A[\alpha]$, it follows that $\mathfrak{D}_{B/A}$ divides $(f'(\alpha))$. There remains to be proved that it is the greatest common divisor, or more precisely that given a prime $\mathfrak{P}$, there exists an α such that

$$\operatorname{ord}_{\mathfrak{P}} \mathfrak{D}_{B/A} = \operatorname{ord}_{\mathfrak{P}} (f'(\alpha)).$$

The proof will be an exercise in techniques revolving around the approximation theorem.

There would be no difficulty if we could write $B = A[\alpha]$ for some α. This is true only locally. Hence we shall use the approximation theorem to reduce our problem to the local case.

Let $v = v_{\mathfrak{p}}$ and $w = w_{\mathfrak{P}}$. Let $\{\sigma\}$ range over the distinct isomorphisms of E into the algebraic closure $\overline{K}_v$ of K. Let σ_1 be one of these, inducing the absolute value $w_{\mathfrak{P}}$ on E. If α is a generator of E over K, and f its irreducible equation over K, then

$$\sigma_1 f'(\alpha) = f'(\sigma_1\alpha) = \prod_{\sigma \neq \sigma_1} (\sigma_1\alpha - \sigma\alpha).$$

We shall write $\sigma \sim \tau$ if σ and τ are conjugate over K_v, i.e. if there exists an isomorphism λ of $\overline{K}_v$ over K_v such that $\tau = \lambda\sigma$ on E.

According to Proposition 3, §1, there exists an element β of B_w such that $B_w = A_v[\beta]$. We observe that any element of B_w which is sufficiently close to β also generates B_w over A_v.

Let λ range over isomorphisms of $\overline{K}_v$ over K_v. There exists an element $a \in A_v$ such that

$$|\lambda\beta - a| = 1$$

for all λ. Such an element exists because the conjugates $\lambda\beta$ have residue classes which are conjugate over $A_v/\mathfrak{p}_v$. If these residue classes are 0, we take $a = 1$. If they are not 0, we take $a = 0$.

Let $\sigma_1, \ldots, \sigma_r$ be representatives of the equivalence classes of the embeddings of E into $\overline{K}_v$. By the approximation theorem, we can find an element α of E such that

$$|\sigma_1\alpha - \beta| \text{ is very small,}$$
$$|\sigma_i\alpha - a| \text{ is very small for } i \neq 1.$$

Without loss of generality, we may assume in addition that α is integral over A and $E = K(\alpha)$. (If necessary, first multiply α by an element of A which is $\equiv 1 \bmod \mathfrak{p}$ and is highly divisible by a finite number of other primes to make it integral, and then add $\pi^\nu\gamma$, where γ is any integral generator, and ν is very large. Then $\alpha + \pi^\nu\gamma$ becomes a generator.)

Since $\sigma_1\alpha$ is very close to β, it follows that $B_w = A_v[\sigma_1\alpha]$, and hence the $\mathfrak{P}$-contribution to the different is given by

$$\operatorname{ord}_{\mathfrak{P}} \mathfrak{D}_{B_w/A_v} = \operatorname{ord}_{\mathfrak{P}} \prod_{\substack{\sigma\sim\sigma_1 \\ \sigma\neq\sigma_1}} (\sigma_1\alpha - \sigma\alpha).$$

We must now show that the other factors do not give any $\mathfrak{P}$-contribution.

Suppose that σ is not conjugate to σ_1 over K_v. We can write $\sigma = \lambda\sigma_i$, $i \neq 1$. Then

$$|\sigma_1\alpha - \sigma\alpha| = |\sigma_1\alpha - \lambda\sigma_i\alpha| = |\lambda^{-1}\sigma_1\alpha - \sigma_i\alpha|$$
$$= |\lambda^{-1}\sigma_1\alpha - a + a - \sigma_i\alpha|.$$

But $|\sigma_i\alpha - a|$ is very small, and $\lambda^{-1}\sigma_1\alpha$ is very close to $\lambda^{-1}\beta$. Since $|\lambda^{-1}\beta - a| = 1$, it follows that $|\lambda^{-1}\sigma_1\alpha - a| = 1$ also. Hence $|\sigma_1\alpha - \sigma\alpha| = 1$. This proves our last assertion.

§3. *The discriminant*

Throughout this section, A is a Dedekind ring, K its quotient field, E a finite separable extension of K of degree n, and B the integral closure of A in E.

Let $W = (w_1, \ldots, w_n)$ be any set of n elements of E. We define the **discriminant**

$$D_{E/K}(W) = \det(\sigma_i w_j)^2$$

to be the square of the determinant taken with σ_i ranging over the n distinct embeddings of E in a given algebraic closure of K.

Assume that W and $V = (v_1, \ldots, v_n)$ are two sets of elements of E, and that there is a matrix $X = (x_{ij})$ of elements of K such that $W = XV$. From this we see that

$$D_{E/K}(W) = \det(X)^2 D_{E/K}(V).$$

If the matrix X has entries in A, then $\det(X)^2$ lies in A. Hence whenever W and V generate the same module over A, the matrix X is invertible in A, and its determinant is a unit in A. Thus the two discriminants differ by the square of a unit in A.

In particular, if $A = \mathbf{Z}$ is the ring of ordinary integers, the discriminant is uniquely determined by the module. If the module is the ring of algebraic integers $\mathfrak{o}_K$, then its discriminant will be called simply THE discriminant (or also the discriminant of K), and will be denoted by D_K.

Proposition 9. *Notation as above, the discriminant $D_{E/K}(W)$ lies in K, and lies in A if the components of W lie in B. The discriminant is $\neq 0$ if and only if W is a basis of E over K.*

Proof. Applying any isomorphism σ of E over K to the determinant $\det(\sigma_i w_j)$ interchanges the rows, hence multiplies the determinant by ± 1. Taking the square gets rid of ± 1. If α is a generator of E over K, i.e. $E = K(\alpha)$, then the discriminant $D_{E/K}(1, \alpha, \ldots, \alpha^{n-1})$ is the Vandermonde determinant, and hence is $\neq 0$. The same holds therefore for any basis V of E over K by a preceding remark concerning the change of the discriminant under linear transformations. If the coordinates of W are linearly dependent over K, it is clear that the discriminant is 0. If they are all integral over A, it is also clear that the discriminant lies in A (because the integral closure of A in a Galois extension containing E is a ring). This proves our proposition.

If M is a free module of rank n over A (contained in E), then we can define the discriminant of M by means of a basis of M over A. It is well defined up to the square of a unit in A.

Proposition 10. *Let $M_1 \subset M_2$ be two free modules of rank n over A, contained in E. Then $D_{E/K}(M_1)$ divides $D_{E/K}(M_2)$ (as principal ideals). If $D_{E/K}(M_1) = D_{E/K}(M_2)u$ for some unit u of A, then $M_1 = M_2$.*

Proof. The first statement is obvious. The second statement asserts that the matrix going from a basis of M_1 to a basis of M_2 is invertible in A, and hence that $M_1 = M_2$.

In general, it is not true that every fractional ideal of B is a free module over A. For the moment, if $\mathfrak{b}$ is a fractional ideal of B, we denote by $D_{E/K}(\mathfrak{b})$ the A-module generated by all $D_{E/K}(W)$ as W ranges over bases of E over K such that all $w_i \in \mathfrak{b}$, and call this the **discriminant of the fractional ideal.** Since there exists an element $c \neq 0$ in A such that $c\mathfrak{b} \subset B$, it follows at once that the discriminant is a fractional ideal of A.

Proposition 11. *Let $\mathfrak{b}$ be a fractional ideal of B and S a multiplicative subset of A. Then*

$$S^{-1}D_{E/K}(\mathfrak{b}) = D_{E/K}(S^{-1}\mathfrak{b}).$$

Proof. Trivial from the definitions.

This proposition allows us to localize. If $\mathfrak{p}$ is a prime of A, we can compute the $\mathfrak{p}$-component of the discriminant by localizing at $\mathfrak{p}$. The great advantage of this is that $A_{\mathfrak{p}}$ becomes a discrete valuation ring, and thus that every fractional ideal of B becomes a free $A_{\mathfrak{p}}$-module when localized at $\mathfrak{p}$. Furthermore, $B_{\mathfrak{p}}$ has only a finite number of primes above $\mathfrak{p}$, and is a principal ideal ring. Thus we are reduced to computing Vandermonde determinants.

Proposition 12. *Assume in addition that A is a discrete valuation ring. Let $\mathfrak{b}$ be a fractional ideal of B, $\mathfrak{b} = (\beta)$ for some $\beta \neq 0$ in E. Then*

$$D_{E/K}(\mathfrak{b}) = (N_K^E(\beta))^2 D_{E/K}(B).$$

Proof. Let W be a basis of B over A. Then βW is a basis of $\mathfrak{b}$ over A, and the assertion is obvious from the definitions.

Using the localizing process, we can extend the above proposition to the case when A is not necessarily local.

Proposition 13. *Let A be arbitrary again, and $\mathfrak{b}$ a fractional ideal of B. Then*

$$D_{E/K}(\mathfrak{b}) = (N_K^E(\mathfrak{b}))^2 D_{E/K}(B),$$

the norm being the norm of ideals as in Chapter I, §7.

Proof. It suffices to verify this relation for each $\mathfrak{p}$-component, $\mathfrak{p}$ a prime of A. Thus we may assume that A is a discrete valuation ring by Proposition 11. In that case $\mathfrak{b} = (\beta)$ for some $\beta \in E$, and our assertion follows from Proposition 23 of Chapter I, §7.

Proposition 14. *The discriminant and different are related by the formula*

$$N_K^E \mathfrak{D}_{B/A} = D_{E/K}(B).$$

Proof. Using Proposition 6 of §1 and Proposition 11, we may assume that A is a discrete valuation ring, and hence that B is a free module over A. If W is a basis for B over A, then $D_{E/K}(B)$ is generated by $D_{E/K}(W)$. Let W' be the complementary basis to W under the trace. Then the complementary module B' is generated by W' over A. Thus

$$D_{E/K}(B') = D_{E/K}(W')A.$$

But we see directly from the definition of the discriminant of a basis that

$$D_{E/K}(W)D_{E/K}(W') = 1.$$

Hence $D_{E/K}(B)D_{E/K}(B') = A$. Using Proposition 4 of §1 and Proposition 13 yields what we want.

Finally, consider a finite separable extension E of degree n over K, and let β be an element of E, $\beta \neq 0$, such that $E = K(\beta)$. We define the **different** $\mathfrak{D}_{E/K}(\beta)$ and the **discriminant** $D_{E/K}(\beta)$ of this element by

$$\mathfrak{D}_{E/K}(\beta) = \prod_{\sigma \neq id} (\beta - \sigma\beta)$$

$$D_{E/K}(\beta) = D_{E/K}(1, \beta, \ldots, \beta^{n-1}).$$

Proposition 15. *We have*

$$D_{E/K}(\beta) = (-1)^{n(n-1)/2} N_K^E \mathfrak{D}_{E/K}(\beta).$$

Proof. Exercise in permuting the rows of a determinant.

Proposition 16. *Let $\alpha \in B$ and let $\mathfrak{p}$ be a prime of A. If $\mathfrak{p}$ does not divide $D_{E/K}(\alpha)/D_{E/K}(B)$ then $B_{\mathfrak{p}} = A_{\mathfrak{p}}[\alpha]$.*

Proof. By Theorem 1 of Chapter I, §2 we know that $B_{\mathfrak{p}}$ is a free module over $A_{\mathfrak{p}}$. Furthermore

$$D_{E/K}(1, \alpha, \ldots, \alpha^{n-1}) = D_{E/K}(B)c^2$$

where c is an element of $A_{\mathfrak{p}}$. By hypothesis, this element c is a unit in $A_{\mathfrak{p}}$, and hence our proposition follows from Proposition 10.

Remark 1. In Proposition 16, we formulated a local version. One obtains immediately a global version in special cases using Proposition 18 of Chapter I, §7, which states that two A-modules are equal if and only if all their localizations are equal.

Remark 2. Instead of using the discriminant, we could have formulated our hypothesis in terms of the different. Indeed, the condition

$$\mathfrak{p}B \text{ is relatively prime to } (f'(\alpha))/\mathfrak{D}_{E/K}$$

where f is the irreducible polynomial of α over K *is equivalent with the condition*

$$\mathfrak{p} \text{ does not divide } D_{E/K}(\alpha)/D_{E/K}(B).$$

The equivalence is seen at once by taking the norm, and using the fact that the norm of the different is equal to the discriminant.

The following result is sometimes useful to analyse the discriminant and verify that the hypothesis of Proposition 16 is satisfied.

Stickelberger's criterion. *Let E be an extension of degree n over $\mathbf{Q}$, and let $\alpha_1, \ldots, \alpha_n$ be algebraic integers in E, linearly independent over $\mathbf{Q}$. Then*

$$D_{E/\mathbf{Q}}(\alpha_1, \ldots, \alpha_n) \equiv 0 \text{ or } 1 \mod 4.$$

Proof. The determinant $\det(\sigma_i\alpha_j)$ has an expansion as a sum of terms with plus and minus signs in front of them. Let P be the sum of terms with plus signs, and N the sum of terms with minus signs, so that the discriminant is equal to

$$(P - N)^2 = (P + N)^2 - 4PN.$$

But $P + N$ and PN are both invariant under any σ_i, and hence are rational integers. The assertion follows at once.

Example. Let $E = \mathbf{Q}(\alpha)$ where $\alpha^3 = 2$, say α is the real cube root of 2. Let $f(X) = X^3 - 2$. Then $f'(\alpha) = 3\alpha^2$, and $D_{E/\mathbf{Q}}(\alpha) = -3^3 2^2$. Let B

be the ring of algebraic integers in E. Note that 2 is ramified in E with ramification index 3, and hence $D_{E/\mathbf{Q}}(B)$ is divisible by 2, whence by 2^2, by Stickelberger's criterion. Furthermore 3 must have some ramified factor in E, for otherwise all the conjugates of E would be unramified over 3, so that the splitting field $\mathbf{Q}(\alpha, \sqrt{-3})$ would also be unramified over 3, which is obviously not the case. The polynomial $X^3 - 2$ is irreducible over the 3-adic field $\mathbf{Q}_3$ because already the congruence

$$X^3 \equiv 2 \pmod 9$$

has no solution in the 3-adic integers. Thus there is only one prime in E lying above (3), and therefore the ramification index must be 3. Thus we have

$$3B = \mathfrak{P}^3.$$

We see that in fact, $\mathfrak{P}$ is strongly ramified, and by Proposition 8 of §2 we conclude that $\mathfrak{P}^3$ divides the different of $E/\mathbf{Q}$. Since $\mathbf{N}\mathfrak{P} = 3$, it follows that 3^3 divides the discriminant, and we now see that $3^3 2^2$ divides the discriminant $D_{E/\mathbf{Q}}$. By Proposition 10, we conclude finally that $B = \mathbf{Z}[\alpha]$.

Proposition 17. *Let K, E be two number fields. Assume that their discriminants are relatively prime and that the fields are linearly disjoint (i.e. if $w_1, \ldots, w_n$ is a basis of K over $\mathbf{Q}$ and $v_1, \ldots, v_m$ is a basis of E over $\mathbf{Q}$, then $\{w_i v_j\}$ is a basis of KE over $\mathbf{Q}$). Then*

$$\mathfrak{o}_{KE} = \mathfrak{o}_K \mathfrak{o}_E$$

and

$$D_{KE} = D_K^m D_E^n.$$

Proof. From the fundamental properties of the different, we know that $\mathfrak{D}_{KE/\mathbf{Q}}$ is equal to

$$\mathfrak{D}_{KE/K}\mathfrak{D}_{K/\mathbf{Q}} = \mathfrak{D}_{KE/E}\mathfrak{D}_{E/\mathbf{Q}}.$$

But $\mathfrak{D}_{E/\mathbf{Q}}$ and $\mathfrak{D}_{K/\mathbf{Q}}$ have no factor in common (viewed as ideals of $\mathfrak{o}_{KE}$). The same holds for the other two factors. Hence

$$\mathfrak{D}_{KE/E} = \mathfrak{D}_{K/\mathbf{Q}} \quad \text{and} \quad \mathfrak{D}_{KE/K} = \mathfrak{D}_{E/\mathbf{Q}}.$$

Let W be a basis for $\mathfrak{o}_K$ over $\mathbf{Z}$ and V a basis for $\mathfrak{o}_E$ over $\mathbf{Z}$. Then the above remark implies that the complementary basis W' of W, which generates $\mathfrak{D}_{K/\mathbf{Q}}^{-1}$, also generates $\mathfrak{D}_{KE/E}^{-1}$. This is the complementary module of $\mathfrak{o}_{KE}$ relative to $\mathfrak{o}_E$. Dualizing again shows that W generates $\mathfrak{o}_{KE}$ over

$\mathfrak{o}_E$ and proves the assertion concerning the rings of integers. We leave the assertion on the discriminants as an exercise.

Examples of the situation in Proposition 17 arise, for instance, with two distinct quadratic extensions, with relatively prime discriminants, or with cyclotomic extensions of relatively prime degrees, as we shall see in the next chapter. It will in fact be used to determine the ring of algebraic integers for an arbitrary cyclotomic extension when we know the ring of integers in cyclotomic extensions of a prime power root of unity. Thus the next chapter gives us further examples for the use of the discriminant.

CHAPTER IV

Cyclotomic Fields

This chapter achieves two purposes simultaneously. It gives examples for the theory, and also describes in greater details the cyclotomic fields which exert a great deal of control over algebraic number theory in general. The extent to which they exert this control is in fact not yet clearly understood, but one knows for instance that the heart of the proofs of class field theory is concentrated in the cyclotomic fields.

§1. *Roots of unity*

Let ω be an n-th root of unity, i.e. $\omega^n = 1$. The extension $\mathbf{Q}(\omega)$ is normal over $\mathbf{Q}$. Indeed, if ω is a primitive n-th root of unity (i.e. has period exactly n), and if σ is any isomorphism of $\mathbf{Q}(\omega)$ over $\mathbf{Q}$, then $(\sigma\omega)^n = \sigma(\omega^n) = 1$, so that $\sigma\omega$ is an n-th root of unity also. Hence $\sigma\omega = \omega^i$ for some integer $i = i(\sigma)$, uniquely determined mod n. Hence $\mathbf{Q}(\omega)$ is mapped into itself by σ, and hence is normal over $\mathbf{Q}$. If τ is another isomorphism of $\mathbf{Q}(\omega)$ over $\mathbf{Q}$, then $\sigma\tau\omega = \omega^{i(\sigma)i(\tau)}$. Since σ, τ are isomorphisms, it follows that $i(\sigma)$, $i(\tau)$ are prime to n. Hence the map

$$\sigma \mapsto i(\sigma)$$

is a homomorphism of the Galois group G of $\mathbf{Q}(\omega)$ over $\mathbf{Q}$ into the multiplicative group of residue classes mod n, prime to n, and is injective. If we let φ be the Euler φ-function, then $\varphi(n)$ is the order of this multiplicative group. We shall see below that $[\mathbf{Q}(\omega) : \mathbf{Q}] = \varphi(n)$. This will determine the Galois group of $\mathbf{Q}(\omega)$ over $\mathbf{Q}$, i.e. prove that the map $\sigma \mapsto i(\sigma)$ is surjective.

Let K be a number field. Then the Galois group of $K(\omega)$ over K is a subgroup of G, and hence is abelian.

Let K be a number field, and let us fix an algebraic closure $\overline{K}$ of K. A **cyclotomic extension** of K is one which is contained in a field $K(\omega)$, where ω is a root of unity ($\omega^n = 1$ for some n). Since $K(\omega)$ is abelian over K, a cyclotomic extension of K is abelian. We say that K is **cyclotomic** if it is a cyclotomic extension of $\mathbf{Q}$.

Consider now the case $K = \mathbf{Q}(\omega)$.

Let p be a prime number and ω a primitive p-th root of unity. Then ω is a root of the polynomial

$$X^p - 1 = (X - 1)(X^{p-1} + \cdots + 1).$$

Hence $[\mathbf{Q}(\omega) : \mathbf{Q}] \leqq p - 1$. We contend that

$$[\mathbf{Q}(\omega) : \mathbf{Q}] = p - 1.$$

In fact, let $\pi = 1 - \omega$. Then π is integral over $\mathbf{Z}$. If i is an integer prime to p, then ω^i is also a primitive p-th root of unity, and

$$\frac{1 - \omega^i}{1 - \omega} = 1 + \omega + \cdots + \omega^{i-1}$$

is an algebraic integer. But $\omega = (\omega^i)^j$ for some integer j (such that $ji \equiv 1 \pmod{p}$), and hence the above quotient is a unit in the ring $\mathfrak{o}_K$ of algebraic integers of K.

Let $\mathfrak{p}$ be a prime of $\mathfrak{o}_K$ lying above (p), and let

$$f(X) = X^{p-1} + \cdots + 1.$$

Then ω^i $(i = 1, \ldots, p - 1)$ is a root of $f(X)$ (because it is a root of $X^p - 1$), and hence

$$f(X) = \prod_{i=1}^{p-1} (X - \omega^i).$$

Therefore

$$p = f(1) = \prod_{i=1}^{p-1} (1 - \omega^i).$$

For any i, j prime to p we have seen that

$$\frac{1 - \omega^i}{1 - \omega^j}$$

is a unit in $\mathfrak{o}_K$. All elements $1 - \omega^i$ have the same absolute value at $\mathfrak{p}$. Hence for the absolute value $|\ | = |\ |_{\mathfrak{p}}$ we have

$$|\pi|^{p-1} = |p|.$$

This implies that the ramification index of $\mathfrak{p}$ is at least $p - 1$. By Proposition 21 of Chapter I, §7 it follows that

$$e_{\mathfrak{p}} = p - 1 = [\mathbf{Q}(\omega) : \mathbf{Q}]$$

and that $\mathfrak{p}$ is the only prime of $\mathfrak{o}_K$ above (p), which is totally ramified.

Since ω also satisfies the equation $X^p - 1 = 0$, we see that any prime number not equal to p is unramified in $\mathbf{Q}(\omega)$, because the derivative $p\omega^{p-1}$ is divisible only by p. (Use Proposition 8 of Chapter III, §2.)

We now consider the prime-power case, and let $m = p^r$, r an integer > 0. Let $Y = X^{p^{r-1}}$ and consider

$$X^{p^r} - 1 = Y^p - 1 = (Y - 1)(Y^{p-1} + \cdots + 1).$$

Let

$$f(X) = \frac{X^{p^r} - 1}{X^{p^{r-1}} - 1} = Y^{p-1} + \cdots + 1.$$

The degree of f is $\varphi(p^r) = (p - 1)p^{r-1}$. Let ω be a primitive p^r-th root of unity. Let i be integer. Then ω^i is also a primitive p^r-th root of unity if and only if i is prime to p. Thus there are $\varphi(p^r)$ primitive p^r-th roots of unity. Then

$$f(X) = \prod_{\zeta} (X - \zeta) = \prod_{(i,p)=1} (X - \omega^i),$$

the product over ζ being taken over primitive p^r-th roots of unity, and the product over i being taken over distinct residue classes of $\mathbf{Z}/p^r\mathbf{Z}$ prime to p.

Just as we saw for p-th roots of unity, we see that

$$\frac{1 - \omega^i}{1 - \omega^j}$$

is a unit if i, j are prime to p. Let $\pi = 1 - \omega$. Then from

$$(*) \qquad f(1) = p = \prod_{(i,p)=1} (1 - \omega^i)$$

we conclude that

$$|\pi|^{\varphi(p^r)} = |p|$$

at any absolute value extending the p-adic absolute value on $\mathbf{Q}$, and hence p is totally ramified. We therefore have:

Theorem 1. *Let ω be a primitive p^r-th root of unity, and $K = \mathbf{Q}(\omega)$. Then $[K : \mathbf{Q}] = \varphi(p^r) = (p - 1)p^{r-1}$. There is only one prime $\mathfrak{p}$ of $\mathfrak{o}_K$ lying above p, and it is totally ramified. All other primes of $\mathfrak{o}_K$ are unramified.*

Corollary. *Let n be an integer > 1, and assume that n is not a prime power. Let ω be a primitive n-th root of unity. Then*

$$\prod_{j=1}^{n-1} (1 - \omega^j) = 1.$$

Proof. Let S_d be the set of primitive d-th roots of unity. Let

$$f_d(X) = \prod_{\zeta \in S_d} (X - \zeta).$$

Let

$$g(X) = \frac{X^n - 1}{X - 1} = X^{n-1} + X^{n-2} + \cdots + X + 1.$$

Then

$$g(X) = \prod_{\substack{d|n \\ d>1}} f_d(X).$$

Hence

$$n = g(1) = \prod_{\substack{d|n \\ d>1}} f_d(1).$$

If p is a prime dividing n, then among the divisors of n we get $p, p^2, \ldots, p^r$ (where r is the highest power of p dividing n). We know from (*) that $f_{p^k}(1) = p$. Hence

$$\prod_{k=1}^{r} f_{p^k}(1) = p^r.$$

Thus from the prime powers dividing n we already get a contribution of n for $g(1)$. This implies that for the composite divisors of n, the values $f_d(1)$ (which are algebraic integers, rational, hence ordinary integers) must be 1 or -1. Assume inductively that for $d|n$ and $d < n$ the value $f_d(1)$ is equal to 1. Then we see from our product that $f_n(1) = 1$, thus proving our corollary. (I am indebted to Bass for this proof.)

The last statement in Theorem 1 actually can be strengthened as follows.

Theorem 2. *Let m be a positive integer and ω a primitive m-th root of unity. Then $[\mathbf{Q}(\omega):\mathbf{Q}] = \varphi(m)$. The only ramified primes p in $\mathbf{Q}(\omega)$ are those dividing m. If*

$$m = p_1^{r_1} \cdots p_s^{r_s}$$

is the prime power decomposition of m, ω_j is a primitive p^{r_j}-th root of unity, then

$$\mathbf{Q}(\omega) = \mathbf{Q}(\omega_1, \ldots, \omega_s) = \mathbf{Q}(\omega_1) \ldots \mathbf{Q}(\omega_s)$$

is the compositum of the $\mathbf{Q}(\omega_j)$.

Proof. Let $g(X) = X^m - 1$. Then ω satisfies $g(X) = 0$, and

$$g'(\omega) = m\omega^{m-1}$$

is divisible only by primes dividing m. Hence any other prime is unramified in $\mathbf{Q}(\omega)$. For any $j > 1$, the field $\mathbf{Q}(\omega_j)$ is an abelian extension of $\mathbf{Q}$

whose intersection with $\mathbf{Q}(\omega_1, \ldots, \omega_{j-1})$ is $\mathbf{Q}$, because p_j is totally ramified in $\mathbf{Q}(\omega_j)$ and unramified in the other field. Hence $\mathbf{Q}(\omega_1, \ldots, \omega_j)$ has degree $\varphi(p^{r_j})$ over $\mathbf{Q}(\omega_1, \ldots, \omega_{j-1})$. This proves our theorem.

If G is the Galois group of $\mathbf{Q}(\omega)$ over $\mathbf{Q}$, then any automorphism σ of $\mathbf{Q}(\omega)$ over $\mathbf{Q}$ must map ω on some primitive root ω^i, i prime to m. Since $[\mathbf{Q}(\omega): \mathbf{Q}] = \varphi(m)$, it follows that for any such i there exists $\sigma \in G$ such that $\sigma\omega = \omega^i$. Thus G is isomorphic to the multiplicative group of residue classes of $\mathbf{Z}/m\mathbf{Z}$ which are prime to m. Observe also that if m, n are two relative prime integers > 0, and ζ_n, ζ_m denote primitive m-th and n-th roots of unity respectively, then

$$\mathbf{Q}(\zeta_n) \cap \mathbf{Q}(\zeta_m) = \mathbf{Q}.$$

Theorem 3. *Let ω be a primitive p^r-th root of unity, and $K = \mathbf{Q}(\omega)$. Then $\mathfrak{o}_K = \mathbf{Z}[\omega]$. The discriminant is given by*

$$D_K = \pm p^{p^{r-1}(pr-r-1)},$$

where the $-$ sign holds when $p^r = 4$ or $p \equiv 3 \pmod 4$, and the $+$ sign holds otherwise.

Proof. We shall give the proof only when $r = 1$. The principle is the same in general. Thus we deal with the p-th roots of unity. Let $B = \mathbf{Z}[\omega]$. To prove that $B = \mathfrak{o}_K$ it suffices to prove that the discriminant of B and $\mathfrak{o}_K$ as modules over $\mathbf{Z}$ coincide as $\mathbf{Z}$-ideals by Proposition 10 of Chapter III, §3. To do this, it suffices to prove it locally for each prime. All primes except p are unramified, and consequently such primes do not contribute either to the discriminant of $\mathfrak{o}_K$ or of B. As for p, it is totally ramified, and using Proposition 23 of Chapter I, §7, we conclude that $S_p^{-1}B = S_p^{-1}\mathfrak{o}_K$ if S_p is the complement of the principal ideal (p) in $\mathbf{Z}$. Hence the p-component of the discriminants is the same in both cases. This proves that $B = \mathfrak{o}_K$. The assertion concerning the exact value of the discriminant comes from taking the discriminant of the element ω itself, and paying attention to the sign. There is no difficulty in this (use Proposition 15 of Chapter III, §3).

To deal with an arbitrary composite integer m, we use a discriminant criterion.

Theorem 4. *Let m be a positive integer, and ω a primitive m-th root of unity. Then $\mathbf{Z}[\omega]$ is the integral closure of $\mathbf{Z}$ in $\mathbf{Q}(\omega)$.*

Proof. It is clearly the compositum of the rings of integers of various prime power cyclotomic fields which satisfy the conditions of Proposition 17, Chapter III, §3.

§2. *Quadratic fields*

Extensions of degree 2 over the rationals are also worthy of mention as examples.

Theorem 5. *Let m be a square-free integer $\neq 0$, and let $K = \mathbf{Q}(\sqrt{m})$. If $m \equiv 2$ or $3 \pmod 4$, then $[1, \sqrt{m}]$ is a basis for $\mathfrak{o}_K$ over $\mathbf{Z}$. If $m \equiv 1 \pmod 4$, then*

$$\left[1, \frac{1+\sqrt{m}}{2}\right]$$

is a basis for $\mathfrak{o}_K$ over $\mathbf{Z}$.

Proof. Exercise. To verify that an element $x + y\sqrt{m}$ with $x, y \in \mathbf{Q}$ is integral over $\mathbf{Z}$, it is necessary and sufficient that its norm and trace lie in $\mathbf{Z}$. From this, there is no difficulty in verifying the assertion of the theorem.

For instance, if $m = -3$, then

$$\frac{1+\sqrt{-3}}{2}$$

is a cube root of unity, and hence is integral over $\mathbf{Z}$.

Before proving the next result, we make some observations on finite fields.

Let F_q be the finite field with q elements, q equal to a power of the prime number p. Then F_q^* has $q - 1$ elements, and is a cyclic group. Hence we get the index

$$(F_q^* : F_q^{*2}) = 2.$$

If ν is an integer $\not\equiv 0 \bmod p$, let

$$\left(\frac{\nu}{p}\right) = \begin{cases} 1 & \text{if} \quad \nu \equiv x^2 \pmod p \\ -1 & \text{if} \quad \nu \not\equiv x^2 \pmod p. \end{cases}$$

This is known as the **quadratic symbol,** and depends only on the residue class of ν mod p.

From the preceding remark, we see that there are as many quadratic residues as there are non-residues mod p.

Theorem 6. *Let ζ be a primitive p-th root of unity, and*

$$S = \sum_{\nu} \left(\frac{\nu}{p}\right) \zeta^{\nu},$$

the sum being taken over non-zero residue classes mod p. *Then*

$$S^2 = \left(\frac{-1}{p}\right) p.$$

Every quadratic extension of **Q** *is contained in a cyclotomic extension.*

Proof. The last statement follows at once from the explicit expression of $\pm p$ as a square in $\mathbf{Q}(\zeta)$ and also $(1 + i)^2 = 2i$. As for the sum, we have

$$S^2 = \sum_{\nu,\mu} \left(\frac{\nu\mu}{p}\right) \zeta^{\nu+\mu}.$$

As ν ranges over non-zero residue classes, so does $\nu\mu$ for any fixed μ, and hence replacing ν by $\nu\mu$ yields

$$\begin{aligned} S^2 &= \sum_{\nu,\mu} \left(\frac{\nu\mu^2}{p}\right) \zeta^{\mu(\nu+1)} = \sum_{\nu,\mu} \left(\frac{\nu}{p}\right) \zeta^{\mu(\nu+1)} \\ &= \sum_{\mu} \left(\frac{-1}{p}\right) \zeta^0 + \sum_{\nu \neq -1} \left(\frac{\nu}{p}\right) \sum_{\mu} \zeta^{\mu(\nu+1)}. \end{aligned}$$

But $1 + \zeta + \cdots + \zeta^{p-1} = 0$, and the sum on the right over μ consequently yields -1. Hence

$$\begin{aligned} S^2 &= \left(\frac{-1}{p}\right)(p - 1) + (-1) \sum_{\nu \neq -1} \left(\frac{\nu}{p}\right) \\ &= p\left(\frac{-1}{p}\right) - \sum_{\nu} \left(\frac{\nu}{p}\right) \\ &= \left(\frac{-1}{p}\right) p \end{aligned}$$

as desired.

We see that $\mathbf{Q}(\sqrt{p})$ is contained in $\mathbf{Q}(\zeta, \sqrt{-1})$, or $\mathbf{Q}(\zeta)$, depending on the sign of the quadratic symbol with -1. It is in fact a theorem that every abelian extension of **Q** is cyclotomic, and we shall prove this in the class field theory later.

We now apply Theorem 6 to prove the quadratic reciprocity law. We observe that if p is an odd prime, then

$$\left(\frac{-1}{p}\right) = (-1)^{\frac{p-1}{2}} \quad \text{and} \quad \left(\frac{\nu}{p}\right) \equiv \nu^{\frac{p-1}{2}} \pmod{p}.$$

This is obvious from the definitions, and the fact that $(\mathbf{Z}/p\mathbf{Z})^*$ is cyclic.

Let p, q be odd primes. On the one hand, we get

$$S^q = S(S^2)^{\frac{q-1}{2}} = S(-1)^{\frac{p-1}{2}\frac{q-1}{2}} p^{\frac{q-1}{2}}$$
$$\equiv S(-1)^{\frac{p-1}{2}\frac{q-1}{2}} \left(\frac{p}{q}\right) \pmod{q}.$$

On the other hand, we get

$$S^q \equiv \sum_{\nu=1}^{p-1} \left(\frac{\nu}{p}\right) \zeta^{\nu q} \pmod{q}$$
$$\equiv \left(\frac{q}{p}\right) \sum_{\nu=1}^{p-1} \left(\frac{\nu q}{p}\right) \zeta^{\nu q} \pmod{q}$$
$$\equiv \left(\frac{q}{p}\right) S \pmod{q}.$$

Hence

$$S(-1)^{\frac{p-1}{2}\frac{q-1}{2}} \left(\frac{p}{q}\right) \equiv \left(\frac{q}{p}\right) S \pmod{q}.$$

Multiplying by S and canceling $\pm p$ yields the reciprocity law

$$\boxed{\left(\frac{q}{p}\right) = \left(\frac{p}{q}\right)(-1)^{\frac{p-1}{2}\frac{q-1}{2}}.}$$

A similar argument (but simpler) using the sum $(1+i)^p$ yields the result

$$\boxed{\left(\frac{2}{p}\right) = (-1)^{\frac{p^2-1}{8}}.}$$

We shall now reconsider these results from another point of view, closer to that of class field theory, and having to do with the decomposition laws for primes.

Quadratic Reciprocity Law. *Let p, q be prime numbers.*

Case 1. *If p, q are odd and $p \equiv 1 \pmod{4}$, then* $\left(\frac{p}{q}\right) = \left(\frac{q}{p}\right)$.

Case 2. *If p, q are $\equiv 3 \pmod{4}$, then* $\left(\frac{p}{q}\right) = -\left(\frac{q}{p}\right)$.

Case 3. *If* $q = 2$ *and* p *is odd, then* $\left(\frac{2}{p}\right) = 1$ *if* $p \equiv \pm 1 \pmod 8$ *and* $\left(\frac{2}{p}\right) = -1$ *if* $p \equiv \pm 3 \pmod 8$.

Proof. First deal with Case 1, and consider the field $\mathbf{Q}(\zeta)$ where ζ is a primitive p-th root of unity. Then

$$[\mathbf{Q}(\zeta) : \mathbf{Q}] = p - 1$$

and $\mathbf{Q}(\zeta)$ is cyclic over $\mathbf{Q}$. Hence $\mathbf{Q}(\zeta)$ contains a unique quadratic subfield. Since p is the only ramified prime, this subfield must be obtained by $\sqrt{-p}$ or $\sqrt{p}$, and hence must be $\mathbf{Q}(\sqrt{p})$ since the discriminant is p in the latter case, and $-4p$ in the former.

In the field $\mathbf{Q}(\sqrt{p})$, the prime q splits as follows:

$$(q) = \mathfrak{q}\mathfrak{q}' \text{ with } \mathfrak{q} \neq \mathfrak{q}' \iff \left(\frac{p}{q}\right) = 1,$$

$$(q) = \mathfrak{q} \text{ remains prime} \iff \left(\frac{p}{q}\right) = -1.$$

This is obvious from the definitions.

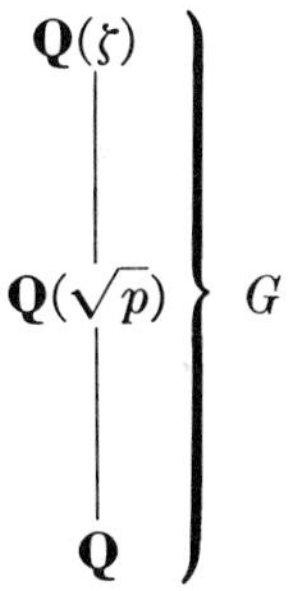

Let $\mathfrak{Q}|q$ in $\mathbf{Q}(\zeta)$. We let f be defined by $\mathbf{N}\mathfrak{Q} = q^f$, so that f is the order of the decomposition group of $\mathfrak{Q}$. We let r be the number of distinct primes of $\mathbf{Q}(\zeta)$ dividing q. Then

$$fr = p - 1.$$

We shall prove that $2|r$ is equivalent with $\left(\frac{p}{q}\right) = 1$ and with $\left(\frac{q}{p}\right) = 1$. This will take care of Case 1.

Assume that $2|r$. If Z is the fixed field of $G_{\mathfrak{Q}}$, i.e. the decomposition field of q, then $[Z : \mathbf{Q}] = r$, so that Z contains the unique quadratic subfield $\mathbf{Q}(\sqrt{p})$. Hence q splits completely in this subfield, and $\left(\frac{p}{q}\right) = 1$.

Conversely, if $\left(\frac{p}{q}\right) = 1$, then q splits completely in $\mathbf{Q}(\sqrt{p})$, which is therefore contained in Z, and hence $2|r$.

Next, let σ be the Frobenius automorphism such that $\sigma\zeta = \zeta^q$. Then $q^f \equiv 1 \pmod p$ and f is the least positive such exponent. If $2|r$, then

$f|(p-1)/2$, and hence

$$q^{\frac{p-1}{2}} \equiv 1 \pmod{p}.$$

It follows that $\left(\frac{q}{p}\right) = 1$. Conversely, if $\left(\frac{q}{p}\right) = 1$, then we get the same congruence, so that $f|(p-1)/2$ and finally $2|r$, thus proving Case 1.

As for Case 2, the proof is just like that of Case 1, except that now, $2|r$ is equivalent with $\left(\frac{p}{q}\right) = -1$.

In Case 3, we take $q = 2$. Let $i = \sqrt{-1}$ so $(1+i)^2 = 2i$, and

$$(1+i)^{2(p-1)/2} = 2^{(p-1)/2} i^{(p-1)/2} = (1+i)^{p-1}.$$

We get

$$(1+i)^p \equiv 1 + i^p \equiv \left(\frac{2}{p}\right) i^{(p-1)/2}(1+i) \pmod{p}.$$

But

$$(1+i^p)(1+i) = \begin{cases} 2i & \text{if } p \equiv 1 \pmod{4} \\ 2 & \text{if } p \equiv -1 \pmod{4}. \end{cases}$$

Hence

$$p \equiv 1 \pmod{4} \quad \text{implies} \quad 2i \equiv \left(\frac{2}{p}\right) i^{(p-1)/2} 2i \pmod{p},$$

$$p \equiv -1 \pmod{4} \quad \text{implies} \quad 2 \equiv \left(\frac{2}{p}\right) i^{(p-1)/2} 2i \pmod{p}.$$

From this Case 3 follows at once.

Note that the three cases can be summarized by the usual formula. The symbol

$$\left(\frac{p}{q}\right)$$

can be extended to more general integers.

Let P be a non-zero integer, written as

$$P = \pm p_1 \cdots p_r$$

where $p_1, \ldots, p_r$ are primes. Let

$$Q = q_1 \cdots q_s$$

be an *odd* positive integer written as a product of primes. We assume that $(P, Q) = 1$. We define

$$\left(\frac{P}{Q}\right) = \prod_{j=1}^{s} \left(\frac{P}{q_j}\right).$$

We call this the **quadratic symbol.** It is then clear from the definition that the following properties hold.

QR 1. *If* $P_1 \equiv P_2 \pmod{Q}$ *then*

$$\left(\frac{P_1}{Q}\right) = \left(\frac{P_2}{Q}\right).$$

QR 2. *The symbol is bi-multiplicative, i.e.,*

$$\left(\frac{P_1P_2}{Q}\right) = \left(\frac{P_1}{Q}\right)\left(\frac{P_2}{Q}\right) \quad \text{and} \quad \left(\frac{P}{Q_1Q_2}\right) = \left(\frac{P}{Q_1}\right)\left(\frac{P}{Q_2}\right).$$

QR 3. *We have* $\left(\frac{-1}{Q}\right) = (-1)^{\frac{Q-1}{2}}$.

Proof. By definition, and the definition of the symbol for primes,

$$\left(\frac{-1}{Q}\right) = \prod_{j=1}^{s} (-1)^{\frac{q_j-1}{2}} = (-1)^{\Sigma\frac{(q_j-1)}{2}}.$$

But

$$Q = \prod_{j=1}^{s} ((q_j - 1) + 1) \equiv \prod_{j=1}^{s} (q_j - 1) + 1 \pmod{4}$$

because $q_j - 1$ is even, and the product of any two or more such terms is $\equiv 0 \bmod 4$. Thus our assertion follows.

QR 4. *If* P, Q *are odd and both* > 0 *then*

$$\left(\frac{P}{Q}\right)\left(\frac{Q}{P}\right) = (-1)^{\frac{P-1}{2}\frac{Q-1}{2}}.$$

Proof. We have

$$\left(\frac{P}{Q}\right)\left(\frac{Q}{P}\right) = \prod_{j,k} \left(\frac{p_k}{q_j}\right)\left(\frac{q_j}{p_k}\right) = (-1)^{\sum_{k,j}\frac{p_k-1}{2}\frac{q_j-1}{2}} = (-1)^{\frac{P-1}{2}\frac{Q-1}{2}}.$$

§3. *Gauss sums*

Sums involving roots of unity appear in many contexts. We have just seen one example in §2. Other examples arise in the functional equation of zeta functions and L-series. We study them here a little for their own sake. We shall use constantly the fact that if G is a finite abelian group and χ is a character of G (i.e. a homomorphism of G into the group of roots of unity) then

$$\sum_{a\in G} \chi(a) = \begin{cases} 0 & \text{if } \chi \neq 1 \\ (G:1) & \text{if } \chi = 1. \end{cases}$$

This is trivially seen, because if $\chi \neq 1$, then there exists $b \in G$ such that $\chi(b) \neq 1$. Then

$$\sum_{a\in G} \chi(a) = \sum_{a\in G} \chi(ba) = \chi(b) \sum_{a\in G} \chi(a),$$

whence $\sum \chi(a) = 0$.

We shall consider Gauss sums relative to $\mathbf{Z}/q\mathbf{Z}$ where q is an integer > 1, and also relative to a finite field with q elements. We begin with the former case.

Gauss sums for $\mathbf{Z}/q\mathbf{Z}$.

The elements of $\mathbf{Z}/q\mathbf{Z}$ represented by integers relative prime to q form a multiplicative group denoted by $(\mathbf{Z}/q\mathbf{Z})^*$. By a **multiplicative character** of $\mathbf{Z}/q\mathbf{Z}$ (or a character mod q) one means a character of this multiplicative group. Such characters are denoted by χ. If $d|q$, then we have a natural homomorphism

$$\mathbf{Z}/q\mathbf{Z} \to \mathbf{Z}/d\mathbf{Z}$$

which is surjective. A multiplicative character for $\mathbf{Z}/d\mathbf{Z}$ composed with this homomorphism induces a character mod q. We say that a character mod q is **primitive** if it cannot be induced by a character mod d for any divisor d of q, $d \neq q$. A character χ is extended to a function on $\mathbf{Z}/q\mathbf{Z}$ by letting

$$\chi(n) = 0 \text{ if } (n, q) > 1.$$

Let ζ be a primitive q-th root of unity. We define the **Gauss sum** for a primitive character χ mod q and an integer n to be

$$\tau(\chi, n) = \sum_{x \bmod q} \chi(x)\zeta^{nx}.$$

This Gauss sum of course depends on ζ. We can always select

$$\zeta = e^{2\pi i/q}$$

as a canonical choice, but we are interested here in algebraic manipulations rather than analytic values, so any *fixed* ζ will do. Observe that $\tau(\chi, n)$ is actually the Fourier transform of χ evaluated at n (actually selecting ζ to be $e^{-2\pi i/q}$!).

If $(n, q) = 1$, then we write

$$\bar{\chi}(n) = \chi(n)^{-1} = \chi(n^{-1})$$

where n^{-1} is the inverse of n mod q.

For any primitive character χ mod q *we have the formula*

$$\boxed{\tau(\chi, n) = \overline{\chi(n)}\tau(\chi, 1).} \tag{1}$$

Proof. Assume first that $(n, q) = 1$. Then

$$\begin{aligned}\overline{\chi(n)}\tau(\chi, 1) &= \sum_x \overline{\chi(n)}\chi(x)\zeta^x \\ &= \sum_x \chi(xn^{-1})\zeta^x = \sum_y \chi(y)\zeta^{ny} = \tau(\chi, n),\end{aligned}$$

because as x ranges over the residue class mod q, so does nx when n is relatively prime to q. This proves our formula, in case $(n, q) = 1$.

Assume now that $(n, q) > 1$. It will suffice to prove that

$$\boxed{\tau(\chi, n) = 0.} \tag{2}$$

Write $q = rd$ and $n = md$ with positive integers r, d, m such that $d > 1$ and $(r, m) = 1$. Then

$$\tau(\chi, n) = \sum_{x \bmod q} \chi(x)\zeta_r^{mx}$$

where $\zeta_r = \zeta_q^d$ is a primitive r-th root of unity. Write

$$x = y + rz \qquad \text{with } y \bmod r \quad \text{and} \quad z \bmod d.$$

Then

$$\tau(\chi, n) = \sum_{y \bmod r} \sum_{z \bmod d} \chi(y + rz)\zeta_r^{my}.$$

Note that the function

$$y \mapsto \sum_{z \bmod d} \chi(y + rz)\zeta_r^{my}$$

depends only on the residue class of y mod r. We get:

$$\begin{aligned}\chi(c)\tau(\chi, n) &= \sum_{y \bmod r} \sum_{z \bmod d} \chi(cy + crz)\zeta_r^{my} \\ &= \sum_{y \bmod r} \sum_{z \bmod d} \chi(y)\zeta_r^{my} = \tau(\chi, n).\end{aligned}$$

It follows that $\tau(\chi, n) = 0$, thus proving our assertion (2).

Finally, we obtain the absolute value of the Gauss sum.

For primitive character χ mod q *and* $(n, q) = 1$, *we have*

(3) $$\boxed{|\tau(\chi, n)| = \sqrt{n}.}$$

Proof. We have:

$$|\tau(\chi, n)|^2 = \tau(\chi, n)\overline{\tau(\chi, n)} = \sum_x \sum_y \chi(x)\overline{\chi(y)}\zeta^{n(x-y)}.$$

Take the sum over all residue class n mod q.

If $x \not\equiv y \pmod q$ then $\sum_{n \bmod q} \zeta^{n(x-y)} = 0.$

If $x \equiv y \pmod q$ then $\sum_{n \bmod q} \zeta^{n(x-y)} = q.$

Since $\chi(x) = 0$ if $(x, q) > 1$, we get

$$\sum_{n \bmod q} |\tau(\chi, n)|^2 = \sum_{x \equiv y} |\chi(x)| q = q\varphi(q).$$

But from (1), we know that

$$|\tau(\chi, n)|^2 = |\chi(n)|^2 |\tau(\chi, 1)|^2.$$

Summing over n and using the fact that $\chi(n) = 0$ if $(n, q) > 1$ we get

$$\varphi(q)|\tau(\chi, n)|^2 = q\varphi(q).$$

This proves our formula $|\tau(\chi, n)| = \sqrt{n}$.

We shall now investigate quadratic sums. For the rest of our discussion, we use the following convention.

Let a, b be non-zero integers, $b > 0$, and $(a, b) = 1$.

Let

$$G(a, b) = \sum_{x \bmod b} e^{\frac{2\pi i}{b} ax^2}.$$

We shall determine the value of this Gauss (quadratic sum). We first give some algebraic reduction steps.

QS 1. *If p is an odd prime, then*

$$\boxed{G(a, p) = \left(\frac{a}{p}\right) G(1, p).}$$

Proof. If $a \equiv c^2 \pmod{p}$ for some c, then we replace x by cx, which also runs over the residue classes mod p, and we see that $G(a, p) = G(1, p)$ in this case. If $a \not\equiv c^2 \pmod{p}$, then we use the fact that

$$\sum_{x \bmod p} e^{\frac{2\pi i}{p} x^2} = 1 + 2 \sum_{r} e^{\frac{2\pi i}{p} r} + 2 \sum_{n} e^{\frac{2\pi i}{p} n},$$

where r denotes the non-zero quadratic residues mod p, and n denotes the non-zero non-residues mod p. The map $x \mapsto x^2$ covers the residues precisely twice (since $(\mathbf{Z}/p\mathbf{Z})^*$ is cyclic), and we also have

$$\sum_{y \bmod p} e^{\frac{2\pi i}{p} y} = 0 = 1 + \sum_{r} e^{\frac{2\pi i}{p} r} + \sum_{n} e^{\frac{2\pi i}{p} n}.$$

From this our assertion is clear.

QS 2. *Let p be an odd prime, and r an integer $\geqq 2$. Then*

$$\boxed{G(a, p^r) = pG(a, p^{r-2}).}$$

Proof. Write

$$x = y + p^{r-1}z, \qquad y \bmod p^{r-1}, \quad z \bmod p.$$

Then $x^2 = y^2 + 2p^{r-1}yz + p^{2r-2}z^2$.

$$G(a, p^r) = \sum_{y} \sum_{z} e^{\frac{2\pi i}{p^r} ay^2} e^{\frac{2\pi i}{p} 2ayz}.$$

Sum separately for $y \equiv 0\ (p)$ and $y \not\equiv 0\ (p)$. If $y \not\equiv 0\ (p)$, then the map $z \mapsto 2ayz$ permutes the residue class mod p, and hence the sum over z in this case is 0. If $y \equiv 0\ (p)$, we write

$$y = pu,$$

and we can take the sum for u mod p^{r-2}. Each term $e^{\frac{2\pi i}{p} 2ayz}$ is $= 1$, and the inner sum over z yields p. Thus we obtain precisely

$$pG(a, p^{r-2}),$$

as desired.

QS 3. *Let $b, c \geqq 1$, $(b, c) = 1$, and $(a, bc) = 1$. Then*

$$\boxed{G(a, bc) = G(ab, c)G(ac, b).}$$

Proof. Write x mod bc as

$$x = yb + zc, \qquad y \text{ mod } c,\ z \text{ mod } b.$$

Then

$$\begin{aligned} G(ab, c)G(ac, b) &= \sum_{y,z} e^{\frac{2\pi i}{c} aby^2} e^{\frac{2\pi i}{b} acz^2} \\ &= \sum_{y,z} e^{\frac{2\pi i}{bc} a[(by)^2 + (cz)^2]} \\ &= G(a, bc) \end{aligned}$$

because

$$\frac{2yzbc}{bc} = 2yz$$

is an integer.

QS 4. *If b is odd $\geqq 1$ then*

$$\boxed{G(a, b) = \left(\frac{a}{b}\right) G(1, b).}$$

Proof. Induction. If b is an odd prime, this is **QS 1.** Assume $b > 3$. If $b = p^r$ and $r \geqq 2$, then

$$\frac{G(a, p^r)}{G(1, p^r)} = \frac{G(a, p^{r-2})}{G(1, p^{r-2})}.$$

Our assertion then follows at once, in the case of prime power.

In the composite case, suppose b, $c > 1$, and $(a, bc) = 1$. Then

$$\begin{aligned} G(a, bc) &= G(ab, c)G(ac, b) \\ &= \left(\frac{ab}{c}\right)\left(\frac{ac}{b}\right) G(1, c)G(1, b) \qquad \text{(by induction)} \\ &= \left(\frac{a}{bc}\right)\left(\frac{b}{c}\right)\left(\frac{c}{b}\right) G(1, c)G(1, b) \\ &= \left(\frac{a}{bc}\right) G(b, c)G(c, b) = \left(\frac{a}{bc}\right) G(1, bc), \end{aligned}$$

and we are done.

There remains to handle the case when $b = 2^r$. We shall compute analytically the value $G(1, b)$ for arbitrary b below, and we shall find:

$$G(1, b) = \begin{cases} (1 + i)\sqrt{b} & \text{if } b \equiv 0 \pmod 4 \\ \sqrt{b} & \text{if } b \equiv 1 \pmod 4 \\ 0 & \text{if } b \equiv 2 \pmod 4 \\ i\sqrt{b} & \text{if } b \equiv 3 \pmod 4. \end{cases}$$

Remember that $b \geqq 1$, and that $\sqrt{b}$ is the ordinary positive square root of b. In view of these values, we define

$$\epsilon(b) = \begin{cases} 1 & \text{if } b \equiv 1 \pmod 4 \\ i & \text{if } b \equiv 3 \pmod 4. \end{cases}$$

We shall use the given values to get $G(a, 2^r)$ as follows.

QS 5. *Let a be odd. Then*

$$G(a, 2^r) = \left(\frac{-2^r}{a}\right) \epsilon(a)G(1, 2^r).$$

Proof. The map

$$\sigma_a : \zeta \mapsto \zeta^a$$

on 2^m-th roots of unity induces an automorphism of the field generated over $\mathbf{Q}$ by 2^m-th roots of unity for all m, and we have

$$G(a, 2^r) = \sigma_a G(1, 2^r) = \sigma_a(1 + i)\sigma_a(2^{r/2}),$$

assuming that $r \geqq 2$ (the case $r = 1$ being trivial). Obviously,

$$\sigma_a(1+i) = 1 + i^a = \begin{cases} 1+i & \text{if } a \equiv 1 \pmod 4 \\ 1-i & \text{if } a \equiv 3 \pmod 4), \end{cases}$$

Since $1 - i = -i(1+i)$, we find that

$$\sigma_a(1+i) = \left(\frac{-1}{a}\right)\epsilon(a)(1+i).$$

Next observe that

$$1 + i = e^{\frac{2\pi i}{8}}\sqrt{2} \quad \text{or} \quad \sqrt{2} = \frac{1+i}{e_8},$$

where $e_8 = e^{\frac{2\pi i}{8}}$. Hence

$$\sigma_a\sqrt{2} = \frac{1+i^a}{e_8^a} = \begin{cases} \sqrt{2} & \text{if } a \equiv \pm 1 \pmod 8 \\ -\sqrt{2} & \text{if } a \equiv \pm 3 \pmod 8). \end{cases}$$

Thus

$$\sigma_a\sqrt{2} = \left(\frac{2}{a}\right)\sqrt{2} = (-1)^{\frac{a^2-1}{8}}\sqrt{2}.$$

If r is even, then $2^{r/2}$ is rational, and if r is odd, then $2^{r/2}$ is a rational number times $\sqrt{2}$. Therefore

$$\sigma_a(2^{r/2}) = \left(\frac{2}{a}\right)^r 2^{r/2} = \left(\frac{2^r}{a}\right)2^{r/2}.$$

This proves **QS 5** and concludes our formalism of the Gauss sums.

There remains to compute $G(1, b)$ for arbitrary $b \geqq 1$. The computation is analytic, and is due to Dirichlet. It uses the fact that if φ is a function which is smooth except for ordinary discontinuities, then its Fourier series converges pointwise to the midpoint of the discontinuity. In particular, if φ is a function which is continuously differentiable on the interval $[0, 1]$, then

$$\frac{\varphi(0) + \varphi(1)}{2} = \sum_m c_m,$$

where c_m is the m-th Fourier coefficient,

$$c_m(\varphi) = \int_0^1 \varphi(x)e^{-2\pi imx}\,dx,$$

and the sum is taken over all integers m.

We shall use the function

$$f(x) = e^{2\pi i x^2/b}, \qquad 0 \leqq x \leqq 1,$$

and its translates, also in the interval $0 \leqq x \leqq 1$, namely

$$f_k(x) = f(x + k), \qquad k = 0, 1, \ldots, b - 1.$$

Then by definition,

$$G(1, b) = \sum_{k=0}^{b-1} \frac{f_k(0) + f_k(1)}{2},$$

whence if $\varphi = f_0 + f_1 + \cdots + f_{b-1}$, we need only compute the sum of the Fourier coefficients for φ to get the value of $G(1, b)$. By definition, and the convergence of the Fourier series, we find

$$\begin{aligned} G(1, b) &= \sum_m \sum_{k=0}^{b-1} \int_0^1 f_k(x) e^{-2\pi i m x}\, dx \\ &= \sum_m \int_0^b e^{2\pi i x^2/b} e^{-2\pi i m x}\, dx \\ &= \sum_m \int_0^b e^{\frac{2\pi i}{b}(x^2 - bmx)}\, dx. \end{aligned}$$

We complete the square,

$$x^2 - bmx = \left(x - \frac{bm}{2}\right)^2 - \frac{b^2 m^2}{4},$$

and find that our last expression is

$$= \sum_m e^{-\pi i b m^2/2} \int_0^b e^{\frac{2\pi i}{b}(x - \frac{bm}{2})^2}\, dx.$$

If m is even, then $e^{-\pi i b m^2/2} = 1$. If m is odd, then $e^{-\pi i b m^2/2} = i^{-b}$. We split the sum over even m and odd m. A trivial computation putting $m = 2r$ or $m = 2r + 1$ shows that the sums of the integrals over m even and m odd are equal to the same value, namely

$$I_b = \int_{-\infty}^{\infty} e^{\frac{2\pi i}{b} y^2}\, dy,$$

so that

$$G(1, b) = (1 + i^{-b}) I_b.$$

This integral converges at both ends, for if $0 < A < B$, then changing variables, $t = y^2$, $dt = 2ydy$, and integrating by parts shows that

$$\int_A^B e^{2\pi i y^2/b}\,dy = O\left(\frac{1}{\sqrt{A}}\right).$$

Thus the tail ends of the integral are arbitrarily small. Finally, let

$$u = \frac{y}{\sqrt{b}} \quad \text{and} \quad du = \frac{dy}{\sqrt{b}}.$$

Changing variables shows that

$$\int_{-\infty}^{\infty} e^{\frac{2\pi i}{b}y^2}\,dy = \sqrt{b}\int_{-\infty}^{\infty} e^{2\pi i u^2}\,du = \sqrt{b}\,I,$$

where I is the universal integral constant on the right. The integral I is simply I_1, whose value is obtained from the relation

$$1 = G(1, 1) = (1 + i^{-1})I_1.$$

Thus we find

$$\boxed{G(1, b) = \frac{1 + i^{-b}}{1 + i^{-1}}\sqrt{b},}$$

as desired.

Character sums over finite fields

For the rest of this section, we let F be a finite field with q elements, and $q = p^f$. We let F_p be $\mathbf{Z}/p\mathbf{Z}$. We denote elements of F by x, and elements of the multiplicative group F^* of F by a. We let $\omega = e^{2\pi i/p}$. We let $\mathbf{Tr} = \mathrm{Tr}_{F/F_p}$ be the absolute trace from F to F_p. Let $\mathfrak{F}$ be the vector space of complex valued functions on F.

If $\lambda : F \to \mathbf{C}^*$ is a non-trivial character, then λ induces a self duality of F, by means of the pairing

$$(x, y) \mapsto \lambda(xy).$$

Indeed, if λ_x is the map such that $\lambda_x(y) = \lambda(xy)$, then $x \mapsto \lambda_x$ is an injective homomorphism of F into its dual group, whence an isomorphism because these two groups have the same order. *We shall always use the fixed λ such that*

$$\boxed{\lambda(x) = \omega^{\mathbf{Tr}(x)}}$$

If $f \in \mathfrak{F}$, we define the (essentially Fourier) transform Tf by

$$Tf(y) = \sum_{x \in F} f(x)\lambda(xy).$$

Thus Tf is again a function on F (identified with its character group by λ), and $T\colon \mathfrak{F} \to \mathfrak{F}$ is a linear map.

Theorem 7. *We have $T^2 f = qf^-$, i.e. $T^2 f(z) = qf(-z)$.*

Proof. We have

$$\begin{aligned} T^2 f(z) &= \sum_y \sum_x f(x)\lambda(yx)\lambda(zy) \\ &= \sum_x f(x - z) \sum_y \lambda(yx) \\ &= qf(-z), \end{aligned}$$

as desired.

Theorem 7 is the analogue of the Fourier inversion formula. We see in particular that T is an automorphism of $\mathfrak{F}$.

We define the **convolution** $f * g$ between functions by the usual formula

$$(f * g)(y) = \sum_x f(x)g(y - x).$$

A change of vaiiables shows that

$$f * g = g * f.$$

Theorem 8. *For complex functions f, g on F, we have*

$$T(f * g) = (Tf)(Tg)$$

$$T(fg) = \frac{1}{q} Tf * Tg.$$

Proof. For the first formula, we have

$$T(f * g)(z) = \sum_y (f * g)(y)\lambda(zy) = \sum_y \sum_x f(x)g(y - x)\lambda(zy).$$

We change the order of summation, let $y - x = t$, $y = x + t$, and find

$$\sum_x f(x)\lambda(zx) \sum_t g(t)\lambda(zt),$$

which is precisely $(Tf)(Tg)(z)$, thus proving the first formula. The second formula follows from the first because T is an isomorphism on $\mathfrak{F}$, so that we can write $f = Tf_1$, $g = Tg_1$ for some functions f_1, g_1. We then combine the first formula with Theorem 7 to get the second.

We let χ denote a character of the multiplicative group F^*, and define $\chi(0) = 0$.

Example. If p is odd, we could take the character χ_2 defined by

$$\chi_2(a) = \left(\frac{a}{p}\right),$$

i.e. the quadratic residue symbol. This character is trivial on F^{*2}.

We are concerned with the Gauss sums which generalize the sum S considered in §2, and which are defined by

$$\tau(\chi) = \sum_{a \in F^*} \chi(a)\lambda(a) = \sum_x \chi(x)\lambda(x).$$

This can also be written as

$$\tau(\chi) = \chi(-1)(\chi * \lambda)(0) = (T\chi)(1),$$

using our convention that $\chi(0) = 0$. The Gauss sum has the following properties.

GS 1. *For any character $\chi \neq 1$, we have $T\chi = \tau(\chi)\chi^{-1}$.*

Proof. We have

$$T\chi(y) = \sum_x \chi(x)\lambda(yx).$$

If $y = 0$, then $T\chi(y) = 0$. If $y \neq 0$, we make a change of variables, $x = ty^{-1}$, and we find precisely the desired value $\tau(\chi)\chi(y^{-1})$.

GS 2. $\tau(\chi)\tau(\chi^{-1}) = \chi(-1)q$.

Proof. Note that $T^2\chi = T(\tau(\chi)\chi^{-1}) = \tau(\chi)\tau(\chi^{-1})\chi$. But we also know that $T^2\chi = q\chi^{-}$. This proves **GS 2.**

GS 3. $|\tau(\chi)| = \sqrt{q}$.

Proof. For the complex conjugate, we have

$$\overline{\tau(\chi)} = \sum_a \chi^{-1}(a)\lambda(-a) = \chi^{-1}(-1)\sum_a \chi^{-1}(a)\lambda(a)$$
$$= \chi(-1)\tau(\chi^{-1}).$$

Hence $\tau(\chi)\overline{\tau(\chi)} = q$, and our property follows.

GS 4. *Let*

$$\psi(\chi_1, \chi_2) = \chi_1 * \chi_2(1) = \sum_x \chi_1(x)\chi_2(1-x).$$

If $\chi_1\chi_2 \neq 1$, then

$$\tau(\chi_1)\tau(\chi_2) = \psi(\chi_1, \chi_2)\tau(\chi_1\chi_2).$$

Proof. We compute from the definitions:

$$\begin{aligned}\tau(\chi_1)\tau(\chi_2) &= \sum_x \sum_y \chi_1(x)\chi_2(y)\lambda(x+y)\\ &= \sum_x \sum_y \chi_1(x)\chi_2(y-x)\lambda(y)\\ &= \sum_x \sum_{a\neq 0} \chi_1(x)\chi_2(a-x)\lambda(a) + \sum_x \chi_1(x)\chi_2(-x).\end{aligned}$$

Since $\chi_1\chi_2 \neq 1$, the last sum on the right is equal to 0. In the other sum, we interchange the order of summation, replace x by ax, and find

$$\sum_a \chi_1\chi_2(a)\lambda(a) \cdot \sum_x \chi_1(x)\chi_2(1-x),$$

which proves **GS 4.**

GS 5. *For any positive integer* r, *we have* $\tau(\chi^{p^r}) = \tau(\chi)$.

Proof. This is obvious because raising to the p-th power is an automorphism of F, and therefore $\mathbf{Tr}(x^p) = \mathbf{Tr}(x)$.

We shall now consider the prime factorization of $\tau(\chi)$. To begin with, we observe that $\tau(\chi)$ is an algebraic integer in $\mathbf{Q}(\omega)$. Furthermore, since $\tau(\chi)\tau(\chi^{-1}) = \pm q$, it follows that the only primes dividing $\tau(\chi)$ are those which divide p.

We let K be the extension of $\mathbf{Q}$ obtained by adjoining the p-th roots of unity and the $(q-1)$-th roots of unity, so that K contains roots of unity as representatives of the elements of the finite field F with q elements. *We fix a homomorphism*

$$\varphi : \mathfrak{o}_K \to \overline{F}_p$$

of $\mathfrak{o}_K$ into the algebraic closure of F_p, and write mod p for this homomorphism. This homomorphism induces an isomorphism between the group of $(q-1)$-th roots of unity in K and the multiplicative group F^*, because the polynomial $X^{q-1} - 1$ has no multiple root mod p. If W_{q-1} is the cyclic group of $(q-1)$-th roots of unity, then

$$\varphi : W_{q-1} \to F^*$$

is this isomorphism. We can define a generator χ_φ for the character group of F^* by letting χ_φ be the character such that

$$\varphi\chi_\varphi(a) = a^{-1}.$$

Then χ_φ has order $q-1$, and any character χ is a power of χ_φ.

Theorem 9. *Let χ be a character of F^* and let $\chi = \chi_\varphi^\nu$, with*

$$1 \leqq \nu < q - 1.$$

Write ν in the p-adic expansion

$$\nu = \nu_0 + \nu_1 p + \cdots + \nu_{f-1} p^{f-1}$$

with $0 \leqq \nu_i \leqq p - 1$, and not all $\nu_i = 0$ or $p - 1$. Let

$$s(\nu) = \sum_{i=0}^{f-1} \nu_i \quad \text{and} \quad \gamma(\nu) = \prod_{i=0}^{f-1} (\nu_i!) \pmod{p}.$$

Then $\gamma(\nu) \not\equiv 0 \pmod{p}$ and

$$\varphi\left[\frac{\tau(\chi)}{(\omega - 1)^{s(\nu)}}\right] = \frac{-1}{\gamma(\nu)} \pmod{p}.$$

In particular, for any absolute value $|\ |_p$ extending the p-adic absolute value on the rationals, we get

$$|\tau(\chi)|_p = |\omega - 1|_p^{s(\nu)}.$$

Proof. We use induction on ν. Take first $\nu = 1$ so $\chi = \chi_\varphi$. We have

$$\tau(\chi_\varphi) = \sum_a \chi_\varphi(a)\omega^{\mathbf{Tr}(a)}.$$

Write

$$\omega^{\mathbf{Tr}(a)} = (1 + \omega - 1)^{\mathbf{Tr}(a)} = 1 + \mathbf{Tr}(a)(\omega - 1) + \xi(\omega - 1)^2$$

with some algebraic integer ξ depending on a. We interpret $\mathbf{Tr}(a)$ to be any representative in $\mathfrak{o}_K$ for the element in F. Then

$$\frac{\tau(\chi_\varphi)}{\omega - 1} = \sum_a \chi_\varphi(a)[\mathbf{Tr}(a) + \xi(\omega - 1)],$$

and hence

$$\begin{aligned}\varphi\left(\frac{\tau(\chi_\varphi)}{\omega - 1}\right) = \sum_a a^{-1}\mathbf{Tr}(a) &= \sum_a a^{-1}(a + a^p + \cdots + a^{p^{f-1}}) \\ &= \sum_a (1 + a^{p-1} + \cdots + a^{p^{f-1}-1}) \\ &= q - 1 \equiv -1 \pmod{p}\end{aligned}$$

because $a \mapsto a^{p^r - 1}$ is a multiplicative character. This settles the case $\nu = 1$.

Assume next that $1 < \nu < q - 1$ and that the statement is true for χ_φ^μ with $1 \leqq \mu < \nu$. We distinguish two cases.

Case 1. $p|\nu$. Then $\nu = p\mu$ and $\chi_\varphi^\nu = (\chi_\varphi^\mu)^p$, so that by **GS 5** we have

$$\tau(\chi_\varphi^\nu) = \tau(\chi_\varphi^\mu).$$

But obviously

$$s(\mu) = s(\nu) \qquad \text{and} \qquad \gamma(\nu) = \gamma(\mu).$$

This case is taken care of.

Case 2. $p \nmid \nu$. Then $\nu_0 \not\equiv 0$. We shall use **GS 4**. We have

$$\begin{aligned} \varphi(\psi(\chi_\varphi, \chi_\varphi^{\nu-1})) &= \varphi\Big(\sum_{a\neq 0,1} \chi_\varphi(a)\chi_\varphi^{\nu-1}(1-a)\Big) \\ &= \sum_{a\neq 0,1} a^{-1}(1-a)^{-(\nu-1)}, \end{aligned}$$

and after inserting $q - 1$ as an exponent of $(1 - a)$, using the fact that $(1 - a)^{q-1} = 1$, we find that this is

$$\begin{aligned} &= \sum_{a\neq 0} \sum_{j=0}^{q-\nu} (-1)^j \binom{q-\nu}{j} a^{j-1} \\ &= (q-1)(-1)(q-\nu) \end{aligned}$$

(because $a \mapsto a^{j-1}$ is a multiplicative character)

$$= -\nu = -\nu_0 \pmod{p}.$$

Note that in the present case,

$$s(\nu) = s(\nu - 1) + 1 \qquad \text{and} \qquad \gamma(\nu) = \nu_0 \cdot \gamma(\nu - 1).$$

Hence

$$\begin{aligned} \varphi\left(\frac{\tau(\chi_\varphi^\nu)}{(\omega-1)^{s(\nu)}}\right) &= \varphi\left(\frac{\tau(\chi_\varphi)\tau(\chi_\varphi^{\nu-1})}{(\omega-1)(\omega-1)^{s(\nu)-1}\psi(\chi_\varphi, \chi_\varphi^{\nu-1})}\right) \\ &= (-1)\frac{-1}{\gamma(\nu-1)}\frac{-1}{\nu_0} \\ &= -\frac{1}{\gamma(\nu)}, \end{aligned}$$

thus proving our theorem.

For an application in the next section, we obtain another expression for $s(\nu)$. As usual, $[x]$ is the largest integer $\leqq x$, and $\{x\} = x - [x]$.

Lemma. *If ν is a positive integer, $\nu = \nu_0 + \nu_1 p + \cdots + \nu_{f-1}p^{f-1}$ with $0 \leqq \nu_i \leqq p - 1$, then*

$$s(\nu) = \nu - (p-1)\sum_{j=0}^{f-1}\left[\frac{p^j\nu}{q-1}\right].$$

Proof. The expression on the right is equal to

$$(p-1)\sum_{j=0}^{f-1}\left(\frac{p^j\nu}{q-1} - \left[\frac{p^j\nu}{q-1}\right]\right) = (p-1)\sum_{j=0}^{f-1}\left[\frac{p^j\nu}{q-1}\right].$$

We note that this expression depends only on the residue class of $\nu \pmod{q-1}$. We consider therefore ν such that $0 \leqq \nu < q - 1$. For $j = 0, \ldots, f-1$, we have

$$\nu_j = \left[\frac{\nu}{p^j}\right] - p\left[\frac{\nu}{p^{j+1}}\right],$$

and $[\nu/p^f] = 0$. Taking the sum yields

$$s(\nu) = \nu - (p-1)\sum_{j=0}^{f-1}\left[\frac{\nu}{p^{j+1}}\right] = \nu - (p-1)\sum_{j=0}^{f-1}\left[\frac{\nu p^j}{q}\right].$$

It will now suffice to prove that

$$\left[\frac{\nu p^j}{q}\right] = \left[\frac{\nu p^j}{q-1}\right].$$

Suppose otherwise. Then for some integer n we have

$$\frac{\nu p^j}{q} < n \leqq \frac{\nu p^j}{q-1},$$

whence

$$\nu < \frac{nq}{p^j} \leqq \frac{\nu q}{q-1} = \nu + \frac{\nu}{q-1} < \nu + 1,$$

a contradiction which proves our lemma.

§4. *Relations in ideal classes*

Throughout this section we let $k = \mathbf{Q}(\zeta)$ where ζ is a primitive m-th root of unity. We let p be a prime number, $p \nmid m$, and we let $\mathfrak{p}$ be a prime in k such that $\mathfrak{p}|p$. We let ω be a primitive p-th root of unity. If μ is a positive integer prime to m, we let σ_μ be the automorphism of k such that

$$\sigma_\mu\zeta = \zeta^\mu.$$

We know that p is totally ramified in $\mathbf{Q}(\omega)$, and hence $\mathfrak{p}$ is totally ramified in $\mathbf{Q}(\zeta, \omega) = k(\omega)$. Thus there exists a unique prime $\mathfrak{P}$ in $k(\omega)$ such that $\mathfrak{P}|\mathfrak{p}$, and we have

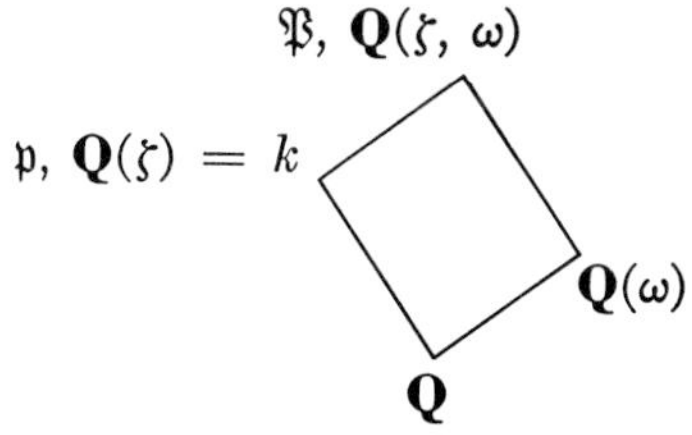

$$\mathfrak{p} = \mathfrak{P}^{p-1}.$$

Theorem 10. *Let f be the order of p* mod m, *and $q = p^f$. Let χ be a character of $F = F_q$ such that*

$$\chi(a) \equiv a^{-(q-1)/m} \pmod{\mathfrak{p}}.$$

Then for any integer $r \geqq 1$ we have the factorization

$$\tau(\chi^r) \sim \mathfrak{P}^{\alpha(r)},$$

where $\alpha(r)$ is the element of the group ring given by

$$\alpha(r) = \frac{1}{f}\sum_{\mu} s\left(\frac{(q-1)\mu r}{m}\right)\sigma_\mu^{-1},$$

and the sum is taken over all μ mod m, *prime to m.*

Proof. This is essentially a reformulation of Theorem 9. Let $K = \mathbf{Q}(\zeta, \omega)$ and let φ be a homomorphism of $\mathfrak{o}_K$ into $\overline{F}_p$ corresponding to $\mathfrak{P}$, i.e. inducing an injection

$$\mathfrak{o}_K/\mathfrak{P} \to \overline{F}_p.$$

Then we may assume that $\chi^r = \chi_\varphi^{(q-1)r/m}$. We know from §1 that $\omega - 1$ is a prime element in $\mathbf{Q}(\omega)$, and remains unramified in K. Hence by Theorem 9,

$$\operatorname{ord}_{\mathfrak{P}} \tau(\chi^r) = s\left(\frac{(q-1)r}{m}\right).$$

We also have

$$\sigma_\mu\tau(\chi^r) = \tau(\chi^{r\mu}),$$

so that

$$\operatorname{ord}_{\sigma_\mu^{-1}\mathfrak{P}} \tau(\chi^r) = \operatorname{ord}_{\mathfrak{P}} \sigma_\mu\tau(\chi^r) = s\left(\frac{(q-1)r\mu}{m}\right).$$

As μ ranges over $(\mathbf{Z}/m\mathbf{Z})^*$, each conjugate of $\mathfrak{P}$ appears f times. This proves Theorem 10.

Theorem 11. *Let $k = \mathbf{Q}(\zeta_m)$ where ζ_m is a primitive m-th root of unity. Let p be a prime number, $p \nmid m$, and let $\mathfrak{p}|p$ in k. For positive integers a, b let*

$$\theta_{a,b} = \sum_{\mu} \left(\left[\frac{(a+b)\mu}{m} \right] - \left[\frac{a\mu}{m} \right] - \left[\frac{b\mu}{m} \right] \right) \sigma_{\mu}^{-1}.$$

Then $\mathfrak{p}^{\theta_{a,b}}$ is principal, and in fact

$$\mathfrak{p}^{\theta_{a,b}} \sim \psi(\chi^a, \chi^b),$$

where χ is the character described in Theorem 10.

Proof. We just transform the expression of Theorem 10 and use **GS 4.** We have

$$\psi(\chi^a, \chi^b) = \frac{\tau(\chi^a)\tau(\chi^b)}{\tau(\chi^{a+b})}$$

and hence

$$\psi(\chi^a, \chi^b) \sim \mathfrak{P}^{\beta(a,b)},$$

where

$$\beta(a, b) =$$

$$\frac{1}{f} \sum_{\mu} \left(s\left(\frac{(q-1)a\mu}{m}\right) + s\left(\frac{(q-1)b\mu}{m}\right) - s\left(\frac{(q-1)(a+b)\mu}{m}\right)\right) \sigma_{\mu}^{-1}$$

$$= \frac{p-1}{f} \sum_{\mu} \left(\sum_{j=0}^{f-1} \left[\frac{(a+b)p^j\mu}{m} \right] - \left[\frac{ap^j\mu}{m} \right] - \left[\frac{bp^j\mu}{m} \right] \right) \sigma_{\mu}^{-1},$$

using the lemma at the end of §3. The decomposition group $G_{\mathfrak{p}}$ of $\mathfrak{p}$ in k is $\{1, \sigma_p, \sigma_{p^2}, \ldots\}$. Hence we can replace σ_μ by $\sigma_{p^j\mu}$, and since μ ranges over $(\mathbf{Z}/m\mathbf{Z})^*$, so does $p^j\mu$. Consequently we find

$$\beta(a, b) = (p-1)\theta_{a,b}.$$

Since $\mathfrak{p} = \mathfrak{P}^{p-1}$, we see that Theorem 11 is proved.

The special case of Theorems 10 and 11 when m is prime is already in Hilbert's Zahlbericht. The general case is due to MacKenzie ("Class group relations in cyclotomic fields", *Am. J. Math.*, **74**, 1952, pp. 759–763). Here, I have followed an exposition given by Tate in a seminar around 1951. The significance of Theorem 11 is that it gives a relation in the ideal class group of $\mathbf{Q}(\zeta)$, since every ideal class contains infinitely many primes (a fact which will be proved later in this book).

CHAPTER V

Parallelotopes

This chapter gives quantitative results concerning the distribution of elements of a number field in parallelotopes.

If we impose certain bounds on the absolute values of elements α in a number field k, then we can ask for the number of field elements satisfying such conditions. It turns out that this number is asymptotic to the volume of the region (in a suitable space) determined by the inequalities.

Next, we shall reproduce the classical theory of Minkowski concerning the units and discriminant of the number field, and obtain the Minkowski constant.

§1. *The product formula*

Let $M_{\mathbf{Q}}$ be the canonical set of absolute values on the rational numbers $\mathbf{Q}$. Then for any element $\alpha \in \mathbf{Q}$, $\alpha \neq 0$, we have

$$\prod_{v \in M_{\mathbf{Q}}} |\alpha|_v = 1.$$

Indeed, if α is a prime number l, then

$$|l|_p = \begin{cases} 1 & \text{if } \ p \text{ is a prime number} \neq l \\ 1/p & \text{if } \ p = l. \end{cases}$$

The ordinary absolute value will be called (by abuse of language) a **prime at infinity.** Since $|l|_\infty = l$, the product formula is satisfied for prime numbers. It follows for any element of $\mathbf{Q}^*$ by multiplicativity.

Let k be a finite extension of $\mathbf{Q}$ and M_k the set of absolute values of k extending those of $M_{\mathbf{Q}}$. Then by Corollary 2 of Theorem 2, Chapter II, §1, we obtain for $\alpha \in k^*$:

$$\begin{aligned} 1 &= \prod_{v_0 \in M_{\mathbf{Q}}} |N^k_{\mathbf{Q}}(\alpha)|_{v_0} = \prod_{v_0 \in M_{\mathbf{Q}}} \prod_{v \mid v_0} |\alpha|_v^{N_v} \\ &= \prod_{v \in M_k} |\alpha|_v^{N_v} = \prod_{v \in M_k} \|\alpha\|_v. \end{aligned}$$

Thus the product formula is also satisfied, with multiplicities

$$N_v = [k_v : \mathbf{Q}_{v_0}].$$

If k is a number field, we denote by S_∞ the set of archimedean absolute values in M_k. We let r_1 and r_2 be the number of real and complex absolute values respectively. Then

$$r_1 + 2r_2 = [k : \mathbf{Q}]$$

and we denote this degree by N. We also let $r = r_1 + r_2 - 1$. The local degree N_v is 1 if v is real, and 2 if v is complex.

We shall now prove the classical theorems concerning the finiteness of class number and the unit theorem.

To begin with the class number, we shall prove that *there exists a constant C depending only on k, such that for any ideal $\mathfrak{a}$ (always assumed $\neq 0$), there exists an ideal $\mathfrak{b}$ in the linear equivalence class of $\mathfrak{a}$ such that* $\mathbf{N}\mathfrak{b} \leqq C$.

This implies that *the number of ideal classes is finite*, because there is only a finite number of ideals with bounded norms. (In fact, there is only a finite number of prime numbers bounded by a given constant, and for each prime number p, there is only a finite number of prime ideals $\mathfrak{p}$ of $\mathfrak{o}_k$ lying above p.) This number is called the **class number** of k.

Let $\omega_1, \ldots, \omega_N$ be a basis of $\mathfrak{o}_k$ over $\mathbf{Z}$, and let S be the set of elements of $\mathfrak{o}_k$ of type

$$a_1\omega_1 + \cdots + a_N\omega_N$$

with integers a_i such that

$$0 \leqq a_i \leqq (\mathbf{N}\mathfrak{a})^{1/N} + 1.$$

Then there are more than $\mathbf{N}\mathfrak{a}$ elements in S, and thus there are two distinct elements α, β in S such that $\alpha - \beta = \xi$ will map into 0 in the homomorphism

$$\mathfrak{o}_k \to \prod \mathfrak{o}_k/\mathfrak{p}^{\operatorname{ord}_\mathfrak{p}\mathfrak{a}}.$$

(Cf. Proposition 24 of Chapter I, §7.) It follows that there exists an ideal $\mathfrak{b}$ such that $(\xi) = \mathfrak{a}\mathfrak{b}$. On the other hand, we estimate the norm

$$N_{\mathbf{Q}}^k(\xi) = \prod_\sigma |c_1\omega_1^\sigma + \cdots + c_N\omega_N^\sigma|,$$

where $0 \leqq |c_i| \leqq (\mathbf{N}\mathfrak{a})^{1/N} + 1$. We see that there is a constant C (depending on the maximum of the archimedean absolute values of the ω_i and on N) such that

$$|N_{\mathbf{Q}}^k(\xi)| \leqq C \cdot \mathbf{N}\mathfrak{a}.$$

Using Proposition 22 of Chapter I, §7 we get $\mathbf{N}\mathfrak{b} \leqq C$ and $\mathfrak{b} \sim \mathfrak{a}^{-1}$ by definition. This proves our assertion.

Next, we shall prove the unit theorem, as in Artin-Whaples. We first discuss some general notions.

We define an $\boldsymbol{M_k}$**-divisor** $\mathfrak{c}$ to be a real valued function of absolute values v in M_k such that:

(1) $\mathfrak{c}(v) > 0$ for all v in M_k.

(2) $\mathfrak{c}(v) = 1$ for all but a finite number of v in M_k.

(3) If v is a discrete valuation, then there exists an element α in k such that $\mathfrak{c}(v) = |\alpha|_v$.

We shall sometimes write $|\mathfrak{c}|_v$ or $\mathfrak{c}_v$ instead of $\mathfrak{c}(v)$, and when we have the multiplicities N_v, we write

$$\|\mathfrak{c}\|_v = \mathfrak{c}(v)^{N_v}.$$

We define the $\boldsymbol{k}$**-size** or simply size of our M_k-divisor to be

$$\|\mathfrak{c}\|_k = \prod_v \mathfrak{c}(v)^{N_v}.$$

We denote by $L(\mathfrak{c})$ the set of elements $x \in k$ such that for each $v \in M_k$ we have

$$|x|_v \leqq \mathfrak{c}(v).$$

Each element $\alpha \in k^*$ determines an M_k-divisor whose value at v is simply $|\alpha|_v$. The product of two M_k-divisors is an M_k-divisor, and if $\mathfrak{c}$ is an M_k-divisor, then $\alpha\mathfrak{c}$ is the M_k-divisor such that

$$(\alpha\mathfrak{c})(v) = |\alpha|_v\mathfrak{c}(v).$$

In view of the product formula, we have

$$\|\alpha\mathfrak{c}\|_k = \|\mathfrak{c}\|_k.$$

In other words, the size of $\mathfrak{c}$ is the same as the size of $\alpha\mathfrak{c}$.

If $\alpha \in k^*$, then $L(\alpha\mathfrak{c})$ and $L(\mathfrak{c})$ are in canonical bijection under the mapping

$$x \mapsto \alpha x, \qquad x \in L(\mathfrak{c}).$$

We denote the number of elements of $L(\mathfrak{c})$ by $\lambda(\mathfrak{c})$. Then

$$\lambda(\alpha\mathfrak{c}) = \lambda(\mathfrak{c}).$$

If we think of $\mathfrak{c}$ as prescribing the sides of a box, all but a finite number of which are 1, then $\lambda(\mathfrak{c})$ may be interpreted as the number of field elements in the box. The size of $\mathfrak{c}$ may be interpreted as the volume of the box. We shall now prove that the number of elements in the box is approximately equal to the volume. In the next section, we shall obtain a stronger asymptotic result, by different methods.

Theorem 0. *Let k be a number field. There exist two numbers $c_1, c_2 > 0$ depending only on k, such that for any M_k-divisor $\mathfrak{c}$, we have*

$$c_1\|\mathfrak{c}\|_k < \lambda(\mathfrak{c}) \leqq \sup\,[1, c_2\|\mathfrak{c}\|_k].$$

Proof. Suppose that there is at least one complex absolute value v_0 in M_k. We identify k_{v_0} with the complex plane, and consider the square centered at the origin, with sides of length $2\mathfrak{c}(v_0)$. Let m be an integer such that

$$m < \lambda(\mathfrak{c})^{1/2} \leqq m + 1.$$

Without loss of generality, we may assume that $m \neq 0$, and so $m \geqq 1$. Cut up each side of the square into m equal parts, thus giving rise to m^2 small squares inside the big one. Our set $L(\mathfrak{c})$ is embedded inside the big square at k_{v_0}. Since it contains more than m^2 elements, there exist two distinct elements $x, y \in L(\mathfrak{c})$ lying in the same small square. Hence we can estimate their difference by

$$|x - y|_{v_0} \leqq \frac{2\sqrt{2}\,\mathfrak{c}(v_0)}{m}.$$

If v is any other archimedean absolute value of M_k, then

$$|x - y|_v \leqq 2\mathfrak{c}(v),$$

and if v is non-archimedean, then

$$|x - y|_v \leqq \mathfrak{c}(v).$$

Taking the product, we obtain

$$1 = \prod_{v \in M_k} |x - y|_v^{N_v} \leqq \frac{c_3\|\mathfrak{c}\|_k}{m^2}$$

with a suitable constant c_3. Since $(m + 1)^2 \leqq 4m^2$, the inequality on the right in Theorem 0 follows immediately.

If there is no complex absolute value in M_k, then we proceed in a similar manner, using a real one v_0, and cut up the interval centered at the origin of length $2\mathfrak{c}(v_0)$ into m equal parts, giving rise to m small intervals, with

$$m < \lambda(\mathfrak{c}) \leqq m + 1.$$

The arguments then proceed in the same way.

Let us prove the other inequality. Let $\omega_1, \ldots, \omega_N$ be a basis for $\mathfrak{o}_k$ over $\mathbf{Z}$. Put

$$c_0 = N \sup_{v,i} |\omega_i|_v,$$

the sup being taken over the archimedean absolute values v in M_k, and over i. This is a number depending only on k.

Let $\mathfrak{c}$ be our given M_k-divisor. By the approximation theorem, there exists an element $\alpha \in k^*$ such that

$$c_0 \leqq |\alpha\mathfrak{c}|_v \leqq 2c_0$$

for each archimedean absolute value v in M_k. We now select an element $a \in \mathbf{Z}$, $a \neq 0$, such that $a\alpha\mathfrak{c}$ has absolute value $\leqq 1$ at all non-archimedean $v \in M_k$, just by taking a highly divisible at a lot of prime numbers. In view of the fact that $\lambda(\mathfrak{c})$ and $\|\mathfrak{c}\|_k$ do not change if we multiply $\mathfrak{c}$ by an element of k^*, we may therefore assume, without loss of generality, that our M_k-divisor satisfies the inequalities

$$c_0|a|_v \leqq |\mathfrak{c}|_v \leqq 2c_0|a|_v$$

for some element $a \in \mathbf{Z}$, $a > 0$, and all $v \in S_\infty$.

We must exhibit elements of $L(\mathfrak{c})$. For this purpose, consider the set L of elements of $\mathfrak{o}_k$ consisting of those which can be expressed in the form

$$a_1\omega_1 + \cdots + a_N\omega_N$$

with $a_i \in \mathbf{Z}$, and $0 \leqq a_i \leqq a$. Then our set L contains more than a^N elements.

Each non-archimedean v in M_k corresponds to a prime $\mathfrak{p}$ of $\mathfrak{o}_k$, and using the third condition in the definition of an M_k-divisor, we have in an obvious manner the notion of $\operatorname{ord}_\mathfrak{p} \mathfrak{c}$. Let $n_\mathfrak{p} = \operatorname{ord}_\mathfrak{p} \mathfrak{c}$. The additive group

$$\mathfrak{o}_k/\prod \mathfrak{p}^{n_\mathfrak{p}}$$

has $\prod(\mathbf{N}\mathfrak{p})^{n_\mathfrak{p}}$ elements. We look at the image of L under the canonical homomorphism of $\mathfrak{o}_k$ into this additive group. There will be a subset L' of L with at least

$$\frac{a^N}{\prod(\mathbf{N}\mathfrak{p})^{n_\mathfrak{p}}}$$

elements, all of which have the same image. Take one fixed element $x \in L'$, and let y range over L'. Then for each non-archimedean absolute value v in M_k, we have

$$|x - y|_v \leqq \mathfrak{c}(v),$$

because $\operatorname{ord}_{\mathfrak{p}}(x - y) \geqq \operatorname{ord}_{\mathfrak{p}} \mathfrak{c}$. If v is archimedean, then by an obvious estimate, we have

$$|x - y|_v \leqq c_0 |a|_v \leqq \mathfrak{c}(v).$$

Thus our element $x - y$ lies in $L(\mathfrak{c})$. We have therefore proved that

$$\lambda(\mathfrak{c}) \geqq a^N \prod \frac{1}{\mathbf{N}\mathfrak{p}^{n_{\mathfrak{p}}}} \cdot$$

We observe finally that

$$a^N = \prod_{v \mid v_\infty} |a|_v^{N_v} > c_1 \prod_{v \mid v_\infty} |\mathfrak{c}|_v^{N_v},$$

the product being taken over the archimedean absolute values, and c_1 being an obvious constant, while

$$\frac{1}{\mathbf{N}\mathfrak{p}^{n_{\mathfrak{p}}}} = \|\mathfrak{c}\|_v,$$

if v is the non-archimedean absolute value belonging to $\mathfrak{p}$. Taking the full product over all absolute values proves our inequality on the left in Theorem 0.

Let k be a number field, and S a finite subset of M_k containing the archimedean absolute values. Let s be the number of elements of S. We define the set of **S-units** k_S to be the set of elements in k^* such that

$$|\alpha|_v = 1$$

for $v \notin S$. If $S = S_\infty$, the S-units are also called the **units** of k. Strictly speaking, they are the units (invertible elements) of the ring of algebraic integers $\mathfrak{o}_k$.

We map k_S into Euclidean s-space as follows. Let $v_1, \ldots, v_s$ be the absolute values of S. Map

$$x \mapsto (\log \|x\|_1, \ldots, \log \|x\|_s),$$

and call this map

$$\log\colon k_S \to \mathbf{R}^s.$$

By the product formula, the image of k_S is contained in the hyperplane defined by the equation

$$\xi_1 + \cdots + \xi_s = 0,$$

so that this image is at most $(s - 1)$-dimensional.

Unit Theorem. *The image* $\log(k_S)$ *is an* $(s - 1)$*-dimensional lattice in* $\mathbf{R}^s$.

By saying that it is a lattice, we mean that it is a discrete subgroup of $\mathbf{R}^s$, and by saying that it is $(s-1)$-dimensional, we mean that the vector space generated by it is the entire hyperplane mentioned above. Thus in particular, it follows that $\log(k_S)$ is a free abelian group on $s-1$ generators. The kernel of our log mapping is clearly the set of roots of unity in k because the kernel is a group, and its elements have bounded absolute values, hence form a finite group.

Corollary. *Let k be a number field and S a finite subset of M_k containing the archimedean absolute values. Then k_S modulo the group of roots of unity in k is a free abelian group on $s-1$ generators ($s =$ number of elements of S).*

Observe, however, that the statement of the unit theorem is stronger than the statement of the corollary. The unit theorem is actually equivalent with a compactness statement, which we shall give in Chapter VII, §3.

We shall now prove the unit theorem.

Let us begin by observing that in any bounded region of $\mathbf{R}^s$ there exists only a finite number of elements of $\log(k_S)$. Indeed, if $\log(x)$ lies in such a region, then the absolute values of x and its conjugates must be bounded, and hence x can satisfy only a finite number of equations of degree $\leqq [k:\mathbf{Q}]$ over $\mathbf{Q}$, because the coefficients of such equations are elementary symmetric functions of x and its conjugates. By a well-known property of Euclidean space, whose proof we shall recall at the end, it follows that $\log(k_S)$ is a discrete, finitely generated subgroup of $\mathbf{R}^s$. We must prove that it has dimension $s-1$.

For this purpose, we shall first prove that given an index i, there exists a vector $(\xi_1, \ldots, \xi_s)$ in $\log(k_S)$ such that $\xi_i > 0$ and $\xi_j < 0$ for $j \neq i$. We shall then prove that any $s-1$ such vectors are linearly independent over $\mathbf{R}$.

We need the following lemma.

Lemma. *Given $v_0 \in M_k$ there exists a number $c(v_0) > 0$ such that for any M_k-divisor $\mathfrak{c}$ there exists $\beta \in k^*$ such that*

$$1 \leqq \|\beta\mathfrak{c}\|_v \leqq c(v_0)$$

for all $v \neq v_0$ in M_k.

Proof. Let c_1 be the number of Theorem 0. Let $c_0 = 1$ if v_0 is archimedean, and let $c_0 = \mathbf{N}\mathfrak{p}_0$ if $\mathfrak{p}_0$ is the prime of v_0. Let $\mathfrak{c}'$ be an M_k-divisor which differs from $\mathfrak{c}$ only at v_0, and such that

$$1/c_1 \leqq \|\mathfrak{c}'\|_k \leqq c_0/c_1.$$

If v_0 is archimedean, we can adjust the v_0-component as we please, in a continuous fashion. If v_0 is discrete, the value group ranges over powers of $\mathbf{N}\mathfrak{p}_0$, and so we can also find the $\mathfrak{c}'$ subject to our condition. We set $c(v_0) = c_0/c_1$.

By Theorem 0, $\lambda(\mathfrak{c}') > 1$, and hence there exists an element $\alpha \neq 0$ in $L(\mathfrak{c}')$, that is,

$$\|\alpha\|_v \leqq \|\mathfrak{c}'\|_v$$

for all $v \in M_k$. We put $\beta = 1/\alpha$. Then the inequality on the left in the lemma is satisfied. For the inequality on the right, we have

$$\|\beta\mathfrak{c}'\|_v = \frac{\|\beta\mathfrak{c}'\|_k}{\prod_{w \neq v} \|\beta\mathfrak{c}'\|_w} \leq \|\beta\mathfrak{c}'\|_k = \|\mathfrak{c}'\|_k$$

for all $v \in M_k$. The product is taken over all $w \in M_k$, $w \neq v$. Since $\mathfrak{c}'$ is like $\mathfrak{c}$ except at v_0, we have also proved the inequality on the right.

We return to the main proof. If $v \notin S$, then the value group of v is infinite cyclic, generated by $\mathbf{N}\mathfrak{p}$, and there is only a finite number of primes such that

$$\mathbf{N}\mathfrak{p} \leqq c(v_0).$$

Consequently, by the lemma, there is a finite set of absolute values $S' \supset S$ having the following property. If $\mathfrak{c}$ is an M_k-divisor, then there exists $\beta \in k^*$ such that

$$1 = \|\beta\mathfrak{c}\|_v, \qquad \text{all } v \notin S'.$$

Consider only such $\mathfrak{c}$ that $\mathfrak{c}(v) \geqq 1$ for all v and $\mathfrak{c}(v) = 1$ for all $v \notin S$. For such $\mathfrak{c}$ there exists β with

$$1 = \|\beta\mathfrak{c}\|_v = \|\beta\|_v, \qquad v \notin S'$$
$$1 \leqq \|\beta\mathfrak{c}\|_v \leqq \mathfrak{c}(v_0), \qquad v \neq v_0.$$

Let B be the set of all such β. Map B into $\mathbf{R}^{S'-S}$ by

$$\beta \mapsto \{\|\beta\|_v\}_{v \in S'-S}.$$

The image of B is finite. Let $\beta_1, \ldots, \beta_m$ be representatives in B for the elements of this image. Let

$$b = \operatorname*{Min}_{\substack{v \in S'-S \\ j=1,\ldots,m}} \|\beta_j\|_v.$$

Then $b > 0$, and for all $\beta \in B$ there exists an S-unit $u_\beta \in k_S$ and some j such that

$$\beta = u_\beta \beta_j.$$

For all $\mathfrak{c}$ as above, we can therefore find $u \in k_S$ satisfying

$$\|u\mathfrak{c}\|_v < \frac{c(v_0)}{b}, \qquad \text{all } v \neq v_0.$$

We select $\mathfrak{c}$ such that $\mathfrak{c}(v)$ is very large for all $v \in S$. Then $\|u\|_v$ is very small for all $v \neq v_0$, $v \in S$. By the product formula, it follows that $\|u\|_{v_0}$ is very large. The log of u has the desired property. This achieves the first of our objectives.

As to the second, we have found elements $x_1, \ldots, x_{s-1} \in k_S$ such that

$$\begin{aligned} \log x_1 &= (\xi_{11}, \ldots, \xi_{1s}) \\ &\vdots \\ \log x_{s-1} &= (\xi_{s-1,1}, \ldots, \xi_{s-1,s}), \end{aligned}$$

and such that the matrix of signs of the ξ_{ij} is as follows:

$$\begin{bmatrix} + & - & - & \cdots & - & - \\ - & + & - & \cdots & - & - \\ & & & \vdots & & \\ - & - & - & \cdots & + & - \end{bmatrix}.$$

Let $Y_1, \ldots, Y_s$ be the column vectors. We must show that the first $s - 1$ are linearly independent over $\mathbf{R}$. Suppose that

$$a_1 Y_1 + \cdots + a_{s-1} Y_{s-1} = 0,$$

not all the coefficients being 0. Say $a_1 > 0$ and $a_1 \geqq a_j$ for any j. Then looking at the sum just in the first row, we get

$$\begin{aligned} 0 &= a_1 \xi_{11} + a_2 \xi_{12} + \cdots + a_{s-1} \xi_{1,s-1} \\ &\geqq a_1 \xi_{11} + a_1 \xi_{12} + \cdots + a_1 \xi_{1,s-1} \\ &= a_1(\xi_{11} + \xi_{12} + \cdots + \xi_{1,s-1}) \end{aligned}$$

because ξ_{1j} is negative for $j = 2, \ldots, s - 1$. By the product formula, we must have

$$\xi_{11} + \xi_{12} + \cdots + \xi_{1,s-1} > 0,$$

contradiction.

For the convenience of the reader, we repeat the proof that a discrete subgroup of Euclidean space is a free abelian group. We do this by induction on the dimension of the subgroup, i.e. the maximal number of linearly independent elements over $\mathbf{R}$.

Let Γ be our subgroup and $\xi_1, \ldots, \xi_m$ a maximal set of independent vectors in Γ. Let Γ_0 be the subgroup of Γ contained in the subspace spanned by $\xi_1, \ldots, \xi_{m-1}$. By induction, we may assume that any vector of Γ_0 is a linear integral combination of $\xi_1, \ldots, \xi_{m-1}$.

Consider the subset T of all ξ in Γ of the form

$$\xi = a_1\xi_1 + \cdots + a_m\xi_m$$

with real coefficients a_i satisfying

$$0 \leqq a_i < 1, \qquad i = 1, \ldots, m-1$$
$$0 \leqq a_m \leqq 1.$$

It is a bounded set. Let ξ'_m be a vector of T with the smallest $a_m \neq 0$, say

$$\xi'_m = b_1\xi_1 + \cdots + b_m\xi_m.$$

Starting with any vector ξ of Γ, we can select integral coefficients $c_1, \ldots, c_m$ in such a way that

$$\xi' = \xi - c_m\xi'_m - c_1\xi_1 - \cdots - c_{m-1}\xi_{m-1}$$

lies in T, and the coefficient of ξ_m is $> b_m$ and $\geqq 0$. This coefficient must therefore be 0, and ξ' lies in Γ_0. From this our result is clear.

Remark. It is sometimes useful to consider subgroups of finite index in the unit group. They may arise in the following way. Let M be an additive subgroup of the algebraic integers $\mathfrak{o}$, of finite index. An equivalent condition is that M has rank $[k:\mathbf{Q}]$. Let u be a unit in $\mathfrak{o}$. The map

$$x \mapsto ux$$

is an additive automorphism of $\mathfrak{o}$, which maps M on an additive subgroup uM. We have isomorphisms of factor groups,

$$\mathfrak{o}/M \approx \mathfrak{o}/uM,$$

and hence the same index,

$$(\mathfrak{o}:M) = (\mathfrak{o}:uM).$$

If $m = (\mathfrak{o}:M)$, then every element of $\mathfrak{o}/M$ has period m, and hence

$$\mathfrak{o} \supset M \supset m\mathfrak{o}.$$

Since $\mathfrak{o}/m\mathfrak{o}$ is finite, we conclude that there is only a finite number of subgroups of $\mathfrak{o}$ lying between $\mathfrak{o}$ and $m\mathfrak{o}$. The unit group U is represented in the finite group of permutations of such subgroups of $\mathfrak{o}$. We conclude that the subgroup U_M consisting of all units $u \in U$ such that $uM = M$ is a subgroup of finite index in U.

Let

$$r = r_1 + r_2 - 1.$$

If $\alpha \in k$, we let $\alpha^{(j)}$ be the j-th conjugate of α for $j = 1, \ldots, r_1 + r_2$. Let

$$\{u_1, \ldots, u_r\}$$

be a set of generators for the ordinary unit group U, modulo roots of unity. The absolute value of the determinant

$$\begin{vmatrix} N_1 \log |u_1^{(1)}| & \cdots & N_1 \log |u_r^{(1)}| \\ \vdots & & \vdots \\ N_r \log |u_1^{(r)}| & \cdots & N_r \log |u_r^{(r)}| \end{vmatrix}$$

is independent of the choice of our generators $u_1, \ldots, u_r$ and is called the **regulator** $R_k = R$ of the field k. Since the log vectors of the units are linearly independent, it follows that the regulator is not 0. We note that this regulator, like all determinants, can be interpreted as a volume of a parallelotope in r-space. The regulator occasionally occurs in the form

$$\pm 2^{-r_2} NR = \begin{vmatrix} 1 & \log |u_1^{(1)}| & \cdots & \log |u_r^{(1)}| \\ \vdots & \vdots & & \vdots \\ 1 & \log |u_1^{(r+1)}| & \cdots & \log |u_r^{(r+1)}| \end{vmatrix}.$$

To see this, we multiply the i-th row of the determinant on the right by N_i, and add the sum of the first r rows to the last row. Then we get N in the lower left-hand corner, 0 in the rest of the last row, and our assertion is obvious.

The reason for the regulator appearing in the second form is as follows. Let

$$G = \mathbf{R}^+ \times \cdots \times \mathbf{R}^+$$

be the direct product of $r_1 + r_2$ copies of the multiplicative group of positive reals. Map each unit u into G by

$$u \mapsto (|u^{(1)}|, \ldots, |u^{(r+1)}|).$$

This is a homomorphism of U into G, whose kernel consists of the roots of unity. Let V be the image of U in G. Then V is contained in G^0, the subgroup consisting of all elements

$$y = (y_1, \ldots, y_{r+1})$$

such that

$$y = \prod_{i=1}^{r+1} y_i^{N_i} = 1.$$

Let $u_1, \ldots, u_r$ be a set of independent generators for U modulo roots of unity, and let $\eta_1, \ldots, \eta_r$ be their respective images in G. Then we have an isomorphism

$$g:\mathbf{R}^+ \times \mathbf{R}^r \to G$$

given by

$$g(t, z) = t^{1/N}\eta_1^{z_1}\cdots\eta_r^{z_r},$$

and the Jacobian matrix of this mapping is

$$\mathrm{Jac}_g\,(t, z) = \begin{pmatrix} y_1\dfrac{1}{Nt} & y_1 \log \eta_{11} & \cdots & y_1 \log \eta_{r1} \\ \vdots & \vdots & & \vdots \\ y_{r+1}\dfrac{1}{Nt} & y_{r+1} \log \eta_{1,r+1} & \cdots & y_{r+1} \log \eta_{r,r+1} \end{pmatrix}.$$

Hence the Jacobian determinant is

$$\Delta_g(t, z) = \frac{y_1\cdots y_{r+1}}{Nt}\begin{vmatrix} 1 & \log |u_1^{(1)}| & \cdots & \log |u_r^{(1)}| \\ \vdots & \vdots & & \vdots \\ 1 & \log |u_1^{(r+1)}| & \cdots & \log |u_r^{(r+1)}| \end{vmatrix}$$

from which we see the determinant as indicated above.

Observe that our map g gives us a natural parametrization of G^0 in terms of a Euclidean space $\mathbf{R}^r$.

§2. *Lattice points in parallelotopes*

In this section, we shall give a refinement of Theorem 0.

Theorem 1. *Let k be a number field, $[k:\mathbf{Q}] = N$. Let B_k be the constant*

$$B_k = \frac{2^{r_1}(2\pi)^{r_2}}{|D_k|^{1/2}}\cdot$$

Then, for $\mathfrak{c}$ ranging over M_k-divisors, the number $\lambda(\mathfrak{c})$ of elements of $L(\mathfrak{c})$ is given by

$$\lambda(\mathfrak{c}) = B_k\|\mathfrak{c}\|_k + O(\|\mathfrak{c}\|_k^{1-1/N}), \qquad \|\mathfrak{c}\|_k \to \infty.$$

In other words, there exist constants $b_1, b_2 > 0$ depending only on k such that for $\|\mathfrak{c}\|_k > b_2$ we have

$$|\lambda(\mathfrak{c}) - B_k\|\mathfrak{c}\|_k| \leqq b_1(\|\mathfrak{c}\|_k^{1-1/N}).$$

Proof. We shall first make some remarks concerning M_k-divisors. Given an M_k-divisor $\mathfrak{c}$, there exists a fractional ideal $\mathfrak{a}$ of $\mathfrak{o}_k$ such that $\alpha \in \mathfrak{a}$ if and only if

$$|\alpha|_\mathfrak{p} \leqq \mathfrak{c}(v_\mathfrak{p})$$

for all primes $\mathfrak{p}$ of $\mathfrak{o}_k$. This follows at once from the definitions. Thus $L(\mathfrak{c})$ consists of those elements of $\mathfrak{a}$ which satisfy certain inequalities at the archimedean absolute values. We call $\mathfrak{a}$ the **fractional ideal associated with** $\mathfrak{c}$.

Given $\beta \in k^*$, we have $\lambda(\beta\mathfrak{c}) = \lambda(\mathfrak{c})$. Hence to compute $\lambda(\mathfrak{c})$, we may change $\mathfrak{c}$ by an element of k^*.

We know that the group of ideal classes of $\mathfrak{o}_k$ is a finite group. Let $\mathfrak{a}_1, \ldots, \mathfrak{a}_h$ be ideal representatives of the elements of this group. Multiplying $\mathfrak{c}$ by a suitable element of k^*, we may assume that the fractional ideal $\mathfrak{a}$ associated with $\mathfrak{c}$ is equal to one of the $\mathfrak{a}_i$.

Let $\mathfrak{c}$ be an M_k-divisor, and $\mathfrak{a}$ its associated fractional ideal. Then

$$\|\mathfrak{c}\|_k = \frac{1}{\mathbf{N}\mathfrak{a}} \prod_{v \in S_\infty} \mathfrak{c}_v^{N_v}$$

where we write $\mathfrak{c}_v$ instead of $\mathfrak{c}(v)$ to simplify the notation.

Lemma 1. *Assume that the associated fractional ideal $\mathfrak{a}$ is equal to one of the fixed representatives $\mathfrak{a}_i$. There exists a unit u of $\mathfrak{o}_k$ such that we have, for all $v \in S_\infty$,*

$$c_1(k)\|\mathfrak{c}\|_k^{1/N} \leqq |u\mathfrak{c}|_v \leqq c_2(k)\|\mathfrak{c}\|_k^{1/N},$$

where $c_1(k)$, $c_2(k)$ are two constants > 0, depending only on k.

Proof. Let $V = \|\mathfrak{c}\|_k$ and let $\mathfrak{c}'_v = \mathfrak{c}_v(V\mathbf{N}\mathfrak{a})^{-1/N}$ for all $v \in S_\infty$. Then

$$\prod_{v \in S_\infty} \mathfrak{c}_v'^{N_v} = 1.$$

Consider now the log vector

$$\log(\mathfrak{c}') = (\ldots, \log \|\mathfrak{c}'_v\|_v, \ldots)_{v \in S_\infty}.$$

Since the log vectors of units form a lattice of maximal rank in the hyperplane of vectors such that the sum of the components is 0, it follows that there exists a unit u such that

$$|\log(\mathfrak{c}') - \log(u^{-1})| < c_3(k)$$

for some constant $c_3(k)$. The absolute value is the ordinary norm of a vector in Euclidean space. From this we conclude that $\log(u\mathfrak{c})$ is a vector of bounded length, i.e. that there exist constants c_4, $c_5 > 0$ such that

$$c_4 \leqq |u\mathfrak{c}'_v|_v \leqq c_5$$

for all $v \in S_\infty$. We get the assertion of the lemma by substituting the definition of $\mathfrak{c}'_v$.

We let

$$A_k(\infty) = \prod_{v \in S_\infty} k_v.$$

We can identify this product with $\mathbf{R}^N$, because we have a product of r_1 copies of the real numbers, and r_2 copies of the complex numbers. If v is complex, we fix an isomorphism of k_v with $\mathbf{C}$. (We have a choice of two such isomorphisms.)

Each ideal of $\mathfrak{o}_k$ is a lattice of rank N in this Euclidean space, if we view $\mathfrak{o}_k$ as embedded in the natural way on the diagonal. The inequalities imposed by our M_k-divisor at absolute values $v \in S_\infty$ can be viewed as determining a region in this Euclidean space, and our problem has therefore been reduced to the following.

Given a lattice L of rank N in Euclidean N-space, show that under certain circumstances, the number of lattice points in a parallelotope is approximately equal to the volume of the parallelotope. This is precisely what we shall do.

Let $\xi_1, \ldots, \xi_N$ be linearly independent vectors in $\mathbf{R}^N$. The abelian group generated by them is a lattice. By definition, a **fundamental domain** for the lattice is any (measurable) set such that every vector of $\mathbf{R}^N$ is congruent to exactly one vector in the set modulo the lattice. For fundamental domain, we shall always select the set F of points

$$t_1 \xi_1 + \cdots + t_N \xi_N$$

with $0 \leqq t_i < 1$.

If $\mathfrak{c}$ is an M_k-divisor, we denote by $P_\mathfrak{c}$ the set of vectors x in

$$\prod_{v \in S_\infty} k_v = \mathbf{R}^N$$

such that

$$|x|_v \leqq \mathfrak{c}_v \qquad \text{for all } v \in S_\infty$$

and call $P_\mathfrak{c}$ the **parallelotope** determined by $\mathfrak{c}$ (at infinity).

Let $n(\mathfrak{c})$ be the number of translations F_x of F which are contained in $P_\mathfrak{c}$ for some $x \in L$.

Let $m(\mathfrak{c})$ be the number of translations F_x of F which intersect $P_\mathfrak{c}$ for some $x \in L$.

Let $l(\mathfrak{c})$ be the number of lattice points in the parallelotope $P_\mathfrak{c}$. Then clearly

$$n(\mathfrak{c})\ \mathrm{Vol}(F) \leqq \mathrm{Vol}(P_\mathfrak{c}) \leqq m(\mathfrak{c})\ \mathrm{Vol}(F)$$

where Vol means volume in Euclidean space.

The only lattice point in F_x is x itself. Thus

$$n(\mathfrak{c}) \leqq l(\mathfrak{c}) \leqq m(\mathfrak{c}).$$

We shall now prove a theorem concerning any lattice in $\mathbf{R}^N$.

Theorem 2. *Let $\mathfrak{c}$ range over M_k-divisors such that for all $v \in S_\infty$ we have*

$$c_6 \operatorname{Vol}(P_\mathfrak{c})^{1/N} \leqq \mathfrak{c}_v \leqq c_7 \operatorname{Vol}(P_\mathfrak{c})^{1/N},$$

with constants $c_6, c_7 > 0$. Let L be a fixed lattice in $\mathbf{R}^N$. Then, whenever $\operatorname{Vol}(P_\mathfrak{c}) > c'$, we have

$$l(\mathfrak{c}) = \frac{\operatorname{Vol}(P_\mathfrak{c})}{\operatorname{Vol}(F)} \pm c'' \operatorname{Vol}(P_\mathfrak{c})^{1-1/N},$$

with constants c', c'' depending only on c_6, c_7, and L.

Proof. It suffices to prove that $m(\mathfrak{c}) - n(\mathfrak{c})$ is bounded by a term of order of magnitude $B^{1-1/N}$ if we set $B = \operatorname{Vol}(P_\mathfrak{c})$.

If a translation F_x of our fundamental domain by an element x in L is not contained in $P_\mathfrak{c}$ but intersects $P_\mathfrak{c}$, then it intersects the boundary of $P_\mathfrak{c}$. (Namely, the line segment between a point in $F_x \cap P_\mathfrak{c}$ and a point in F_x but not in $P_\mathfrak{c}$ is contained in the convex set F_x and crosses the boundary of $P_\mathfrak{c}$.) We can write

$$P_\mathfrak{c} = \prod_{v \in S_\infty} D_v,$$

where D_v is the closed interval or the closed disc of radius $\mathfrak{c}_v$, according as v is real or complex. Then the boundary of D_v consists of two points or a circle, and

$$\partial P_\mathfrak{c} = \bigcup_{v_0 \in S_\infty} \left[\partial D_{v_0} \times \prod_{v \neq v_0} D_v\right].$$

The dimension of the boundary is therefore $N - 1$. It will now suffice to give an upper bound of the desired kind for the number of translations F_x which intersect each

$$\partial D_{v_0} \times \prod_{v \neq v_0} D_v$$

because there are at most N such terms in the union. This will be done by parametrizing the boundary by a map having suitable partial derivatives. We recall that if φ is a differentiable map with derivative φ', then for any two vectors y, z we have

$$|\varphi(y) - \varphi(z)| \leqq |\varphi'|\,|y - z|,$$

where $|\ |$ is Euclidean norm, and $|\varphi'|$ is the maximum of the norm of the derivative of φ on the segment between y and z. (This is the mean value theorem.)

We parametrize $P_{\mathfrak{c}}$ by a map

$$\varphi : I^N \to P_{\mathfrak{c}}$$

sending the N-cube with sides of length equal to 1 onto $P_{\mathfrak{c}}$ as follows. If v is real, we map

$$t \mapsto 2\mathfrak{c}_v(t - \tfrac{1}{2}), \qquad 0 \leqq t \leqq 1$$

and if v is complex, we use polar coordinates, and map

$$(u, \theta) \mapsto (\mathfrak{c}_v u, 2\pi\theta), \qquad \begin{matrix} 0 \leqq u \leqq 1 \\ 0 \leqq \theta \leqq 1. \end{matrix}$$

Each partial derivative of φ is then bounded by $\mathfrak{c}_v$ times a constant (2 or 2π), and hence there is a constant c_8 $(= 2\pi N c_7)$ such that $|\varphi'| \leqq c_8 B^{1/N}$.

The boundary of $P_{\mathfrak{c}}$ is then parametrized by the $(N - 1)$-cube I^{N-1}. If we cut each side of I^{N-1} into $[B^{1/N}]$ segments of equal length, we get a decomposition of I^{N-1} into

$$[B^{1/N}]^{N-1}$$

small cubes, of diameter $\leqq (N - 1)^{1/2}/[B^{1/N}]$. The image of such a small cube under φ has diameter

$$\begin{aligned} &\leqq \frac{(N-1)^{1/2}}{[B^{1/N}]} c_8[B^{1/N}] \\ &\leqq c_9. \end{aligned}$$

The number of translations F_x $(x \in L)$ which meet a region of diameter $\leqq c_9$ is bounded by a constant c_{10} depending only on c_9 and the diameter of F. Thus the image of a small cube under φ meets at most c_{10} translates F_x of F by lattice points. Since we have $[B^{(N-1)/N}]$ small cubes, we see that $\varphi(I^{N-1})$ meets at most $c_{10}[B^{(N-1)/N}]$ translates of F. The boundary of $P_{\mathfrak{c}}$ consists of at most N pieces, each of which can be parametrized as indicated. This proves our theorem.

The next lemma determines the volume of the fundamental domain of an ideal $\mathfrak{a}$ of $\mathfrak{o}_k$ viewed as a lattice in Euclidean space

$$\mathbf{R}^N = \prod_{v \in S_\infty} k_v.$$

Lemma 2. *Let $\mathfrak{a}$ be an ideal of the ring of integers of k, and let F be a fundamental domain of $\mathfrak{a}$, as lattice in $\mathbf{R}^N$. Then*

$$\mathrm{Vol}(F) = 2^{-r_2}|D_{k/\mathbf{Q}}(\mathfrak{a})|^{1/2} = 2^{-r_2}\mathbf{N}\mathfrak{a}\sqrt{|D_k|}.$$

Proof. The ideal $\mathfrak{a}$ has a basis $\alpha_1, \ldots, \alpha_N$ over $\mathbf{Z}$.

Let $\sigma_1, \ldots, \sigma_{r_1}$ be the real embeddings of k. Let $\tau_1, \ldots, \tau_{r_2}$ and their conjugates be the complex ones. Each α in k maps on the vector

$$(\sigma_1\alpha, \ldots, \sigma_{r_1}\alpha, \tau_1\alpha, \ldots, \tau_{r_2}\alpha).$$

Let us write

$$\tau_j\alpha = x_j + \sqrt{-1}\, y_j,$$

where (x_j, y_j) are real coordinates in the complex numbers $\mathbf{C}$. Thus

$$\tau_j\alpha_\nu = x_{j\nu} + \sqrt{-1}\, y_{j\nu}, \qquad \nu = 1, \ldots, N.$$

The discriminant of $\mathfrak{a}$ as a module over $\mathbf{Z}$ is the square of the determinant

$$\begin{vmatrix} \sigma_1\alpha_1 & \cdots & \sigma_1\alpha_N \\ \vdots & & \vdots \\ x_{11} + iy_{11} & \cdots & x_{1N} + iy_{1N} \\ \vdots & & \vdots \\ x_{11} - iy_{11} & \cdots & x_{1N} - iy_{1N} \\ \vdots & & \vdots \end{vmatrix} \begin{matrix} \}r_1 \\ \\ \}r_2 \\ \\ \}r_2 \end{matrix}$$

Adding the last set of r_2 rows to the middle rows, and then subtracting again, we see that this determinant, up to a sign, is equal to

$$2^{r_2}\begin{vmatrix} \sigma_1\alpha_1 & \cdots & \sigma_1\alpha_N \\ \vdots & & \vdots \\ x_{11} & \cdots & x_{1N} \\ \vdots & & \vdots \\ y_{11} & \cdots & y_{1N} \\ \vdots & & \vdots \end{vmatrix}$$

and the determinant obtained here is the determinant of a set of basis vectors for $\mathfrak{a}$ as a lattice in $\mathbf{R}^N$ having all their components in the direction of the canonical unit vectors of $\mathbf{R}^N$. Thus we obtain

$$\sqrt{|D_{k/\mathbf{Q}}(\mathfrak{a})|} = 2^{r_2}\,\mathrm{Vol}(F)$$

as desired.

We can finally show how Theorem 2 implies Theorem 1. We had seen that we could assume our M_k-divisor such that the condition of Theorem 2 was satisfied, and also such that its associated ideal $\mathfrak{a}$ is one of a finite number of representatives of the ideal classes.

For any M_k-divisor $\mathfrak{c}$, we find

$$\mathrm{Vol}(P_{\mathfrak{c}}) = \prod_{v\ \mathrm{real}} (2\mathfrak{c}_v) \prod_{v\ \mathrm{complex}} (\pi \mathfrak{c}_v^2) = 2^{r_1}\pi^{r_2} \prod_{v \in S_\infty} \mathfrak{c}_v^{N_v}$$

$$\mathrm{Vol}(F) = 2^{-r_2}\mathbf{N}\mathfrak{a}\sqrt{|D_k|}$$

whence

$$\frac{\mathrm{Vol}(P_{\mathfrak{c}})}{\mathrm{Vol}(F)} = \frac{2^{r_1}(2\pi)^{r_2}}{|D_k|^{1/2}}\,\|\mathfrak{c}\|_k$$

thereby proving Theorem 1.

§3. *A volume computation*

We begin with some remarks on convex bodies in Euclidean space $\mathbf{R}^N$. We let μ be the ordinary measure in $\mathbf{R}^N$.

A subset C of $\mathbf{R}^N$ is said to be **convex** if, whenever x, y are points of C, then

$$tx + (1 - t)y, \qquad 0 \leqq t \leqq 1$$

also lies in C (in other words, the line segment between x and y lies in C).

We say that C is **symmetric** (with respect to the origin) if $x \in C$ implies $-x \in C$.

Theorem 3. *Let L be a lattice of dimension N in $\mathbf{R}^N$, and let C be a closed, convex, symmetric subset of $\mathbf{R}^N$. If*

$$\mu(C) \geqq 2^N\mu(F),$$

where F is a fundamental domain for L, then there exists a lattice point $\neq 0$ in C.

Proof. We shall first prove the theorem under the assumption $\mu(C) > 2^N\mu(F)$.

Under this assumption, we contend that there exist two elements in $\frac{1}{2}C$ whose difference is in L. Indeed, we have

$$\tfrac{1}{2}C = \bigcup_{x \in L} (\tfrac{1}{2}C \cap F_x) \qquad \text{(disjoint)}$$

and

$$\begin{aligned}\mu(\tfrac{1}{2}C) &= \sum_{x\in L} \mu(\tfrac{1}{2}C \cap F_x) \\ &= \sum_{x\in L} \mu((\tfrac{1}{2}C)_{-x} \cap F).\end{aligned}$$

But $\mu(\frac{1}{2}C) = 1/2^N \cdot \mu(C)$. Hence the sets $(\frac{1}{2}C)_{-x} \cap F$ cannot be disjoint (otherwise the assumption on the measure of F would be contradicted). This means that there exist two vectors $y_1, y_2 \in C$ such that

$$\tfrac{1}{2}y_1 + x_1 = \tfrac{1}{2}y_2 + x_2$$

with suitable x_1, x_2 in L, and $x_1 \neq x_2$. This proves our contention.

This gives $\frac{1}{2}(y_1 - y_2) \in L$. But $y_2 \in C$ implies $-y_2 \in C$, and so $\frac{1}{2}(y_1 - y_2)$ lies in C by convexity, as desired.

Suppose that $\mu(C) \geqq 2^N\mu(F)$. For every $\epsilon > 0$,

$$\mu((1+\epsilon)C) > \mu(C) \geqq 2^N\mu(F),$$

and hence there is a lattice point in $(1+\epsilon)C$. Letting ϵ tend to 0 shows that one of these lattice points must be in C.

Our next task is to compute a volume.

Lemma 3. *Let*

$$\mathbf{R}^N = \prod_{v\in S_\infty} k_v,$$

where k_v ranges over the reals taken r_1 times, the complex r_2 times, and $N = r_1 + 2r_2$. For each number $a > 0$, let A be the convex region determined by the inequality

$$\sum_{v\in S_\infty} N_v|z_v| \leqq a$$

and denote its volume by $V_{r_1,r_2}(a)$. Then

$$V_{r_1,r_2}(a) = 2^{r_1}4^{-r_2}(2\pi)^{r_2}\frac{1}{N!}a^N.$$

Proof. To begin with, it is clear that

$$V_{r_1,r_2}(a) = a^N V_{r_1,r_2}(1),$$

because

$$\begin{aligned}\sum_{v\in S_\infty} N_v|z_v| &= |z_1| + \cdots + |z_{r_1}| \\ &\quad + |z_{r_1+1}| + |\bar{z}_{r_1+1}| + \cdots + |z_{r_1+r_2}| + |\bar{z}_{r_1+r_2}|.\end{aligned}$$

The complex variables $z_{r_1+1}, \ldots, z_{r_1+r_2}$ will now be replaced by polar coordinates.

We wish to find $V_{r_1,r_2}(1)$. Use polar coordinates (u_j,θ_j) with $0 \leqq \theta_j \leqq 2\pi$ and $0 \leqq u_j$ to describe z_j. We have

$$V_{r_1r_2}(1) = \int u_{r_1+1} \cdots u_{r_1+r_2}\, du_1 \cdots du_{r_1}\, du_{r_1+1} \cdots du_{r_1+r_2}\, d\theta_{r_1+1} \cdots d\theta_{r_1+r_2},$$

the integral being taken over the region

$$|u_1| + \cdots + |u_{r_1}| + 2u_{r_1+1} + \cdots + 2u_{r_1+r_2} \leqq 1.$$

Restricting the region of integration so that $u_i \geqq 0$ for all i multiplies the integral by 2^{r_1}.

We make the change of variables $2\mu_j = w_j$, $2du_j = dw_j$ for $r_1 + 1 \leqq j \leqq r_1 + r_2$. The integral becomes

$$2^{r_1}4^{-r_2}(2\pi)^{r_2}W_{r_1,r_2}(1),$$

where

$$W_{r_1,r_2}(b) = \int u_{r_1+1} \cdots u_{r_1+r_2}\, du_1 \cdots du_{r_1+r_2},$$

the integral taken over the region $u_i \geqq 0$ all i, and

$$u_1 + \cdots + u_{r_1+r_2} \leqq b.$$

But

$$W_{r_1,r_2}(b) = b^N W_{r_1,r_2}(1).$$

We can split off the integral over du_1 between 0 and 1, and write the integral

$$W_{r_1,r_2}(1) = \int_0^1 W_{r_1-1,r_2}(1 - u_1)\, du_1 = \frac{1}{N} W_{r_1-1,r_2}(1),$$

performing a trivial integration on u_1 and using the homogeneity. By induction, we get rid of the first set of variables and get

$$W_{r_1,r_2}(1) = \frac{1}{N(N-1)\cdots(N-r_1+1)} W_{0,r_2}(1).$$

In a similar way, we get

$$W_{0,r_2}(1) = \int_0^1 t_1(1 - t_1)^{2r_2-2}\, dt_1 W_{0,r_2-1}(1),$$

which, after performing the integration and using induction, is

$$= \frac{1}{(2r_2)!} W_{0,0}(1) = \frac{1}{(2r_2)!}.$$

This yields

$$W_{r_1,r_2}(1) = \frac{1}{N!}$$

whence the desired value for V_{r_1,r_2} drops out.

§4. *Minkowski's constant*

Let k be of degree N over $\mathbf{Q}$ and let $\mathfrak{a}$ be an ideal of the integers $\mathfrak{o}_k$, viewed as a lattice in $\mathbf{R}^N$. We select the number a in Lemma 3 such that the region of that lemma has volume at least equal to 2^N times the volume of a fundamental domain for a. We denote by d_k the absolute value of the discriminant D_k. Then the value of a such that

$$a^N = N! 4^{r_2} \pi^{-r_2} \mathbf{N}\mathfrak{a}\, d_k^{1/2}$$

will achieve our purpose, in view of Lemma 2, §2. By Theorem 3 there exists a lattice point in the region of Lemma 3. This means that there exists an element $\alpha \in \mathfrak{a}$, $\alpha \neq 0$ such that

$$|\sigma_1\alpha| + \cdots + |\sigma_N\alpha| \leqq a.$$

The geometric mean being bounded by the arithmetic mean, we get

$$|N_{\mathbf{Q}}^k(\alpha)|^{1/N} \leqq \frac{|\sigma_1\alpha| + \cdots + |\sigma_N\alpha|}{N},$$

whence

$$|N_{\mathbf{Q}}^k(\alpha)| \leqq \frac{a^N}{N^N} = \frac{N!}{N^N} 4^{r_2} \pi^{-r_2} \mathbf{N}\mathfrak{a}\, d_k^{1/2}.$$

We have a factorization of ideals,

$$(\alpha) = \mathfrak{a}\mathfrak{b},$$

where $\mathfrak{b}$ is an ideal. Hence

$$|N_{\mathbf{Q}}^k(\alpha)| = \mathbf{N}\mathfrak{a}\mathbf{N}\mathfrak{b}.$$

Canceling $\mathbf{N}\mathfrak{a}$, we have:

Theorem 4. *In any ideal class, there exists an ideal $\mathfrak{b}$ such that*

$$\mathbf{N}\mathfrak{b} \leqq C_k d_k^{1/2},$$

where C_k *is the Minkowski constant:*

$$C_k = \frac{N!}{N^N}\left(\frac{4}{\pi}\right)^{r_2}.$$

Corollary. *The absolute value of the discriminant* d_k *is* > 1. *There is at least one prime ramified in* k.

Proof. We have $\mathbf{N}\mathfrak{b} \geqq 1$ whence

$$d_k \geqq \left(\frac{\pi}{4}\right)^{2r_2} \frac{N^{2N}}{(N!)^2} \geqq \left(\frac{\pi}{4}\right)^{N} \frac{N^{2N}}{(N!)^2}.$$

If $N = 2$, then we obtain at once $d > \frac{9}{4} > 1$. Our assertion will be proved if we show that the sequence of numbers

$$\left(\frac{\pi}{4}\right)^{N} \frac{N^{2N}}{(N)!^2}$$

is monotone increasing. Taking the ratio of two successive numbers, a trivial computation proves what we want.

I copied the following table of values for the Minkowski constant in a course of Artin 20 years ago.

N	r_1	r_2	$\left(\frac{4}{\pi}\right)^{r_2} \frac{N!}{N^N}$
2	0	1	0.63661
	2	0	0.5
3	1	1	0.28299
	3	0	0.22222
4	0	2	0.15198
	2	1	0.11937
	4	0	0.09375
5	1	2	0.06225
	3	1	0.04889
	5	0	0.0384

For large N, we see that $d_k \geqq (1/N)(\pi e^2/4)^N$.

We conclude by an example of which Artin was very fond. Consider the equation $f(X) = X^5 - X + 1$. The discriminant Δ of a root of $X^5 + aX + b$ is $5^5b^4 + 2^8a^5$. In this special case,

$$\Delta = 2869 = 19 \cdot 151.$$

Each prime factor occurs to the first power.

Let α be a root of $f(X)$ and $k = \mathbf{Q}(\alpha)$. Then α is integral over $\mathbf{Z}$. Since $f(X)$ is irreducible mod 5, it is irreducible over $\mathbf{Z}$ (or $\mathbf{Q}$) and k is of degree 5 over $\mathbf{Q}$. The discriminant of $\mathbf{Z}[\alpha]$ as a module over $\mathbf{Z}$ has no square factors. Hence it must be equal to $D(\mathfrak{o}_k)$, because it differs from $D(\mathfrak{o}_k)$ by a square. Hence $\mathbf{Z}[\alpha] = \mathfrak{o}_k$ by Proposition 10 of Chapter III, §3.

It is not difficult to show that the Galois group of the polynomial is the full symmetric group. Hence the splitting field K has degree 120 over $\mathbf{Q}$.

By the Minkowski theorem, every ideal class has an ideal $\mathfrak{b}$ such that $\mathbf{N}\mathfrak{b} < 4$ (using the value for the Minkowski constant in the table and trivial estimates). Since $\mathbf{N}\mathfrak{b}$ is an integer, it is either 1, 2, or 3. If $\mathbf{N}\mathfrak{b} \neq 1$, the only possibility is that $\mathfrak{b}$ is a prime ideal $\mathfrak{p}$ with $\mathbf{N}\mathfrak{p} = 2$ or 3. This would mean that the residue class field $\mathfrak{o}_k/\mathfrak{p}$ has degree 1 over $\mathbf{Z}/p\mathbf{Z}$ and hence that f has a root mod 2 or mod 3. This is impossible (direct computation), and hence the only possibility is that $\mathbf{N}\mathfrak{b} = 1$. But then $\mathfrak{b} = (1)$ and (oh miracle!) every ideal is principal. The ring of integers is a principal ideal ring.

As Artin noticed, it can be shown that the splitting field K is unramified over the extension $\mathbf{Q}(\sqrt{D}) = \mathbf{Q}(\sqrt{19 \cdot 151})$.

Artin's example also gives an example of an unramified extension whose Galois group is the icosahedral group. As he once pointed out, given any Galois extension K of a number field k, with group G, there exist infinitely many finite extensions E of k such that $K \cap E = k$ and KE is unramified over E. To obtain such E, it suffices to construct an extension which absorbs locally all the ramification of K (this puts a finite number of conditions on E, which can be realized by the approximation theorem), and one must insure that $E \cap K = k$. To do this, one can for instance use the existence of primes and density theorems proved in a later chapter. We leave it as an exercise.

As a final application of the Minkowski theorem, we shall prove:

Theorem 5. *If k is a number field, denote by N_k and d_k the degree $[k:\mathbf{Q}]$ and absolute value of the discriminant respectively. Then the quotient $N_k/\log d_k$ is bounded for all $k \neq \mathbf{Q}$. Furthermore, there exists only a finite number of fields k having a given value of the discriminant.*

Proof. The first assertion follows from a trivial computation involving the inequality of the Corollary to Theorem 4, and the standard estimate from Sterling's formula

$$N! = N^N e^{-N} \sqrt{2\pi N}\, e^{\theta/12N}.$$

We leave it to the reader. This shows that the degree is bounded when the discriminant is bounded. Hence to prove the second assertion, we must show that there is only a finite number of number fields k having given degree N and given absolute value of the discriminant d.

Consider Euclidean N-space

$$\mathbf{R}^N = \prod_{v \in S_\infty} k_v.$$

Suppose that there is at least one complex absolute value v_0. Consider the domain defined by the inequalities

$$\begin{aligned} |z_{v_0} - \bar{z}_{v_0}| &\leqq C_1 d^{1/2} \\ |z_{v_0} + \bar{z}_{v_0}| &< \tfrac{1}{2} \\ |z_v| &< \tfrac{1}{2}, \qquad\qquad v \neq v_0, \end{aligned}$$

where C_1 is a large constant, depending on N. Here we denote by z_v an element of k_v identified with $\mathbf{C}$ or $\mathbf{R}$ as the case may be.

Then our domain is convex and symmetric with respect to the origin. Consequently it must contain an element $\alpha \neq 0$ in $\mathfrak{o}_k$. Since the norm of α has absolute value $\geqq 1$ (being a non-zero rational integer), it follows from the first inequality that the absolute value of the imaginary part of α is greater than 1. Hence the two conjugates of α corresponding to v_0 are distinct. Furthermore, α is distinct from any other conjugate, since already its absolute value at v_0 is distinct from its absolute value at $v \neq v_0$. Hence α is a generator for k over $\mathbf{Q}$. Its equation over $\mathbf{Z}$ has coefficients which are elementary symmetric functions of α and its conjugates, and are therefore bounded as a function of d and N. Hence such α can satisfy only a finite number of equations over $\mathbf{Z}$, thereby proving our theorem if there is a complex v_0. If all absolute values are real, the proof is even easier, since we can replace the first pair of conditions simply by

$$|z_{v_0}| \leqq C_1 d^{1/2}$$

and argue in the same way.

CHAPTER VI

The Ideal Function

§1. *Generalized ideal classes*

Let k be a number field, and let I denote the multiplicative group of non-zero fractional ideals. Let P be the subset of principal ideals. If $\mathfrak{a}$, $\mathfrak{b}$ are fractional ideals (which we say from now on, instead of non-zero ideals, unless otherwise specified), then we write $\mathfrak{a} \sim \mathfrak{b}$ ($\mathfrak{a}$ is equivalent to $\mathfrak{b}$) if there exists $\alpha \in k$ such that $\mathfrak{a} = (\alpha)\mathfrak{b}$, i.e. $\mathfrak{a}\mathfrak{b}^{-1}$ is a principal fractional ideal. Then the equivalence classes of fractional ideals form a finite group (as we saw in Chapter V, §1), which we call the **ideal class group.** Its order is usually denoted by h, and is called the **class number** of k.

We shall now refine the notion of ideal class group. By a **cycle** (of k) we shall mean a formal product

$$\mathfrak{c} = \prod_{v \in M_k} v^{m(v)},$$

where v ranges over the normalized absolute values of k (inducing the ordinary absolute value of a p-adic absolute value on $\mathbf{Q}$), with exponents $m(v)$ which are integers $\geqq 0$, and such that $m(v) = 0$ for all but a finite number of v. Thus we are interested in assigning a multiplicity $\geqq 0$ to each absolute value. Actually, we shall not care about the complex v, and if v is real, then we only care whether $m(v) = 0$ or $m(v) > 0$. Thus for our purposes, we could take $m(v) = 0$ or 1 in case v is real, and leave out the complex v altogether.

From a notational point of view, the literature extends the notation $\mathfrak{p}$ to apply to the archimedean absolute values in M_k, and also to say that such v are "primes", or "primes at infinity".

We shall avoid this, and reserve $\mathfrak{p}$ to denote (non-zero) prime ideals of $\mathfrak{o}$. If $v = v_{\mathfrak{p}}$ for some prime $\mathfrak{p}$, we do however also write $m(\mathfrak{p})$ instead of $m(v)$. We write $\mathfrak{p}|\mathfrak{c}$ or $v|\mathfrak{c}$ if $m(\mathfrak{p})$ [or $m(v)$] is > 0, and we also say in that case that v (or $\mathfrak{p}$) **divides** $\mathfrak{c}$. We call $m(v)$ the **multiplicity** of v in $\mathfrak{c}$. We let

$$\mathfrak{c}_{\mathfrak{p}} = \mathfrak{p}^{m(\mathfrak{p})} \qquad \text{or} \qquad \mathfrak{c}_v = v^{m(v)}$$

denote the local v-component of $\mathfrak{c}$, if $\mathfrak{p}$ corresponds to v.

We denote by $\mathfrak{c}_0$ the product

$$\mathfrak{c}_0 = \prod_{\mathfrak{p} \neq v_\infty} \mathfrak{p}^{m(\mathfrak{p})}$$

taken over all prime ideals $\mathfrak{p}$, and call it the **finite part** of $\mathfrak{c}$.

We let $I(\mathfrak{c})$, or $I(k, \mathfrak{c})$, or $I_k(\mathfrak{c})$, denote the set of fractional ideals relatively prime to $\mathfrak{c}_0$ (or as we shall also say, prime to $\mathfrak{c}$). Thus $I(\mathfrak{c})$ is the set of fractional ideals not divisible by any prime ideal $\mathfrak{p}$ having a multiplicity > 0 in $\mathfrak{c}$.

Next, we introduce a subgroup of k^* as follows. If $\alpha \in k^*$, we define

$$\alpha \equiv 1 \pmod{^* \mathfrak{c}}$$

to mean that α satisfies the following two conditions:

(i) If $\mathfrak{p}$ is a prime ideal with multiplicity $m(\mathfrak{p}) > 0$, then α lies in the local ring $\mathfrak{o}_\mathfrak{p}$, and

$$\alpha \equiv 1 \pmod{\mathfrak{m}_\mathfrak{p}^{m(\mathfrak{p})}},$$

where $\mathfrak{m}_\mathfrak{p}$ is the maximal ideal of $\mathfrak{o}_\mathfrak{p}$. Symbolically, we also write this congruence in the form

$$\alpha \equiv 1 \pmod{\mathfrak{c}_\mathfrak{p}}.$$

(ii) If v is a real absolute value in M_k having multiplicity $m(v) > 0$ in c, and σ_v is the corresponding embedding of k in $\mathbf{R}$, then

$$\sigma_v \alpha > 0.$$

It is clear that those elements of k^* satisfying (i) and (ii) form a group, and we denote this group by $k_\mathfrak{c}$. We observe that elements of $k_\mathfrak{c}$ are necessarily $\mathfrak{p}$-units if $\mathfrak{p}$ is a prime dividing $\mathfrak{c}$. [As a matter of notation, we write $X(\mathfrak{c})$ to denote the subset of X consisting of those elements prime to $\mathfrak{c}$, and $X_\mathfrak{c}$ to denote the subset of X consisting of those elements satisfying the congruence relations (i) and (ii).]

We denote by $P_\mathfrak{c}$ the subgroup of P consisting of those principal fractional ideals (α) with $\alpha \in k_\mathfrak{c}$. Then it is clear that $P_\mathfrak{c}$ is a subgroup of $I(\mathfrak{c})$. The factor group $I(\mathfrak{c})/P_\mathfrak{c}$ will be called the group of **$\mathfrak{c}$-ideal classes.** We shall see in a moment that it is finite, and has the ordinary group of ideal classes as factor group. If $\mathfrak{c} = 1$, we agree to the convention that $I(1) = I$ is the group of fractional ideals, and $P_1 = P$.

First, we observe that every ideal class in I/P has a representative in $I(\mathfrak{c})$, i.e. has a representative ideal prime to $\mathfrak{c}$. To see this, let $\mathfrak{a}$ be an (integral) ideal in a given class mod P. If $\operatorname{ord}_\mathfrak{p} \mathfrak{a} = r(\mathfrak{p})$ for a prime ideal $\mathfrak{p} | \mathfrak{c}$, we solve the congruences

$$\alpha \equiv \pi_\mathfrak{p}^{r(\mathfrak{p})} \pmod{\mathfrak{p}^{r(\mathfrak{p})+1}}$$

for $\mathfrak{p}|\mathfrak{c}$, using the Chinese remainder theorem. We use the notation $\pi_{\mathfrak{p}}$ for an element of order 1 at $\mathfrak{p}$. Then $\mathfrak{a}(\alpha^{-1})$ is prime to $\mathfrak{c}$. Again using the Chinese remainder theorem, we can multiply $\mathfrak{a}(\alpha^{-1})$ by a suitable algebraic integer in k, prime to $\mathfrak{c}$, to make it an ideal (i.e. not fractional). Thus the inclusions

$$\begin{array}{ccc} I(\mathfrak{c}) & \to & I \\ | & & | \\ P \cap I(\mathfrak{c}) & \to & P \end{array}$$

induce an isomorphism of factor groups

$$I(\mathfrak{c})/P(\mathfrak{c}) \approx I/P, \tag{1}$$

where $P(\mathfrak{c})$ denotes the group of principal fractional ideals prime to $\mathfrak{c}$, so that

$$P(\mathfrak{c}) = P \cap I(\mathfrak{c}).$$

We note that $P(\mathfrak{c})$ contains $P_{\mathfrak{c}}$, and we have the tower of subgroups

$$I(\mathfrak{c}) \supset P(\mathfrak{c}) \supset P_{\mathfrak{c}}.$$

We therefore have a surjective homomorphism

$$I(\mathfrak{c})/P_{\mathfrak{c}} \to I(\mathfrak{c})/P(\mathfrak{c}) \approx I/P.$$

Its kernel is $P(\mathfrak{c})/P_{\mathfrak{c}}$, which we shall now analyze.

We have the surjective homomorphism $k^* \to P$, which to each $\alpha \in k^*$ associates the principal fractional ideal (α). Its kernel is the group of units U. Similarly, if $k(\mathfrak{c})$ denotes the subgroup of k^* consisting of those elements whose ideal is prime to $\mathfrak{c}$, then we have a surjective homomorphism

$$k(\mathfrak{c}) \to P(\mathfrak{c})$$

given by

$$\alpha \mapsto (\alpha).$$

The inverse image of $P_{\mathfrak{c}}$ is precisely the subgroup $Uk_{\mathfrak{c}}$, where U denotes the group of units of k, thus giving rise to the diagram

$$\begin{array}{ccc} k(\mathfrak{c}) & \to & P(\mathfrak{c}) \\ | & & | \\ Uk_{\mathfrak{c}} & \to & P_{\mathfrak{c}} \end{array}$$

and the isomorphism

$$k(\mathfrak{c})/Uk_{\mathfrak{c}} \approx P(\mathfrak{c})/P_{\mathfrak{c}}. \tag{2}$$

Let $\mathbf{R}^+$ denote the multiplicative group of real numbers > 0. If v is a real absolute value, then $k_v^+ = \mathbf{R}^+$, and $k_v^*/k_v^+ \approx \{1, -1\}$. For $\mathfrak{p}|\mathfrak{c}_0$ let

$m(\mathfrak{p})$ be its multiplicity. We consider the map

$$k(\mathfrak{c}) \to \prod_{\mathfrak{p}|\mathfrak{c}_0} (\mathfrak{o}_\mathfrak{p}/\mathfrak{m}_\mathfrak{p}^{m(\mathfrak{p})})^* \times \prod_{\substack{v|\mathfrak{c}\\ v \text{ real}}} k_v^*/k_v^+ \tag{3}$$

which to each $\alpha \in k(\mathfrak{c})$ associates its residue class in the corresponding factor. If $\mathfrak{p}$ is a prime ideal, then $(\mathfrak{o}_\mathfrak{p}/\mathfrak{m}_\mathfrak{p}^{m(\mathfrak{p})})^*$ is the group of units (invertible elements) in the residue class ring $\mathfrak{o}_\mathfrak{p}/\mathfrak{m}_\mathfrak{p}^{m(\mathfrak{p})}$. Using the approximation theorem, one sees at once that our map is surjective, and from the definitions, it follows directly that its kernel is precisely $k_\mathfrak{c}$. Thus we have a good description of the factor group $k(\mathfrak{c})/k_\mathfrak{c}$ as a direct product of local factors shown in (3).

As in the rational case, we define the Euler φ-function. We let

$$\varphi_\mathfrak{p}(\mathfrak{c}_0) = \text{order of the group } (\mathfrak{o}_\mathfrak{p}/\mathfrak{m}_\mathfrak{p}^{m(\mathfrak{p})})^*$$

and

$$\varphi(\mathfrak{c}_0) = \prod_{\mathfrak{p}|\mathfrak{c}_0} \varphi_\mathfrak{p}(\mathfrak{c}_0).$$

It is clear that

$$\varphi_\mathfrak{p}(\mathfrak{c}_0) = (\mathbf{N}\mathfrak{p} - 1)\mathbf{N}\mathfrak{p}^{m(\mathfrak{p})-1}.$$

We already see that $I(\mathfrak{c})/P_\mathfrak{c}$ is finite, and the order of $k(\mathfrak{c})/k_\mathfrak{c}$ is given in terms of the Euler function.

Finally, we have the tower

$$k(\mathfrak{c}) \supset Uk_\mathfrak{c} \supset k_\mathfrak{c},$$

and we look at the factor group

$$Uk_\mathfrak{c}/k_\mathfrak{c} \approx U/(U \cap k_\mathfrak{c}) = U/U_\mathfrak{c}, \tag{4}$$

where $U_\mathfrak{c}$ consists of those units $\equiv 1 \pmod{^*\ \mathfrak{c}}$. In the above manner we have unscrewed the group of $\mathfrak{c}$-ideal classes into various constituents, which in particular allow us to write down a formula for its order. For clarity, we write down the diagram of what we have done.

$$\begin{array}{ccccccc}
 & & & & I(\mathfrak{c}) & \to & I \\
 & & & & | & & | \\
 & & k(\mathfrak{c}) & \to & P(\mathfrak{c}) & \to & P \\
 & & | & & | & & \\
U & \to & Uk_\mathfrak{c} & \to & P_\mathfrak{c} & & \\
| & & | & & & & \\
U_\mathfrak{c} & \to & k_\mathfrak{c} & & & &
\end{array}$$

Two opposite vertical bars represent isomorphisms of factor groups. For each horizontal arrow, the group on the left is the inverse image of the group on the right under the corresponding homomorphism.

Theorem 1. *The group of* $\mathfrak{c}$*-ideal classes* $I(\mathfrak{c})/P_{\mathfrak{c}}$ *is finite. If* h *is the class number of* k, *and* $h_{\mathfrak{c}}$ *is the order of* $I(\mathfrak{c})/P_{\mathfrak{c}}$, *and* $s(\mathfrak{c})$ *is the number of real* $v|\mathfrak{c}$, *then*

$$h_{\mathfrak{c}} = \frac{h\varphi(\mathfrak{c}_0)2^{s(\mathfrak{c})}}{(U:U_{\mathfrak{c}})}.$$

It is a reasonable convention to define

$$\varphi(\mathfrak{c}) = \varphi(\mathfrak{c}_0)2^{s(\mathfrak{c})},$$

so as to include the archimedean v into the definition of the Euler function. Then we can write

$$h_{\mathfrak{c}} = \frac{h\varphi(\mathfrak{c})}{(U:U_{\mathfrak{c}})}.$$

We note that $U_{\mathfrak{c}}$ being of finite index in U, it has also

$$r = r_1 + r_2 - 1$$

independent units, and the additive group of "log vectors" of elements of $U_{\mathfrak{c}}$ is a lattice in $\mathbf{R}^r$.

If $\{\epsilon_1, \ldots, \epsilon_r\}$ are independent units generating U modulo roots of unity, and if $\{\eta_1, \ldots, \eta_r\}$ are independent units generating $U_{\mathfrak{c}}$ modulo roots of unity, then the logs of these units respectively generate lattices in $\mathbf{R}^r$, denoted by $\log U$ and $\log U_{\mathfrak{c}}$ respectively. We can define the **$\mathfrak{c}$-regulator** $R_{\mathfrak{c}}$ by

$$R_{\mathfrak{c}} = |\det(\log|\sigma_j\eta_i|^{N_j})|,$$

with $i = 1, \ldots, r$ and $j = 1, \ldots, r$. Just as the regulator R can be interpreted as the volume of a fundamental domain, so can we interpret $R_{\mathfrak{c}}$ as the volume of a fundamental domain for $\log U_{\mathfrak{c}}$ in $\mathbf{R}^r$.

Example. We conclude this section by an example which is in some sense "typical". Let $k = \mathbf{Q}$. Each prime ideal is represented by a prime number p, and we let v_∞ denote the real absolute value. Let m be a positive integer, representing an ideal (m), and let $\mathfrak{c} = mv_\infty$. Then U_{mv_∞} consists of 1 alone. The group $I(\mathfrak{c})$ consists of those ideals prime to m, and $\mathbf{Q}_{mv_\infty}$ consists of those positive rational numbers α such that

$$\alpha \equiv 1 \pmod{^* m}.$$

Any class of $I(mv_\infty)/P_{mv_\infty}$ can be represented by an arithmetic progression of positive integers prime to m. The generalized ideal class group is isomorphic to $(\mathbf{Z}/m\mathbf{Z})^*$, namely the multiplicative group of integers prime to m, mod m. *Thus we can view our generalized ideal classes as generalizations of arithmetic progressions in number fields.*

§2. *Lattice points in homogeneously expanding domains*

By a lattice in $\mathbf{R}^N$, we mean as usual a discrete subgroup of rank N. Let L be such a lattice, and let D be a subset of $\mathbf{R}^N$. We denote by ∂D the boundary of D (set of points in the closure of D, not lying in the interior). We let tD denote the set of points tx, for $t \in \mathbf{R}$ and $x \in D$. Then $\partial(tD) = t\,\partial D$. We are interested in an asymptotic formula for the number of points of L in tD. To get this, one has to make some assumption on the smoothness of the boundary, as follows. Let S be a subset of some euclidean space. A map

$$\varphi : S \to \mathbf{R}^N$$

is said to satisfy a Lipschitz condition if there exists a constant C such that for all x, $y \in S$ we have

$$|\varphi(x) - \varphi(y)| \leqq C|x - y|.$$

Let I^k denote the unit cube in k-space, that is the set of points $(x_1, \ldots, x_k)$ with $0 \leqq x_i \leqq 1$. A subset T of $\mathbf{R}^N$ is said to be **k-Lipschitz parametrizable** if there exists a finite number of Lipschitz maps $\varphi_j \colon I^k \to T$ whose images cover T.

Let $\omega_1, \ldots, \omega_N$ be a basis for the lattice L over $\mathbf{Z}$. The set F of all points

$$t_1\omega_1 + \cdots + t_N\omega_n, \qquad (0 \leqq t_i < 1)$$

will be called a **fundamental domain** for L. Denote it by F. Then the translations F_l of F by elements $l \in L$ cover $\mathbf{R}^N$ and are disjoint. Every element of R^N has a unique representative in F modulo L.

We let Vol denote volume in N-space.

Theorem 2. *Let D be a subset of $\mathbf{R}^N$ and L a lattice in $\mathbf{R}^N$, with fundamental domain F. Assume that the boundary of D is $(N-1)$-Lipschitz parametrizable. Let $\lambda(t) = \lambda(t, D, L)$ be the number of lattice points in tD. Then*

$$\lambda(t) = \frac{\mathrm{Vol}(D)}{\mathrm{Vol}(F)}\, t^N + O(t^{N-1}),$$

where the constant in O depends on L, N, and the Lipschitz constants.

Proof. If a point $l \in L$ lies in tD, then F_l intersects tD. Furthermore, either F_l is contained in the interior of tD, or F_l intersects the boundary of tD. Let:

$$\begin{aligned} n(t) &= \text{number of } l \in L \text{ such that } l \in tD. \\ m(t) &= \text{number of } l \in L \text{ such that } F_l \subset \text{interior of } tD. \\ b(t) &= \text{number of } l \in L \text{ such that } F_l \text{ intersects } \partial tD. \end{aligned}$$

Then

$$m(t) \leqq n(t) \leqq m(t) + b(t),$$

and

$$m(t)\,\mathrm{Vol}(F) \leqq \mathrm{Vol}\,tD \leqq \big(m(t) + b(t)\big)\,\mathrm{Vol}(F).$$

Hence

$$m(t) \leqq \frac{\mathrm{Vol}\,D}{\mathrm{Vol}\,F}\,t^N \leqq m(t) + b(t),$$

and to conclude the proof, it suffices to estimate $b(t)$. Let $\varphi\colon I^{N-1} \to \mathbf{R}^N$ be one of the parametrizing maps for a piece of the boundary of D, with Lipschitz constant C. Then $t\varphi$ parametrizes a corresponding piece of ∂tD. Let $[t]$ denote the largest integer $\leqq t$, as usual. Cut up each side of the unit cube I^{N-1} into sides of length $1/[t]$. We then get $[t]^{N-1}$ small cubes. The image under φ of each small cube has diameter $\leqq C_1/[t]$, and hence the image under $t\varphi$ of each small cube has diameter $\leqq C_2$. The number of $l \in L$ such that F_l intersects the image of such a small cube under $t\varphi$ is then bounded by C', where C' is a constant depending only on L and C. Hence

$$b(t) \leqq C'[t]^{N-1}.$$

This proves our theorem.

§3. *The number of ideals in a given class*

Let I be the group of fractional ideals of k, and P the subgroup of principal fractional ideals. We are interested in an asymptotic formula for the number of ideals $\mathfrak{a}$ in a given class of I/P such that $\mathbf{N}\mathfrak{a} \leqq t$, for $t \to \infty$. More generally, we want such a formula for the ideals in a generalized class of $I(\mathfrak{c})/P_{\mathfrak{c}}$ for some cycle $\mathfrak{c}$. We begin by sketching the argument in the simplest case. We let $\mathfrak{a}$, $\mathfrak{b}$ denote **ideals** (not fractional).

Let $\mathfrak{K}$ be a given ideal class mod P, and let $\mathfrak{b}$ be an ideal in the inverse class. For each ideal $\mathfrak{a} \in \mathfrak{K}$, the ideal $\mathfrak{a}\mathfrak{b}$ is then a principal ideal (ξ) contained in $\mathfrak{b}$ (because we took $\mathfrak{a}$ to be an ideal, so $\mathfrak{a} \subset \mathfrak{o}$). We have

$$\mathbf{N}\mathfrak{a} \leqq t \quad \text{if and only if} \quad \mathbf{N}(\mathfrak{a}\mathfrak{b}) = \mathbf{N}(\xi) \leqq \mathbf{N}\mathfrak{b} \cdot t.$$

Elements α, β of k are called equivalent if there exists a unit u such that $\alpha = u\beta$. Let $j(\mathfrak{K}, t)$ be the number of ideals $\mathfrak{a} \in \mathfrak{K}$ such that $\mathbf{N}\mathfrak{a} \leqq t$. Then $j(\mathfrak{K}, t)$ is the number of equivalence classes of elements $\xi \in \mathfrak{b}$, $\xi \neq 0$, such that $\mathbf{N}\xi \leqq \mathbf{N}\mathfrak{b} \cdot t$. Let U denote the group of units. Then U operates on the number field k, but we may also view U as operating on Euclidean space

$$A_k(\infty) = \mathbf{R}^N = \prod_{v \in S_\infty} k_v.$$

(If v is complex, we fix a definite identification of k_v with $\mathbf{C}$.) Namely, if $u \in U$, and (a_v) is in $\mathbf{R}^N$, then

$$u(a_v) = (\sigma_v u \cdot a_v),$$

where σ_v is the embedding of k in k_v corresponding to v.

Elements ξ, η of $\mathbf{R}^N$ are said to be in the same **orbit** of U if there exists a unit u such that $\xi = u\eta$.

We can define the norm on $\mathbf{R}^N = A_k(\infty)$, namely if $\xi = (\xi_v)$, then we let

$$\mathbf{N}\xi = \prod_{v \in S_\infty} |\xi|_v^{N_v}.$$

If ξ, η are in the same orbit of U, then clearly $\mathbf{N}\xi = \mathbf{N}\eta$. For $\xi \in A_k(\infty)$ we have

$$\mathbf{N}(t\xi) = t^N \mathbf{N}\xi.$$

We are of course interested in elements $\xi \neq 0$ in $\mathfrak{b}$, and hence it is useful to deal with the subset of $A_k(\infty)$ given by

$$J_k(\infty) = \prod_{v \in S_\infty} k_v^*,$$

consisting of those elements having non-zero coordinates at all $v \in S_\infty$. Then $J_k(\infty)$ is stable under the operation of U, and we can define the notion of a fundamental domain D in $J_k(\infty)$, namely a subset such that every orbit of U has a unique element in D. We can then say that $j(\mathfrak{K}, t)$ is the number of elements $\xi \in \mathfrak{b}$ such that

$$\text{(1)} \qquad \mathbf{N}\xi \leqq \mathbf{N}\mathfrak{b} \cdot t \quad \text{and} \quad \xi \in D.$$

If Y is a subset of $A_k(\infty)$ and $t > 0$, we let $Y(t)$ be the subset of Y consisting of those elements ξ such that $\mathbf{N}\xi \leqq t$. *Assume that we are able to construct D such that $tD = D$ for every real $t > 0$. Then*

$$D(t) = t^{1/N} D(1).$$

With this notation, our conditions (1) are equivalent to the condition

$$\text{(2)} \qquad \xi \in D(\mathbf{N}\mathfrak{b} \cdot t),$$

and we get the fundamental formula:

$$\boxed{j(\mathfrak{R}, t) = \lambda\big((\mathbf{N}\mathfrak{b} \cdot t)^{1/N}, D(1), \mathfrak{b}\big).}$$

In other words, the number of ideals $\mathfrak{a} \in \mathfrak{R}$ such that $\mathbf{N}\mathfrak{a} \leqq t$ is equal to the number of points of the lattice $\mathfrak{b}$ lying in the domain

$$(\mathbf{N}\mathfrak{b} \cdot t)^{1/N} D(1) = D(\mathbf{N}\mathfrak{b} \cdot t).$$

This reduces the problem of computing $j(\mathfrak{R}, t)$ to Theorem 2, §2, provided that we can construct $D(1)$ so as to satisfy the hypothesis of that theorem (that is, Lipschitz parametrizable boundary).

For convenience, it is easier to construct a fundamental domain for a free abelian subgroup of the unit group (i.e. disregard the roots of unity). If we do that, and count the number of points of the lattice $\mathfrak{b}$ in such a domain, then we get $w \cdot j(\mathfrak{R}, t)$, where w is the number of roots of unity in k.

The whole discussion can be applied more generally to ideal classes of $I(\mathfrak{c})/P_\mathfrak{c}$ as follows. We shall prove:

Lemma 1. *Let $\mathfrak{c}$ be a cycle of k. Let V be a free subgroup of $U_\mathfrak{c}$ which generates $U_\mathfrak{c}$ modulo roots of unity. Let $J_k(\infty, \mathfrak{c})$ be the subset of $J_k(\infty)$ consisting of those ξ such that $\xi_v > 0$ if v is real, $v|\mathfrak{c}$. There exists a fundamental domain D for the operation of V on $J_k(\infty, \mathfrak{c})$ such that $tD = D$ if $t > 0$, and such that $D(1)$ has an $(N - 1)$-Lipschitz parametrizable boundary.*

Let us postpone for a moment the proof of Lemma 1. *Let $\mathfrak{R}$ be an ideal class of $I(\mathfrak{c})/P_\mathfrak{c}$, and let $j(\mathfrak{R}, t)$ be the number of ideals $\mathfrak{a} \in \mathfrak{R}$ such that* $\mathbf{N}\mathfrak{a} \leqq t$. *Select* $\mathfrak{b} \in \mathfrak{R}^{-1}$. The map

$$\mathfrak{a} \mapsto \mathfrak{a}\mathfrak{b} = (\xi)$$

establishes a bijection between ideals of $\mathfrak{a} \in \mathfrak{R}$, and $U_\mathfrak{c}$-equivalence classes of elements ξ satisfying the pair of conditions:

$$\xi \equiv 1 \pmod{^* \mathfrak{c}}, \qquad \xi \equiv 0 \pmod{\mathfrak{b}}.$$

If $w_\mathfrak{c}$ denotes the number of roots of unity in $U_\mathfrak{c}$, then we see that:

$w_\mathfrak{c} j(\mathfrak{R}, t)$ is equal to the number of elements ξ satisfying

$$\begin{cases} \xi \in \mathfrak{b}, \\ \xi \equiv 1 \pmod{\mathfrak{c}_0}, \\ \xi \in D(\mathbf{N}\mathfrak{b} \cdot t) = (\mathbf{N}\mathfrak{b} \cdot t)^{1/N} D(1). \end{cases}$$

We wrote $\xi \equiv 1 \pmod{\mathfrak{c}_0}$ rather than $\xi \equiv 1 \pmod{^* \mathfrak{c}}$ because our third condition, that $\xi \in D$, already guarantees that $\sigma_v \xi > 0$ if v is real, $v|\mathfrak{c}$, since D is contained in $J_k(\infty, \mathfrak{c})$. The two congruences

$$\xi \equiv 0 \pmod{\mathfrak{b}} \qquad \text{and} \qquad \xi \equiv 1 \pmod{\mathfrak{c}_0}$$

define a translation of the lattice (ideal) $\mathfrak{b}\mathfrak{c}_0$ in $\mathbf{R}^N = A_k(\infty)$, because if ξ_0 is one solution of these congruences, then the map

$$\xi \mapsto \xi - \xi_0$$

gives a bijection of the set of solutions of these congruences and $\mathfrak{b}\mathfrak{c}_0$. [Note that $\mathfrak{b}$, $\mathfrak{c}_0$ are relatively prime, and the Chinese remainder theorem applies, i.e. $x \equiv 0 \pmod{\mathfrak{b}\mathfrak{c}_0}$ if and only if $x \equiv 0 \pmod{\mathfrak{b}}$ and $x \equiv 0 \pmod{\mathfrak{c}_0}$.] Thus we have shown:

Lemma 2. *Let the notation be as in Lemma 1, and let L be the lattice obtained by translating $\mathfrak{b}\mathfrak{c}_0$ by one solution of the two congruences above. Then $w_{\mathfrak{c}} j(\mathfrak{K}, t)$ is equal to the number of elements of L lying in*

$$(\mathbf{N}\mathfrak{b} \cdot t)^{1/N} D(1).$$

We are therefore in the situation discussed in Chapter V, §2. Observe that the volume of a fundamental domain for $\mathfrak{b}\mathfrak{c}_0$ in $\mathbf{R}^N$ is the same as the volume of a fundamental domain for the translated lattice L.

Theorem 3. *Let $\mathfrak{c}$ be a cycle of k, and let $\mathfrak{K}$ be a class of $I(\mathfrak{c})$ modulo $P_{\mathfrak{c}}$. Then*

$$j(\mathfrak{K}, t) = \rho_{\mathfrak{c}} t + O(t^{1-1/N}),$$

where

$$\rho_{\mathfrak{c}} = \frac{2^{r_1}(2\pi)^{r_2} R_{\mathfrak{c}}}{w_{\mathfrak{c}}\sqrt{d_k}\, \mathbf{N}\mathfrak{c}},$$

and:

$R_{\mathfrak{c}}$ *is the* $\mathfrak{c}$*-regulator,*

$\mathbf{N}\mathfrak{c} = 2^{s(\mathfrak{c})}\mathbf{N}\mathfrak{c}_0,$

$s(\mathfrak{c})$ *is the number of real* $v|\mathfrak{c}$,

$w_{\mathfrak{c}}$ *is the number of roots of unity in* $U_{\mathfrak{c}}$,

d_k *is the absolute value of the discriminant of* k.

In particular, if $\mathfrak{K}$ is an ordinary ideal class modulo principal ideals, then

$$j(\mathfrak{K}, t) = \frac{2^{r_1}(2\pi)^{r_2} R}{w\sqrt{d_k}}\, t + O(t^{1-1/N}),$$

where R is the regulator, w the number of roots of unity in k, and d_k is as above.

Proof. In Chapter V, §2, we had computed the volume of a fundamental domain for the lattice of an ideal $\mathfrak{b}\mathfrak{c}_0$, and found it equal to

$$2^{-r_2}\mathbf{N}\mathfrak{b}\mathbf{N}\mathfrak{c}_0\sqrt{d_k}.$$

In view of Lemma 2, there remains only to prove Lemma 1, i.e. construct a suitable fundamental domain for V in $J_k(\infty, \mathfrak{c})$, and to prove that

$$\boxed{\operatorname{Vol} D(1) = 2^{r_1 - s(\mathfrak{c})}\pi^{r_2}R_{\mathfrak{c}}.}$$

We shall essentially follow Hecke to do this.

We proceed to construct D. Let

$$g : J_k(\infty, \mathfrak{c}) \to \prod_{v \in S_\infty} \mathbf{R}_v$$

be the homogenized log map given by

$$g(\xi) = \left(\dots, \log \frac{\|\xi_v\|}{\mathbf{N}\xi^{N_v/N}}, \dots\right)_{v \in S_\infty}.$$

As usual, $\|\xi_v\| = |\xi_v|^{N_v}$. Then we see at once that the image of g is contained in the hyperplane H consisting of all elements z such that

$$\sum_{v \in S_\infty} z_v = z_1 + \cdots + z_{r_1 + r_2} = 0.$$

Let $\{\eta_1, \dots, \eta_r\}$ be a set of generators for V and let $g(\eta_i) = y_i$. Then $\{y_1, \dots, y_r\}$ is a basis for a lattice in H, and is the usual image of these units under the log mapping, because for any $\eta \in V$ we have $\mathbf{N}\eta = 1$. We let F be the usual fundamental domain for this lattice in H, namely the set of all linear combinations

$$c_1 y_1 + \cdots + c_r y_r, \qquad 0 \leqq c_q < 1.$$

Let

$$D = g^{-1}(F).$$

It is immediately verified that D is a fundamental domain for the action of V on $J_k(\infty, \mathfrak{c})$ and that for any real $t > 0$ we have $tD = D$. This last condition comes from the fact that

$$\frac{\|t\xi_v\|}{\mathbf{N}(t\xi)^{N_v/N}} = \frac{\|\xi_v\|}{\mathbf{N}\xi^{N_v/N}}.$$

We note that $D(1)$ is bounded, because for each coordinate ξ_v of an element of D, we have

$$|\xi_v| \leqq \mathbf{N}\xi^{1/N}e^{Br},$$

where B is a bound for the elements y_i. Hence if $\xi \in D(1)$, we have

$$|\xi_v| \leqq e^{Br}.$$

We shall now simultaneously see that the boundary of $D(1)$ is $(N-1)$-Lipschitz parametrizable, and compute the volume of $D(1)$.

For this purpose, we use polar coordinates, namely

$$(\rho_i, \theta_i) \qquad (i = 1, \ldots, r_1 + r_2)$$

such that $0 \leqq \rho_i$ for all i, and

$$\begin{aligned} \theta_i &= \pm 1 && \text{if } i = 1, \ldots, r_1 \text{ but } \theta_i = 1 \text{ if } v_i | \mathfrak{c} \\ 0 \leqq \theta_i &\leqq 2\pi && \text{if } i = r_1 + 1, \ldots, r_1 + r_2. \end{aligned}$$

The inverse image of our domain $D(1)$ in the polar coordinate space is described by the conditions

$$(3) \qquad \begin{cases} 0 < \prod_{i=1}^{r_1+r_2} \rho_i^{N_i} \leqq 1 \\ \log \rho_j - \dfrac{1}{N} \log \prod_{i=1}^{r_1+r_2} \rho_i^{N_i} = \sum_{q=1}^{r} c_q \log |\sigma_j \eta_q| \end{cases}$$

with $0 \leqq c_q < 1$ for $q = 1, \ldots, r$. These conditions (3) do not involve any of the angles θ_i.

Let us denote by P the set of $(\rho_1, \ldots, \rho_{r_1+r_2})$ satisfying $0 < \rho_i$ and also satisfying conditions (3), i.e. the inverse image of $D(1)$ in the polar coordinate space. For the Lipschitz parametrizability of the boundary of $D(1)$, it will suffice to show that the boundary of P in $(r_1 + r_2)$-space is $(r_1 + r_2 - 1)$-Lipschitz parametrizable. Furthermore, we have

$$\operatorname{Vol} D(1) = 2^{r_1 - s(\mathfrak{c})}(2\pi)^{r_2} \int \cdots \int \rho_{r_1+1} \cdots \rho_{r_1+r_2} \, d\rho_1 \cdots d\rho_{r_1+r_2}.$$

where the integral is taken over P. We change variables, and consider the cube S in $(r_1 + r_2)$-space with variables $(u, c_1, \ldots, c_r)$, satisfying the inequalities

$$(4) \qquad \begin{cases} 0 < u \leqq 1 \\ 0 \leqq c_q < 1. \end{cases}$$

We have a bijection $f: S \to P$ between this cube S and P, given in one direction by

$$\rho_j = u^{1/N} \exp\left(\sum_{q=1}^{r} c_q \log |\sigma_j \eta_q| \right) = f_j(u, c_1, \ldots, c_r).$$

In the other direction, we have

$$u = \prod_{i=1}^{r_1+r_2} \rho_i^{N_i},$$

and the numbers c_q are uniquely determined by $(\rho_1, \ldots, \rho_{r_1+r_2})$ because the determinant det $|\sigma_j \eta_q| (j, q = 1, \ldots, r)$ does not vanish. This determinant is in fact the $R_{\mathfrak{c}}$-regulator, by definition.

The Jacobian determinant of our map is easily computed. For instance, we find

$$\partial \rho_j / \partial u = \frac{1}{N} \frac{\rho_j}{u} \qquad \text{and} \qquad \partial \rho_j / \partial c_q = \rho_j \log |\sigma_j \eta_q|.$$

Hence the Jacobian determinant of f is

$$\frac{1}{N \rho_{r_1+1} \cdots \rho_{r_1+r_2}} \begin{vmatrix} 1 & \log |\sigma_1 \eta_1| & \cdots & \log |\sigma_1 \eta_r| \\ \vdots & \vdots & & \vdots \\ 1 & \log |\sigma_{r_1+r_2} \eta_1| & \cdots & \log |\sigma_{r_1+r_2} \eta_r| \end{vmatrix}.$$

Adding the first r rows to the last after multiplying the j-th row by N_j, we find that this Jacobian determinant is equal to

$$\frac{1}{\rho_{r_1+1} \cdots \rho_{r_1+r_2}} 2^{-r_2} R_{\mathfrak{c}}.$$

Hence

$$\operatorname{Vol} D(1) = 2^{r_1 - s(\mathfrak{c})} (2\pi)^{r_2} \int_S 2^{-r_2} R_{\mathfrak{c}} \, d\mu = 2^{r_1 - s(\mathfrak{c})} \pi^{r_2} R_{\mathfrak{c}},$$

where μ is Lebesgue measure. The volume of the cube S is of course equal to 1, and we have computed the volume of $D(1)$ as desired.

Finally, as to the parametrizability, only the exponent $1/N$ of u is not continuously differentiable. But this is harmless: We just reparametrize the cube, letting say $u = u_1^N$ with another variable u_1. We then get a continuously differentiable parametrization of the closed cube (compact) onto the closure of P, given by

$$\rho_j = u_1 \exp \left(\sum_{q=1}^{r} c_q \log |\sigma_j \eta_q| \right).$$

It follows immediately that the boundary of P is $(r_1 + r_2 - 1)$-Lipschitz parametrizable, because the boundary of our closed cube trivially has this property. This concludes the proof of Lemma 1, and also the proof of our main result, Theorem 3.

CHAPTER VII

Ideles and Adeles

In classical number theory, one embeds a number field in the Cartesian product of its completions at the archimedean absolute values, i.e. in a Euclidean space. In more recent years (more precisely since Chevalley introduced ideles in 1936, and Weil gave his adelic proof of the Riemann-Roch theorem soon afterwards), it has been found most convenient to take the product over the completions at all absolute values, including the p-adic ones, with a suitable restriction on the components, to be explained below. This chapter merely gives the most elementary facts concerning the ideles and adeles (corresponding to a multiplicative and additive construction respectively), and their topologies. In each case, we prove a certain compactness theorem, and construct a fundamental domain. Although we use the existence of fundamental domains later, we shall not need any explicit form for them.

Given any group scheme over the ring of integers $\mathfrak{o}_k$ of a number field, one can take its points in the adele ring, and one can try to prove similar results. This leads into the arithmetic theory of algebraic groups, and we do not deal with it here. Suffice it to say that the ideles turn out to be the points of the multiplicative group scheme in the adele ring.

§1. *Restricted direct products*

Let k be a number field. For each absolute value v on k (normalized to induce one of the standard absolute values on $\mathbf{Q}$), we have the completion k_v of k which is one of three types of fields: The reals, the complex, or a $\mathfrak{p}$-adic field. We call v by the corresponding name.

The additive group k_v (also written k_v^+) is locally compact, and so is the multiplicative group k_v^*. Each one contains a compact subgroup in the $\mathfrak{p}$-adic case, namely the $\mathfrak{p}$-adic integers or the $\mathfrak{p}$-adic units which are open in k_v^+ and k_v^* respectively.

We shall now describe a general procedure which allows us to take a restricted product of these groups.

Let $\{v\}$ be a set of indices, and for each v, let G_v be a locally compact commutative group. For all but a finite number of v, let H_v be a compact open subgroup of G_v. The **restricted direct product** of the G_v with respect to the H_v is the subgroup G of the direct product consisting of elements all but a finite number of whose components lie in H_v.

If S is a finite set of indices v, including at least all v for which H_v is not defined, then we denote by G_S that subgroup of G for which all components outside S are in H_v. Then

$$G_S = \prod_{v \in S} G_v \times \prod_{v \notin S} H_v$$

is a direct product of locally compact groups, all but a finite number of which are compact. Thus G_S is a locally compact group (product topology), and we make G into a locally compact group by decreeing that each such G_S is an open subgroup.

Each G_v is embedded in G on the v-component, as a closed subgroup.

The restricted product of the additive groups k_v with respect to the local integers $\mathfrak{o}_v$ (defined only when $v = v_\mathfrak{p}$ for some $\mathfrak{p}$) is called the **adele group** of k and is denoted by A_k or simply A. We call A_S the S-**adeles.**

The restricted product of the multiplicative groups k_v^* with respect to the units U_v of $\mathfrak{o}_v$ is called the **idele group** of k and is denoted by J_k or simply J. (The topology on the idele group is *not* the topology induced on it as a subset of the adeles!) We call J_S the S-**ideles.**

We can embed the number field k in the adeles on the diagonal. Since an element α of k is a $\mathfrak{p}$-adic integer for all but a finite number of $\mathfrak{p}$, and since we can view α as embedded in each k_v, the vector $(\alpha, \alpha, \alpha, \ldots)$ is an adele.

Similarly, we can embed the multiplicative group k^* in the ideles because a non-zero element of k is a $\mathfrak{p}$-adic unit for all but a finite number of $\mathfrak{p}$.

We can define the trace on adeles. Let E be a finite extension of k and x an adele of E, $x = (x_w)$, $w \in M_E$. We define its trace $\mathrm{Tr}_k^E(x)$ to have v-component

$$\sum_{w|v} \mathrm{Tr}_w(x_w).$$

Then its trace is an adele of k.

Similarly, we define the norm of an idele $a = (a_w)$ of E to be the idele $N_k^E(a)$ whose v-component is

$$\prod_{w|v} N_w(a_w).$$

According to Corollary 3 of Theorem 2, Chapter II, §1, these definitions are consistent with the embedding of k in A and k^* in J, and the usual definition of norm and trace on field elements. In other words, the following diagrams are commutative:

$$\begin{array}{ccc} & E \overset{\subset}{\rightarrow} A_E & \\ \mathrm{Tr} & \downarrow \quad \downarrow & \mathrm{Tr} \\ & k \underset{\subset}{\rightarrow} A_k & \end{array} \qquad \begin{array}{ccc} & E^* \overset{\subset}{\rightarrow} J_E & \\ N & \downarrow \quad \downarrow & N \\ & k^* \underset{\subset}{\rightarrow} J_k & \end{array}$$

Theorem 1. *The additive group k is embedded as a discrete subgroup of the adeles A. The multiplicative group k^* is embedded as a discrete subgroup of J.*

Proof. Let $\alpha \in k$. To say that α is close to 0 in the adele topology means that $|\alpha|_v \leqq 1$ for all but a finite number of v and $|\alpha|_v$ is very small for a finite set of v. By the product formula, this implies that $\alpha = 0$. Hence 0 is an isolated element of k in A. It follows that k is discrete in A. The same argument applied to an element α of k^* close to 1 shows that k^* is discrete in J.

§2. *Adeles*

We observe that the adeles form a topological ring (with zero divisors) if we define multiplication componentwise. If a is an idele and x is an adele, then ax is an adele. The map

$$h_a : A \rightarrow A$$

given for each idele a by the formula $h_a(x) = ax$ is a topological linear automorphism of the additive group A onto itself.

Let us denote by S_∞ the set of archimedean absolute values in the canonical set of absolute values M_k.

Theorem 2. *We have*

$$k + A_{S_\infty} = A.$$

The factor group A/k is compact.

Proof. The first statement means that given any adele x, there exists an element α of k such that $x - \alpha$ has integral components at all valuations v. This is an easy extension of the Chinese remainder theorem, and can be done for instance as follows. Given $x \in A$, let m be a rational integer such that mx has integral components for all non-archimedean v. Let S be the set of primes $\mathfrak{p}$ of $\mathfrak{o}_k$ such that $\mathfrak{p} | m$. We can find an algebraic integer α in k such that

$$mx \equiv \alpha \pmod{\mathfrak{p}^\nu}$$

for all $\mathfrak{p}$ in S and large ν, by the ordinary Chinese remainder theorem. Then $x - \alpha/m$ will be integral for all $\mathfrak{p}$ if ν is sufficiently large.

The field k can be viewed as embedded in Euclidean space

$$\prod_{v \in S_\infty} k_v = \mathbf{R}^N,$$

and in that case, the integers $\mathfrak{o}_k$ form a lattice of rank $N = [k:\mathbf{Q}]$ in $\mathbf{R}^N$.

To show that A/k is compact, we observe that given $x \in A$ we can translate it by an element of k into A_{S_∞}. We can then translate an element of A_{S_∞} by an integer in $\mathfrak{o}_k$ in such a way that the resulting adele has bounded components at all $v \in S_\infty$ because $\mathfrak{o}_k$ has maximal rank in $\mathbf{R}^N$. Hence every element of A/k has a representative in a compact subset of A_{S_∞}. This proves that A/k is compact.

It is in fact easy to construct a fundamental domain for A/k.

Theorem 3. *Let $\omega_1, \ldots, \omega_N$ be a basis for the integers $\mathfrak{o}_k$ of k over $\mathbf{Z}$. Let F_∞ be the subset of*

$$\prod_{v \in S_\infty} k_v$$

spanned by the vectors $\sum t_i \omega_i$ with $0 \leqq t_i < 1$. Then

$$F = \prod_{v \notin S_\infty} \mathfrak{o}_v \times F_\infty$$

is a fundamental domain for A mod *k.*

Proof. Given $x \in A$ we can bring it into A_{S_∞} by translation with an element of k, uniquely determined up to an element of $\mathfrak{o}_k$. Restricting the components t_i to lie in the half-open interval as above determines this algebraic integer uniquely if we require that the translation have a representative in F.

§3. *Ideles*

In this section we carry out an investigation similar to that of the adeles, but applied to the multiplicative ideles.

We denote by S any finite set of absolute values in M_k containing the set S_∞ of archimedean absolute values.

For each $v \in M_k$, corresponding to a $\mathfrak{p}$-adic valuation, we have the $\mathfrak{p}$-adic integers $\mathfrak{o}_v$ and the units U_v of $\mathfrak{o}_v$. Both of these are compact groups.

Each idele a has components $a_v \in k_v^*$, all but a finite number of which lie in U_v. We define

$$\|a\|_v = \|a_v\|_v$$

and

$$\|a\| = \|a\|_k = \prod_{v \in M_k} \|a\|_v.$$

All but a finite number of terms of this product are equal to 1, so the product is well defined. Furthermore, the map

$$a \mapsto \|a\|$$

defines a homomorphism

$$J \to \mathbf{R}^+$$

of J onto the multiplicative group of positive real numbers. This map is obviously continuous, and its kernel is a closed subgroup of J, denoted by J^0.

By the product formula, k^* is contained in J^0, and is a closed discrete subgroup of J^0.

There is a natural homomorphism of J onto the fractional ideals of $\mathfrak{o}_k$. Indeed, given an idele $a = (a_v)$, each a_v lies in k_v. If v is $\mathfrak{p}$-adic, then we can speak of the order of a_v at $\mathfrak{p}$, namely the integers r_v such that we can write

$$a_v = \pi_v^{r_v} u$$

with a prime element π_v and a unit u in U_v. We let

$$r_v = \operatorname{ord}_{\mathfrak{p}} a.$$

Then $r_v = 1$ for almost all v, and therefore

$$\prod_{\mathfrak{p}} \mathfrak{p}^{\operatorname{ord}_{\mathfrak{p}} a}$$

is a fractional ideal, also denoted by (a). The map

$$a \mapsto (a) = \prod \mathfrak{p}^{\operatorname{ord}_{\mathfrak{p}} a}$$

is a homomorphism of J onto the group of fractional ideals I_k, whose kernel is J_{S_∞}.

Thus we have an isomorphism

$$J/k^*J_{S_\infty} \approx I/P,$$

where P is the group of principal fractional ideals, and I/P is the group of ideal classes. This group is finite, and thus if we enlarge S_∞ to a set S which contains enough primes we can find such an S that

$$J = k^*J_S.$$

An element of k^* viewed as an idele is called a **principal idele.** Its associated ideal is a principal ideal. We therefore have an induced homomorphism from J/k^* onto the ideal classes. The factor group J/k^* will be called the group of **idele classes** and will be denoted by C_k (or C if the reference to k is clear). It contains the closed subgroup $C_k^0 = J^0/k^*$.

Let S be a finite subset of M_k containing S_∞. Then J_S is an open subgroup of J, and J_S^0 is an open subgroup of J^0. The intersection

$$J_S \cap k^*$$

will be denoted by k_S and will be called the group of S-**units.** It is a discrete subgroup of J_S (obvious), and if $S = S_\infty$, then k_S is simply the group of units of the ring of integers $\mathfrak{o}_k$, namely it is the set of elements $\alpha \in k^*$ such that $|\alpha_v| = 1$ for $v \notin S_\infty$. The factor group J_S/k_S is called the group of S-**idele classes,** and is denoted by C_S. We have natural inclusions

$$C_S \to C, \qquad C_S^0 \to C^0$$

and under these inclusions, the smaller group is mapped onto an open and closed subgroup of the larger group. (Immediate verification.) In terms of ideles, the first inclusion can be written

$$\begin{aligned} J_S &\overset{\subset}{\to} J \\ k^* \cap J_S = k_S &\overset{\subset}{\to} k^* \\ J_S/k_S &\overset{\subset}{\to} J/k^* \end{aligned}$$

and we have a topological and algebraic isomorphism

$$J/k^*J_S \approx C/C_S.$$

If $S = S_\infty$, then $J/k^*J_{S_\infty}$ is isomorphic to the group of ideal classes (i.e. fractional ideal classes), and is finite. Thus for any S, the group $J/k^*J_S = C/C_S$, which is a homomorphic image of C/C_{S_∞}, is also finite. In particular, $k^*J_{S_\infty}$ can be viewed as the kernel of the homomorphism of J onto the group of ideal classes. We can interpret k^*J_S in a similar way, as the kernel of the homomorphism onto the group of ideal classes represented by ideals "relatively prime to S" (in the obvious meaning to be attached to these words).

Theorem 4. *The factor group $J^0/k^* = C^0$ is compact. So is J_S^0/k_S for any finite set $S \supset S_\infty$.*

Proof. Let

$$\psi : J \to \mathbf{R}^+$$

be the map which to each idele a associates $\psi(a) = \|a\|$. Then $\psi(k^*) = 1$

and so ψ is defined on J/k^*. Its kernel is C^0. For any real number $\rho > 0$, we let $C^\rho = \psi^{-1}(\rho)$. Then C^ρ is topologically isomorphic to C^0. Indeed, if we consider an idele

$$a_\rho = (\rho^{1/N}, \ldots, \rho^{1/N}, 1, 1, \ldots)$$

having component $\rho^{1/N}$ at all $v \in S_\infty$ and 1 otherwise, then $\psi(a_\rho) = \rho$ and $C^\rho = a_\rho C^0$. It will therefore suffice to prove that C^ρ is compact for some ρ.

Lemma. *There exists a constant $c_1(k) > 0$ such that, for $\rho > c_1$ and all $a \in J^\rho$ there exists an element $\alpha \in k^*$ such that*

$$1 \leqq \|\alpha a\|_v \leqq \rho, \qquad \textit{all } v \in M_k.$$

Proof. According to Theorem 0 of §1, Chapter V, there exists an element $\alpha^{-1} \in k^*$ such that

$$|\alpha^{-1}|_v \leqq |a|_v$$

for all $v \in M_k$. This implies

$$1 \leqq \|a\alpha\|_v$$

for all v, and also for any v,

$$\|\alpha a\|_v = \frac{\prod \|\alpha a\|_w}{\prod_{w \neq v} \|\alpha a\|_w} \leqq \frac{\rho}{1} = \rho,$$

as desired.

If $v = v_\mathfrak{p}$ is $\mathfrak{p}$-adic, then the values $\|\alpha a\|_v$ are of the form

$$\ldots, 1/\mathbf{N}\mathfrak{p}, 1, \mathbf{N}\mathfrak{p}, (\mathbf{N}\mathfrak{p})^2, \ldots$$

and there is only a finite number of $\mathfrak{p}$ such that $\mathbf{N}\mathfrak{p} \leqq \rho$. We take $\rho > c_1$ in the lemma. We can conclude that there is a set S such that

$$\begin{aligned} 1 \leqq \|\alpha a\|_v &\leqq \rho, \qquad v \in S \\ \|\alpha a\|_v &= 1, \qquad v \notin S. \end{aligned}$$

Let X be the subset of J defined by these conditions. Then X is of type

$$\prod_{v \in S} (\text{annulus in } k_v^*) \times \prod_{v \notin S} U_v$$

and each factor is compact. (Each annulus is the annulus between 1 and ρ.) Hence X is compact. In the canonical map

$$J \to C$$

the set X maps onto a compact subset of C which contains C^ρ. Hence C^ρ is compact, as was to be shown. The conclusion for J_S^0/k_S follows at once.

We can recover the unit theorem from the compactness of J^0/k^*, without the arguments at the end of §1, Chapter V. We indicate how this can be done.

Given a set $S \supset S_\infty$, let s be the number of elements of S. We map

$$\log: J_S \to \mathbf{R}^s$$

by the log mapping,

$$(\ldots, a_v, \ldots) \mapsto (\ldots, \log \|a\|_v, \ldots)_{v \in S}.$$

Then J_S^0 maps into the hyperplane determined by the equation

$$\xi_1 + \cdots + \xi_s = 0.$$

Call this hyperplane H^{s-1}. The group k_S maps onto a discrete subgroup of $\mathbf{R}^s$. Indeed, in a bounded region of $\mathbf{R}^s$, there is only a finite number of elements of $\log(k_S)$. (This is clear, since prescribing a bounded region of $\mathbf{R}^s$ in effect defines bounds on the absolute values of an element of k, and hence bounds on the coefficients of the equation which this element satisfies over $\mathbf{Z}$.)

Theorem 5. *The image* $\log(k_S)$ *is a discrete subgroup of rank* $s - 1$ *in* H^{s-1}.

Proof. Note first that H^{s-1} is generated (over $\mathbf{R}$) by $\log(J_S^0)$, because we can pick $s - 1$ coordinates in S arbitrarily, and then adjust the last coordinate (at an archimedean absolute value v) so that the sum of the logs is equal to 0. Let W be the subspace generated by $\log(k_S)$. We have a continuous homomorphism

$$J_S^0/k_S \to H^{s-1}/W,$$

and the image of our homomorphism generates H^{s-1}/W as a vector space over $\mathbf{R}$. But this image is the continuous image of a compact set, hence is compact. It follows that $W = H^{s-1}$, thereby proving our assertion.

The kernel of the log mapping consists exactly of the roots of unity in k, because it is a subgroup consisting of elements all of whose absolute values are bounded, and hence is a finite subgroup.

For computational purposes, we shall now describe how to construct a fundamental domain for the factor group J/k^*.

We select one absolute value v_0 in S_∞, and let S'_∞ be the complement of v_0 in S_∞. Then the restriction of the log mapping to $J_{S_\infty}^0$ is denoted by l.

We see that

$$l : J^0_{S_\infty} \to \mathbf{R}^r$$

maps $J^0_{S_\infty}$ onto Euclidean r-space, where $r = r_1 + r_2 - 1$. The surjectivity follows from the fact that we can select r components of an idele in S_∞ arbitrarily, and then adjust the component at v_0 so as to get an element of J^0.

Let $\{\epsilon_i\}$ $(i = 1, \ldots, r)$ be a basis for the group of units modulo roots of unity. Then the vectors $l(\epsilon_i)$ are a basis of $\mathbf{R}^r$, and for any $b \in J^0_{S_\infty}$ we can write

$$l(b) = \sum z_i l(\epsilon_i)$$

with unique real numbers z_i. Let P be the parallelotope in r-space spanned by the vectors $l(\epsilon_i)$, that is the set of all vectors

$$\sum z_i l(\epsilon_i)$$

with $0 \leqq z_i < 1$. Let w be the number of roots of unity in k, and let

$$E^0 = \text{subset of all } b \text{ in } l^{-1}(P) \text{ such that } 0 \leqq \arg b_{v_0} \leqq \frac{2\pi}{w} \cdot$$

Let h be the order of the ideal class group, and let $b^{(1)}, \ldots, b^{(h)}$ be elements of J^0 such that their associated ideals represent the distinct ideal classes. We then have the following result.

Theorem 6. *The subset E of J^0 consisting of*

$$E^0 b^{(1)} \cup \cdots \cup E^0 b^{(h)}$$

is a fundamental domain for J^0 mod k^*.

Proof. Starting with any idele b in J^0 we can change it into an idele which represents a principal ideal by dividing it by a uniquely determined $b^{(\nu)}$. Multiplication by a field element brings us to an idele representing the unit ideal, and therefore takes the idele into $J^0_{S_\infty}$. A change by units lands us in $l^{-1}(P)$, and finally multiplication by a root of unity adjusts the argument at v_0 to land us in E^0. It is clear that this final representative in E^0 is uniquely determined, thereby proving our theorem.

§4. *Generalized ideal class groups; relations with idele classes*

Let $\mathfrak{c}$ be a cycle of k. If $v|\mathfrak{c}$, we may now interpret $\mathfrak{c}_v$ in the completion k_v, as follows. If $v = v_\mathfrak{p}$ for some prime ideal $\mathfrak{p}$, we let $\mathfrak{m}_\mathfrak{p}$ be the maximal ideal *in the completion* $\mathfrak{o}_v = \mathfrak{o}_\mathfrak{p}$. If v has multiplicity $m(v)$ in $\mathfrak{c}$, we let

$$\mathfrak{c}_v = \mathfrak{m}_\mathfrak{p}^{m(\mathfrak{p})}.$$

Let $v = v_{\mathfrak{p}}$. If $a \in k_v$ and $m(v) > 0$, we define $a \equiv 1 \pmod{^* \mathfrak{c}_v}$ to mean that $a \in \mathfrak{o}_v$ and $a \equiv 1 \pmod{\mathfrak{c}_v}$. If v is real, we define $a \equiv 1 \pmod{^* \mathfrak{c}_v}$ to mean $a > 0$. Thus we can extend the notion mod* $\mathfrak{c}$ to ideles. If a is an idele, we define $a \equiv 1 \pmod{^* \mathfrak{c}}$ to mean that $a_v \equiv 1 \pmod{^* \mathfrak{c}_v}$, for all v.

We let $J_{\mathfrak{c}}$ denote the group of ideles a such that $a \equiv 1 \pmod{^* \mathfrak{c}}$. Then it is clear that $k_{\mathfrak{c}} = J_{\mathfrak{c}} \cap k^*$.

For each $v|\mathfrak{c}$ we let $W_{\mathfrak{c}}(v)$ be the subgroup of k_v^* consisting of those elements $a \in k_v^*$ such that $a \equiv 1 \pmod{^* \mathfrak{c}_v}$. If $v \nmid \mathfrak{c}$, then we let $W_{\mathfrak{c}}(v) = U_v$, the group of local units. We let

$$W_{\mathfrak{c}} = \prod_{v|\mathfrak{c}} W_{\mathfrak{c}}(v) \times \prod_{v \nmid \mathfrak{c}} U_v.$$

By convention, if v is real or complex, we let $U_v = k_v^*$.

We can write

$$J_{\mathfrak{c}} = \prod_{v|\mathfrak{c}} W_{\mathfrak{c}}(v) \times \prod_{v \nmid \mathfrak{c}} k_v^*.$$

If v is real, $v|\mathfrak{c}$, then $W_{\mathfrak{c}}(v) = \mathbf{R}^+$ is the group of reals > 0.

If v is complex, then always $W_{\mathfrak{c}}(v) = \mathbf{C}^*$.

If v is non-archimedean, corresponding to the prime $\mathfrak{p}$, and if v has multiplicity $m > 0$ in $\mathfrak{c}$, then

$$W_{\mathfrak{c}}(v) = 1 + \mathfrak{m}_{\mathfrak{p}}^m,$$

where $\mathfrak{m}_{\mathfrak{p}}$ as before is the maximal ideal in the complete local ring $\mathfrak{o}_v$. We may say that $W_{\mathfrak{c}}(v)$ is a disc of center 1 in the $\mathfrak{p}$-adic field.

It is clear that the collection of $W_{\mathfrak{c}}$ forms a fundamental system of open subgroups of the ideles at the identity. In other words, each $W_{\mathfrak{c}}$ is open, and given an open subgroup of J containing 1, there exists some $\mathfrak{c}$ such that this subgroup contains $W_{\mathfrak{c}}$.

We now consider the relations with idele classes. Any idele class (element of J/k^*) has a representative idele in $J_{\mathfrak{c}}$ for any given $\mathfrak{c}$. Indeed, given $a \in J$, by the approximation theorem, there exists $\alpha \in k^*$ such that $\alpha^{-1}a \in J_{\mathfrak{c}}$. (Select α so that $a - \alpha$ is very close to 1 at all $v|\mathfrak{c}$, and then divide by α.) It follows that we have an isomorphism

$$\boxed{J_{\mathfrak{c}}/k_{\mathfrak{c}} \approx J/k^*}$$

for each $\mathfrak{c}$, corresponding to the diagram

$$\begin{array}{ccc} & J_{\mathfrak{c}} & \to & J \\ & | & \to & | \\ J_{\mathfrak{c}} \cap k^* = & k_{\mathfrak{c}} & \to & k^*. \end{array}$$

We have the natural homomorphism

$$J_{\mathfrak{c}} \xrightarrow{\psi} I(\mathfrak{c})$$
$$a \mapsto (a)$$

which to each idele a associates its ideal (a). It is clear that ψ $(= \psi_{\mathfrak{c}})$ is surjective. Furthermore, we have

$$\psi^{-1}(P_{\mathfrak{c}}) = k_{\mathfrak{c}} W_{\mathfrak{c}}.$$

Indeed, if $a \in J_{\mathfrak{c}}$ and $(a) = (\alpha)$ for some $\alpha \in k_{\mathfrak{c}}$, then $(\alpha^{-1}a) = (1)$, whence $\alpha^{-1}a = b$ is an idele all of whose components are units. It is clear that $b \equiv 1 \pmod{{}^* \mathfrak{c}}$, and by definition, $b \in W_{\mathfrak{c}}$. Thus we have a diagram

$$\begin{array}{ccc} & J_{\mathfrak{c}} & \xrightarrow{\psi} & I(\mathfrak{c}) \\ & | & & | \\ \psi^{-1}(P_{\mathfrak{c}}) = & k_{\mathfrak{c}} W_{\mathfrak{c}} & \rightarrow & P_{\mathfrak{c}}. \end{array}$$

and an isomorphism

$$\boxed{J_{\mathfrak{c}}/k_{\mathfrak{c}} W_{\mathfrak{c}} \approx I(\mathfrak{c})/P_{\mathfrak{c}}.}$$

Thus the generalized ideal class group has been expressed as an idele class group.

We now consider certain intermediate groups between $k_{\mathfrak{c}} W_{\mathfrak{c}}$ and $J_{\mathfrak{c}}$, corresponding to norm groups of finite extensions.

Let K/k be a Galois extension. A cycle $\mathfrak{c}$ of k will be said to be **admissible** for K/k if $W_{\mathfrak{c}}(v)$ is contained in the group of local norms $N_w K_w^*$ for each v and $w|v$ in K. Here we abbreviate

$$N_w = N_{k_v}^{K_w}$$

to be the local norm. Since K/k is Galois, we can also write N_v instead of N_w (because all the w above a given v are conjugate by an element of the Galois group).

If v is archimedean, and $w|v$ in K, we say that w is **unramified** over v if $K_w = k_v$. With this convention, if v is *any* absolute value of M_k, and if K/k is unramified over v, then every unit in U_v is a local norm. This is obvious if v is real or complex, and in the non-archimedean case, it follows from Chapter II, §4, Corollary of Proposition 9.

We may say that a cycle $\mathfrak{c}$ is smaller than a cycle $\mathfrak{c}'$ if $\mathfrak{c}|\mathfrak{c}'$. There is obviously a smallest admissible cycle $\mathfrak{f}$ for K/k. It is such that for non-archimedean v corresponding to $\mathfrak{p}$, the open disc $W_{\mathfrak{f}}(v)$ is the largest disc centered at 1, contained in the local norms at v, for all v. Of course, if v is unramified, then $v \nmid \mathfrak{f}$ and this disc is all of U_v.

Let $\mathfrak{N}(\mathfrak{c}) = \mathfrak{N}(\mathfrak{c}, K/k)$ denote the subgroup of $I(\mathfrak{c})$ consisting of all norms $N_k^K\mathfrak{A}$, where $\mathfrak{A}$ is a fractional ideal of K, prime to $\mathfrak{c}$ (i.e. by definition, relatively prime to every prime ideal $\mathfrak{P}$ of K lying above some prime ideal $\mathfrak{p}|\mathfrak{c}$). The subgroup

$$P_{\mathfrak{c}}\mathfrak{N}(\mathfrak{c}) \subset I(\mathfrak{c})$$

is of great importance in class field theory. It is useful only if $\mathfrak{c}$ is admissible for K/k. In that case, we have:

Theorem 7. *Let $\mathfrak{c}$ be admissible for K/k, and let $\mathfrak{f}$ be the smallest admissible cycle for K/k. Then the inclusion*

$$I(\mathfrak{c}) \to I(\mathfrak{f})$$

induces an isomorphism

$$I(\mathfrak{c})/P_{\mathfrak{c}}\mathfrak{N}(\mathfrak{c}) \approx I(\mathfrak{f})/P_{\mathfrak{f}}\mathfrak{N}(\mathfrak{f}). \qquad \begin{array}{ccc} I(\mathfrak{c}) & \to & I(\mathfrak{f}) \\ | & & | \\ P_{\mathfrak{c}}\mathfrak{N}(\mathfrak{c}) & \to & P_{\mathfrak{f}}\mathfrak{N}(\mathfrak{f}) \end{array}$$

We have $P_{\mathfrak{f}}\mathfrak{N}(\mathfrak{f}) \cap I(\mathfrak{c}) = P_{\mathfrak{c}}\mathfrak{N}(\mathfrak{c})$. If $\mathfrak{c}$ is divisible only by the same $\mathfrak{p}$ such that $\mathfrak{p}|\mathfrak{f}$, then $P_{\mathfrak{f}}\mathfrak{N}(\mathfrak{f}) = P_{\mathfrak{c}}\mathfrak{N}(\mathfrak{f})$.

Proof. Let $\mathfrak{a} \in I(\mathfrak{c})$ be such that $\mathfrak{a} = (\alpha)N_k^K\mathfrak{b}$ with some $\mathfrak{b}$ in $I(\mathfrak{f}, K)$ prime to $\mathfrak{f}$, and some $\alpha \in k^*$ such that $\alpha \equiv 1 \pmod{^* \mathfrak{f}}$. We express α as a local norm at all $v|f$, say

$$\alpha = N_{k_v}^{K_w}\gamma_w$$

for $w|v$, $v|\mathfrak{f}$. We can take γ_w to be a unit. By the approximation theorem, there exists $\gamma \in K$ such that $N_k^K\gamma$ is very close to α at all $v|\mathfrak{f}$. (For instance, take γ close to γ_{w_0} for one $w_0|v$, and γ close to 1 for the other $w|v$, and each $v|\mathfrak{f}$.) We can also select γ such that $\operatorname{ord}_{\mathfrak{P}} \gamma = -\operatorname{ord}_{\mathfrak{P}} \mathfrak{b}$ for all $\mathfrak{P}|\mathfrak{p}$, $\mathfrak{p}|\mathfrak{c}$, $\mathfrak{p} \nmid \mathfrak{f}$. Then

$$\alpha N_k^K\gamma^{-1}$$

is close to 1 at all $v|\mathfrak{f}$, $\gamma\mathfrak{b}$ is prime to $\mathfrak{c}$, and

$$\mathfrak{a} = (\alpha N_k^K\gamma^{-1})N_k^K((\gamma)\mathfrak{b}).$$

Since $\mathfrak{a}$ is prime to $\mathfrak{c}$, it follows that $\alpha N_k^K\gamma^{-1}$ is a v-unit at all $v|\mathfrak{c}$. We use the approximation theorem again, and the fact that every v-unit is a norm if $v|\mathfrak{c}$ but $v\nmid\mathfrak{f}$ to find an element γ_1 in K such that γ_1 is a v-unit for all $v|\mathfrak{c}$, and

$$\alpha_1 = \alpha N_k^K\gamma^{-1}N_k^K\gamma_1^{-1}$$

is very close to 1 at all $v|\mathfrak{c}$, specifically $\alpha_1 \equiv 1 \pmod{^* \mathfrak{c}}$. Then

$$\mathfrak{a} = (\alpha_1)N_k^K((\gamma\gamma_1)\mathfrak{b}),$$

so that $\mathfrak{a} \in P_\mathfrak{c}\mathfrak{N}(\mathfrak{c})$, thereby proving both assertions of the theorem.

We are interested also in representing the factor group $I(\mathfrak{c})/P_\mathfrak{c}\mathfrak{N}(\mathfrak{c})$ as a factor group of the ideles. We have a diagram

$$\begin{array}{ccc} J_\mathfrak{c} & \xrightarrow{\psi} & I(\mathfrak{c}) \\ | & & | \\ \psi^{-1}(P_\mathfrak{c}\mathfrak{N}(\mathfrak{c})) & \rightarrow & P_\mathfrak{c}\mathfrak{N}(\mathfrak{c}) \\ | & & | \\ k_\mathfrak{c}W_\mathfrak{c} & \rightarrow & P_\mathfrak{c} \end{array}$$

Let $J_K(1, \mathfrak{c})$ denote the subgroup of K-ideles consisting of those ideles $A \in J_K$ having component $A_w = 1$ at all $w|v$, and $v|\mathfrak{c}$. We contend that

$$\boxed{\psi^{-1}(P_\mathfrak{c}\mathfrak{N}(\mathfrak{c})) = k_\mathfrak{c}W_\mathfrak{c}N_k^K J_K(1, \mathfrak{c}).}$$

To see this, let a be an idele in $J_\mathfrak{c}$ such that $(a) = (\alpha)N_k^K\mathfrak{A}$ for some $\alpha \in k_\mathfrak{c}$ and some ideal $\mathfrak{A}$ of K relatively prime to $\mathfrak{c}$. Let $A \in J_K$ have component $A_w = 1$ for all $w|v$ and $v|\mathfrak{c}$, for all archimedean w, and for all $w_\mathfrak{P}$ such that $\mathfrak{P}$ is relatively prime to $\mathfrak{A}$. If $\mathfrak{P}$ occurs in the factorization of $\mathfrak{A}$, we let $A_{w_\mathfrak{P}}$ have the same order at $\mathfrak{P}$ as $\mathfrak{A}$ itself. Then from the definitions, we see that

$$(N_k^K A) = N_k^K \mathfrak{A}.$$

Therefore $(\alpha N_k^K A) = (a)$, and hence $\alpha N_k^K A$ differs from a by an element of $W_\mathfrak{c}$. This proves one inclusion of our contention, and the reverse inclusion is obvious. We obtain an isomorphism

$$J_\mathfrak{c}/k_\mathfrak{c}W_\mathfrak{c}N_k^K J_K(1, \mathfrak{c}) \approx I(\mathfrak{c})/P_\mathfrak{c}\mathfrak{N}(\mathfrak{c}).$$

On the other hand, corresponding to the inclusion $J_\mathfrak{c} \subset J$, we contend that

$$\boxed{k^* N_k^K J_K \cap J_\mathfrak{c} = \psi^{-1}(P_\mathfrak{c}\mathfrak{N}(\mathfrak{c})),}$$

so that we have the diagram

$$\begin{array}{ccc} J_\mathfrak{c} & \xrightarrow{\text{inc.}} & J \\ | & & | \\ \psi^{-1}(P_\mathfrak{c}\mathfrak{N}(\mathfrak{c})) & \rightarrow & k^* N_k^K J_K \\ | & & | \\ k_\mathfrak{c}W_\mathfrak{c} & \rightarrow & k^* W_\mathfrak{c}. \end{array}$$

The verification uses the same type of trivial technique as above, and the assumption that $W_{\mathfrak{c}} \subset N_k^K J_K$. We leave it to the reader. We then obtain an isomorphism of the corresponding factor groups, which we summarize in a theorem.

Theorem 8. *Let K/k be a Galois extension. Let $\mathfrak{c}$ be admissible for K/k. Then we have an isomorphism*

$$J/k^*N_k^K J_K \approx I(\mathfrak{c})/P_{\mathfrak{c}}\mathfrak{N}(\mathfrak{c}).$$

The isomorphism is induced by the isomorphism

$$J_{\mathfrak{c}}/k_{\mathfrak{c}} \approx J/k^*,$$

followed by the ideal map $b \mapsto (b)$ of $J_{\mathfrak{c}}$ onto $I(\mathfrak{c})$.

Thus in Theorem 7, to each idele a we first select an idele b in the same coset mod k^* such that $b \in J_{\mathfrak{c}}$. We then map b on its ideal (b). We have $(b) \in P_{\mathfrak{c}}\mathfrak{N}(\mathfrak{c})$ if and only if $a \in k^*N_k^K J_K$. In this manner we have represented the idele factor group $J/k^*N_k^K J_K$ as an ideal class factor group. Observe that the norm map applies to the idele classes, and that

$$C_k/N_k^K C_K \approx J_k/k^*N_k^K J_K.$$

Thus the factor group in Theorem 7 can also be viewed as an idele class group. We shall study it especially in the class field theory, and we shall find that if K/k is abelian, then the Galois group $G(K/k)$ is isomorphic to this factor group. We shall also exhibit the isomorphism explicitly.

Example. If we reconsider the example given at the end of Chapter VI, §1, we take $k = \mathbf{Q}$ and let $K = \mathbf{Q}(\zeta_m)$ be the field obtained by adjoining a primitive m-th root of unity to $\mathbf{Q}$. Let $\mathfrak{c} = mv_\infty$. Then it is easily verified that $P_{\mathfrak{c}}\mathfrak{N}(\mathfrak{c})$ is simply the unit class in $(\mathbf{Z}/m\mathbf{Z})^*$, i.e. is represented by the arithmetic progression of positive integers $\equiv 1 \pmod m$. To see this, let p be a prime number, $p \nmid m$, so that p is unramified in K. Let

$$(p) = \mathfrak{p}_1 \ldots \mathfrak{p}_s$$

be the factorization in K, with $\mathfrak{p} = \mathfrak{p}_1$. Let $G_{\mathfrak{p}}$ be the decomposition group of $\mathfrak{p}$ in G. Then $G_{\mathfrak{p}}$ is cyclic, generated by the automorphism σ such that

$$\sigma\alpha \equiv \alpha^p \pmod{\mathfrak{p}}, \qquad (\alpha \in \mathfrak{o}_K)$$

and σ is determined by its effect on ζ_m, which is

$$\sigma : \zeta_m \mapsto \zeta_m^p.$$

Thus the order of σ is the order of $p \pmod m$ in $(\mathbf{Z}/m\mathbf{Z})^*$. If f is the local degree, so that $\mathbf{N}\mathfrak{p} = p^f$, then

$$fs = \varphi(m) = [K : \mathbf{Q}],$$

and f is precisely equal to this order. In particular,

$$p^f \equiv 1 \pmod{m},$$

thus showing that the norms of ideals lie in the unit class.

§5. *Embedding of k_v^* in the idele classes*

We consider the idele class group $C_k = J_k/k^*$. We had embedded the multiplicative group of positive reals $\mathbf{R}^+$ in $J = J_k$, in §3. Let $N = [k : \mathbf{Q}]$. If $\rho \in \mathbf{R}^+$, we denote by a_ρ the idele

$$a_\rho = (\rho^{1/N}, \ldots, \rho^{1/N}, 1, 1, \ldots)$$

or its idele class (to be made clear by the context). The map

$$f : \mathbf{R}^+ \times C_k^0 \to C_k$$

such that

$$(\rho, b) \mapsto a_\rho b$$

is then an algebraic isomorphism of the product onto C_k, and it is obviously continuous. In fact, it is also bicontinuous. This is essentially trivial. If an idele class $\bar{a}$ is close to 1 in C_k, then it can be represented by an idele a close to 1 at a large set of absolute values, and in particular at all $v \in S_\infty$. Thus if $\|a\| = \rho$, then a_ρ is close to 1, and $a^{-1}\bar{a}$ is close to 1 also, thus proving that the inverse of our isomorphism is continuous at 1, whence continuous.

Let v be an absolute value on k. We can embed k_v^* in the ideles, on the v-component, namely if $c \in k_v^*$, then we identify c with the idele

$$c = (\ldots, 1, 1, c, 1, 1, \ldots)$$

having c at the v-component, and 1 at all other components. The composite map

$$k_v^* \to J \to J/k^* = C_k$$

is then obviously a continuous injective homomorphism of k_v^* into C_k. *It is again verified easily that it is a topological embedding, i.e. is bicontinuous.* In fact let v be $\mathfrak{p}$-adic. We can write k_v^* as a direct product

$$k_v^* \to \{\pi\} \times U_v,$$

where $\{\pi\}$ is the cyclic group generated by a prime element π in k_v, and

U_v is the group of local units in k_v. The cyclic group $\{\pi\}$ has the discrete topology, so that

$$k_v^* \approx \mathbf{Z} \times U_v.$$

If the idele class of an element $\pi^m u$ $(u \in U_v)$ is close to 1 in C_k then $\|\pi^m u\| = \|\pi^m u\|_v$ must be close to 1, and this proves the bicontinuity at 1, whence everywhere since our composite map is an algebraic isomorphism between k_v^* and its image in C_k.

Under the isomorphism of C_k with $\mathbf{R}^+ \times C_k^0$, we see that $\{\pi\}$ corresponds to a discrete cyclic subgroup of $\mathbf{R}^+$, namely the subgroup generated by $\mathbf{N}\mathfrak{p}$, and U_v corresponds to a subgroup of C_k^0. Recall that both U_v and C_k^0 are compact. *Thus k_v^* is embedded as a closed subgroup of C_k.*

The situation when v is archimedean is similar. If, say, v is complex, we write

$$k_v^* = \mathbf{C}^* = \mathbf{R}^+ \times \mathbf{C}_1,$$

where $\mathbf{C}_1$ is the multiplicative group of complex numbers of absolute value 1. The argument proceeds as before.

Warning. If S is a finite set of absolute values on k, then one obtains similarly a continuous injective map

$$\prod_{v \in S} k_v^* \to C_k,$$

but this map is **not** bicontinuous, i.e. is **not** a topological embedding if S has more than one element.

§6. *Galois operation on ideles and idele classes*

Let k be a number field as before, and let

$$\sigma : k \to \sigma k$$

be an isomorphism. Each $v \in M_k$ is then mapped on an absolute value $\sigma v \in M_{\sigma k}$, defined by

$$|\sigma x|_{\sigma v} = |x|_v, \qquad x \in k,$$

or

$$|y|_{\sigma v} = |\sigma^{-1} y|_v, \qquad y \in \sigma k.$$

Then σ induces an isomorphism on the completions, uniquely determined by continuity, and again denoted by σ, namely

$$\sigma : k_v \to (\sigma k)_{\sigma v}.$$

We shall apply this to the case of a finite extension E/k. Consider the product

$$\prod_{w \mid v} E_w$$

which occurs as a partial product in the adeles of E. (Putting a star on E would give the same discussion for ideles.) If σ is an isomorphism of E over k, i.e. leaving k fixed, then σ operates on the above product in a natural way, namely if

$$a = \{a_w\}_{w \mid v} \in \prod_{w \mid v} E_w,$$

then

$$(\sigma a)_{\sigma w} = \sigma(a_w),$$

and thus σ induces an isomorphism

$$\prod_{w \mid v} E_w \to \prod_{w' \mid v} (\sigma E)_{w'},$$

where w' ranges over those elements of $M_{\sigma E}$ such that $w' | v$.

In particular, suppose that K is Galois over k and let $\sigma \in G(K/k) = G$. Then σ permutes those $w \in M_K$ such that $w | v$, and hence σ induces an automorphism

$$\prod_{w \mid v} K_w \to \prod_{w \mid v} K_w.$$

The group G permutes the factors K_w transitively, because the elements of G permute the absolute values $w | v$ transitively. The same applies to other products taken for $w | v$, for instance the product

$$\prod_{w \mid v} U_w,$$

where U_w is the group of local units in K_w, in the case when v is $\mathfrak{p}$-adic. This product in that case can also be written

$$\prod_{\mathfrak{P} \mid \mathfrak{p}} U_{\mathfrak{P}}.$$

We shall study this type of operation in greater detail in Chapter IX, §1.

In the operation of G on such a product as

$$\prod_{w \mid v} K_w,$$

the subgroup of G leaving one factor K_w invariant is the subgroup G_w, i.e. the **decomposition group** of w, consisting of all $\sigma \in G$ such that $\sigma w = w$. We had already considered that subgroup in the context of prime ideals, Chapter I, §5.

The above discussion applies to ideles, because the ideles of K are the unions of the subgroups

$$\prod_{v \in S} \prod_{w|v} K_w^* \times \prod_{v \notin S} \prod_{w|v} U_w,$$

where S ranges over finite subsets of M_k, and each partial factor taken over $w|v$ is G-invariant.

Finally, we note that G leaves K^* invariant, and hence induces an automorphism of the idele class group J_K/K^*. Since the operation of an element $\sigma \in G$ on J_K is obviously bicontinuous, it follows that the automorphism induced by σ on C_K is also a topological isomorphism.

CHAPTER VIII

Elementary Properties of the Zeta Function and *L*-series

§1. Lemmas on Dirichlet series

We recall the formula for summation by parts. If $\{a_n\}$ and $\{b_n\}$ are sequences of complex numbers, and if we let

$$A_n = a_1 + \cdots + a_n$$
$$B_n = b_1 + \cdots + b_n$$

be the partial sums, then

$$\sum_{n=1}^{N} a_n b_n = A_N b_N + \sum_{n=1}^{N-1} A_n(b_n - b_{n+1}).$$

We shall consider series

$$\sum_{n=1}^{\infty} \frac{a_n}{n^s},$$

where $\{a_n\}$ is a sequence of complex numbers, and s is a complex variable. We write $s = \sigma + it$ with σ, t real.

Theorem 1. *If the Dirichlet series* $\sum a_n/n^s$ *converges for some* $s = s_0$, *then it converges for any* s *with* $\mathrm{Re}(s) > \sigma_0 = \mathrm{Re}(s_0)$, *uniformly on any compact subset of this region.*

Proof. Write $n^s = n^{s_0}n^{(s-s_0)}$, and sum the following series by parts:

$$\sum \frac{a_n}{n^{s_0}} \frac{1}{n^{(s-s_0)}}.$$

If $P_n(s_0) = \sum_{m=1}^{n} a_m/m^{s_0}$, then the tail ends of this Dirichlet series are given for $n > m$ by

$$\sum_{k=m+1}^{n} \frac{a_k}{k^{s_0}} \frac{1}{k^{s-s_0}} = \frac{P_n(s_0)}{n^{s-s_0}} + \sum_{k=m+1}^{n-1} P_k(s_0)\left[\frac{1}{k^{s-s_0}} - \frac{1}{(k+1)^{s-s_0}}\right].$$

We have

$$\frac{1}{k^{s-s_0}} - \frac{1}{(k+1)^{s-s_0}} = (s - s_0)\int_k^{k+1} \frac{1}{x^{s-s_0+1}}\,dx,$$

which we estimate easily in absolute value. If $\delta > 0$ and $\mathrm{Re}(s) \geqq \sigma_0 + \delta$, then we conclude that our tail end is small uniformly if $|s - s_0|$ is bounded. This proves the theorem.

Assuming that the Dirichlet series converges for some s, if σ_0 is the smallest real number such that the series converges for $\mathrm{Re}(s) > \sigma_0$, then we call σ_0 the **abscissa of convergence,** and we see that the series converges in the half plane to the right of the line $\sigma = \sigma_0$, but does not converge for any s with $\sigma < \sigma_0$.

If the Dirichlet series converges for $s_1 = \sigma_1 + it_1$, then we must have

$$a_n = O(n^{\sigma_1})$$

because the n-th term of the series a_n/n^{s_1} tends to 0. It follows in particular that the Dirichlet series converges absolutely and uniformly for

$$\mathrm{Re}(s) \geqq \sigma_1 + 1 + \delta,$$

if $\delta > 0$. This is immediately seen by comparison with the series $\sum 1/n^{1+\delta}$. We shall now derive a similar criterion using an estimate for the partial sums of the coefficients of the series.

Theorem 2. *Assume that there exists a number C and $\sigma_1 > 0$ such that*

$$|A_n| = |a_1 + \cdots + a_n| \leqq Cn^{\sigma_1}$$

for all n. Then the abscissa of convergence of $\sum a_n/n^s$ is $\leqq \sigma_1$.

Proof. Summing by parts, we find for $n \geqq m$,

$$\begin{aligned} P_n(s) - P_m(s) &= A_n \frac{1}{n^s} + \sum_{k=m+1}^{n-1} A_k \left[\frac{1}{k^s} - \frac{1}{(k+1)^s}\right] \\ &= A_n \frac{1}{n^s} + \sum_{k=m+1}^{n-1} A_k s \int_k^{k+1} \frac{1}{x^{s+1}}\,dx. \end{aligned}$$

Let $\delta > 0$ and let $\mathrm{Re}(s) \geqq \sigma_1 + \delta$. Then

$$\left| A_k \int_k^{k+1} \frac{1}{x^{s+1}}\,dx \right| \leqq C \int_k^{k+1} \frac{1}{x^{\sigma-\sigma_1+1}}\,dx$$

whence taking the sum from $k = m + 1$ to ∞ we find

$$|P_n(s) - P_m(s)| \leqq \frac{C}{n^\delta} + C\frac{|s|}{\delta}\frac{1}{(m+1)^\delta}.$$

This proves our theorem.

Let

$$\zeta(s) = \sum \frac{1}{n^s}.$$

Applying Theorem 2 shows that $\zeta(s)$ is analytic in s, defined by the series for $\mathrm{Re}(s) > 1$. Namely we have $\sigma_1 = 1$ in this case. Furthermore, we have for s real > 1:

$$\frac{1}{s-1} \leqq \int_1^\infty \frac{1}{x^s}\,dx \leqq \zeta(s) \leqq 1 + \frac{1}{s-1}.$$

This follows immediately by comparing the infinite sum with the integral. Hence for $s > 1$, we have

$$1 \leqq (s-1)\zeta(s) \leqq s.$$

We shall prove in a moment that ζ can be continued analytically to the line $\sigma = 0$, and that it is analytic except possibly for a singularity at $s = 1$. The preceding estimate then implies that ζ has a simple pole at $s = 1$, with residue equal to 1.

To get the analytic continuation, we use a simple trick, namely we consider the alternating zeta function

$$\zeta_2(s) = 1 - \frac{1}{2^s} + \frac{1}{3^s} - \cdots.$$

The partial sum of the coefficients of this Dirichlet series are equal to 0 or 1, and therefore are bounded. Theorem 2 shows that $\zeta_2(s)$ is analytic for $\mathrm{Re}(s) > 0$. But

$$\frac{2}{2^s}\zeta(s) + \zeta_2(s) = \zeta(s),$$

and therefore

$$\zeta_2(s) = \left(1 - \frac{1}{2^{s-1}}\right)\zeta(s).$$

By analytic continuation, this already gives an analytic continuation of ζ to the line $\sigma = 0$, and we must still show that there are no poles except at

$s = 1$. This is easily done by considering

$$\zeta_r(s) = \frac{1}{1^s} + \frac{1}{2^s} + \cdots + \frac{1}{(r-1)^s} - \frac{(r-1)}{r^s} + \frac{1}{(r+1)^s} + \cdots$$

with $r = 2, 3, \ldots$. Then just as for $r = 2$, we see that the partial sums of the coefficients of ζ_r are bounded by r, whence ζ_r is analytic for $\mathrm{Re}(s) > 0$. Furthermore, by a similar argument as before, we get

$$\zeta(s) = \frac{\zeta_r(s)}{1 - \dfrac{1}{r^{s-1}}}.$$

From the expression with ζ_2, we see that the only possible poles (other than at $s = 1$) occur when $2^{s-1} = 1$, or equivalently, when

$$s = \frac{2\pi i n}{\log 2} + 1$$

for some integer n. Using ζ_3, we see in the same way that the only such poles occur at

$$s = \frac{2\pi i m}{\log 3} + 1.$$

At any such pole we have $3^n = 2^m$, which is impossible. This proves:

Theorem 3. *The zeta function $\zeta(s)$ is analytic for* $\mathrm{Re}(s) > 0$ *except for a simple pole at $s = 1$, with residue 1. If $\delta > 0$, the series $\sum 1/n^s$ for $\zeta(s)$ converges uniformly and absolutely in the region* $\mathrm{Re}(s) \geqq 1 + \delta$.

For applications to the L-series, we consider a special case of Theorem 2, in which the hypothesis is made more precise.

Theorem 4. *Let $\{a_n\}$ be a sequence of complex numbers, with partial sums A_n. Let $0 \leqq \sigma_1 < 1$, and assume that there is a complex number ρ, and $C > 0$ such that for all n we have*

$$|A_n - n\rho| \leqq Cn^{\sigma_1},$$

or in other words, $A_n = n\rho + O(n^{\sigma_1})$. Then the function

$$f(s) = \sum a_n/n^s$$

defined by the Dirichlet series for $\mathrm{Re}(s) > 1$ *has an analytic continuation to* $\mathrm{Re}(s) > \sigma_1$ *where it is analytic except for a simple pole with residue ρ at $s = 1$.*

Proof. The proof is obtained by considering $f(s) - \rho\zeta(s)$, and applying Theorems 2 and 3 directly.

§2. *Zeta function of a number field*

We have for $\mathrm{Re}(s) > 1$:

$$\zeta(s) = \prod_p \frac{1}{1 - \dfrac{1}{p^s}},$$

the product being taken over all prime numbers p. To see this, recall that if z is a complex number with $|z| < 1$, then $\log(1 + z)$ is defined by the usual series, and $|\log(1 + z)| \leqq |z|$. Thus the sum

$$\sum_p \log\left(1 - \frac{1}{p^s}\right)$$

converges absolutely for $\mathrm{Re}(s) > 1$, and the infinite product converges likewise. Expanding out the series for the log, and reordering the terms, we find that $\zeta(s)$ is given by the infinite product, using the unique factorization of a positive integer into prime powers. Furthermore, we have the expression

$$\log \zeta(s) = \sum_{p,m} \frac{1}{mp^{ms}},$$

the sum being taken over all prime numbers p and all integers $m \geqq 1$. Observe that the sum

$$\sum_{p,m\geqq 2} \frac{1}{mp^{ms}}$$

converges uniformly and absolutely for $\mathrm{Re}(s) \geqq \frac{1}{2} + \delta$, $\delta > 0$. Hence only the sum

$$\sum_p \frac{1}{p^s}$$

contributes to the singularity at $s = 1$.

We use the notation $f(s) \sim g(s)$ to mean that two functions which have a singularity at 1 differ by a function which is analytic at 1. With this notation, we have

$$\zeta(s) \sim \frac{1}{s - 1},$$

and

$$\log \zeta(s) \sim \sum_p \frac{1}{p^s} \sim \log \frac{1}{s - 1}.$$

Next consider a number field k with $[k:\mathbf{Q}] = N$. If $\mathfrak{p}$ is a prime ideal of k and $\mathfrak{p}|p$, and if $\mathbf{N}\mathfrak{p} = p^{f_\mathfrak{p}}$ where $f_\mathfrak{p} = \deg \mathfrak{p}$ is the degree of the residue class field extension, then we have

$$\sum_{\mathfrak{p}|p} f_{\mathfrak{p}} \leqq N.$$

We define the Dedekind zeta function

$$\zeta_k(s) = \prod_{\mathfrak{p}} \frac{1}{1 - \dfrac{1}{\mathbf{N}\mathfrak{p}^s}}\cdot$$

The sum of the logarithms of the terms yields formally

$$\log \zeta_k(s) = \sum_{\mathfrak{p},m} \frac{1}{m\mathbf{N}\mathfrak{p}^{ms}}\cdot$$

For $\mathrm{Re}(s) = \sigma > 1$, this sum is dominated by

$$\sum_{\mathfrak{p},m} \frac{N}{m\mathfrak{p}^{m\sigma}} \leqq N \log \zeta(\sigma).$$

Consequently the sum for the logarithms of the terms of the infinite product for $\zeta_k(s)$ converges absolutely and uniformly for $\sigma \geqq 1 + \delta$, just like the case of $\zeta_{\mathbf{Q}} = \zeta$. We can then exponentiate and multiply out the product. We find the additive expression

$$\zeta_k(s) = \sum_{\mathfrak{a}} \frac{1}{\mathbf{N}\mathfrak{a}^s}$$

taken over all ideals $\mathfrak{a}$ of k. Just as with $\zeta_{\mathbf{Q}}(s)$, we also find

$$\log \zeta_k(s) \sim \sum_{\deg \mathfrak{p}=1} \frac{1}{\mathbf{N}\mathfrak{p}^s}\cdot$$

So far, we have used only the analytic and very simple statements of §1. We shall use the somewhat more refined results of Chapter VI, §3, Theorem 3. For every ideal class $\mathfrak{K}$ of the ideal class group I/P we define

$$\zeta(s, \mathfrak{K}) = \sum_{\mathfrak{a}\in\mathfrak{K}} \frac{1}{\mathbf{N}\mathfrak{a}^s}\cdot$$

Then

$$\zeta_k(s) = \sum_{\mathfrak{K}} \zeta(s, \mathfrak{K}).$$

If we write

$$\zeta(s, \mathfrak{K}) = \sum \frac{a_n}{n^s},$$

then the partial sum $A_n = a_1 + \cdots + a_n$ is equal to $j(\mathfrak{K}, n)$, the number of ideals in $\mathfrak{K}$ with $\mathbf{N}\mathfrak{a} \leqq n$. Combining the result of Chapter VI, §3,

Theorem 3 and Theorem 4 of the preceding section, we find:

Theorem 5. *Let k be a number field, $[k:\mathbf{Q}] = N$, and let $\mathfrak{K}$ be an ideal class. Then $\zeta(s, \mathfrak{K})$ is analytic for $\mathrm{Re}(s) > 1 - 1/N$, except for a simple pole at $s = 1$, with residue ρ, given by*

$$\rho = \frac{2^{r_1}(2\pi)^{r_2}R}{w\sqrt{d_k}}.$$

The same holds for $\zeta_k(s)$, except that the residue is equal to $h\rho$, where h is the class number.

Similarly, using the estimates for the number of ideals in a generalized ideal class, we obtain:

Theorem 5c. *Let $\mathfrak{c}$ be a cycle of k, and let $\mathfrak{K}$ be a class of $I(\mathfrak{c})$ mod $P_\mathfrak{c}$. Then $\zeta(s, \mathfrak{K})$ is analytic for $\mathrm{Re}(s) > 1 - 1/N$, except for a simple pole at $s = 1$ with residue $\rho_\mathfrak{c}$ given in Theorem 3, Chapter VI, §3, depending only on $\mathfrak{c}$ but not on $\mathfrak{K}$.*

With a notation which will not be misleading because of the choice of letters, we can define

$$\zeta_k(s, \mathfrak{c}) = \sum_{(\mathfrak{a},\mathfrak{c})=1} \frac{1}{\mathbf{N}\mathfrak{a}^s}$$

with the sum taken over those ideals prime to $\mathfrak{c}$. Then

$$\zeta_k(s, \mathfrak{c}) = \prod_{\mathfrak{p}\nmid\mathfrak{c}} \frac{1}{1 - \dfrac{1}{\mathbf{N}\mathfrak{p}^s}},$$

the product taken over those prime ideals $\mathfrak{p}$ not dividing $\mathfrak{c}$. We have

$$\zeta_k(s, \mathfrak{c}) = \sum_{\mathfrak{K}\in I(\mathfrak{c})/P_\mathfrak{c}} \zeta(s, \mathfrak{K}),$$

and this yields immediately:

Corollary. *The function $\zeta_k(s, \mathfrak{c})$ is analytic for $\mathrm{Re}(s) > 1 - 1/N$, except for a simple pole at $s = 1$ with residue $h_\mathfrak{c}\rho_\mathfrak{c}$, where $h_\mathfrak{c}$ is the order of the group $I(\mathfrak{c})/P_\mathfrak{c}$.*

The product for $\zeta_k(s, \mathfrak{c})$ differs from the product for $\zeta_k(s)$ by only a finite number of factors, corresponding to those $\mathfrak{p}|\mathfrak{c}$. This yields a relation between ρ and $\rho_{\mathfrak{c}}$, namely

$$h\rho = h_{\mathfrak{c}}\rho_{\mathfrak{c}} \prod_{\mathfrak{p}|\mathfrak{c}} \frac{1}{1 - \dfrac{1}{\mathbf{N}\mathfrak{p}}}\cdot$$

Furthermore, this finite product does not affect the singularity of the logarithm at $s = 1$, and hence we get:

Theorem 6. *The equivalence $\sim$ denoting the property of differing by a function analytic at $s = 1$, we have:*

$$\log \frac{1}{s-1} \sim \log \zeta_k(s) \sim \sum_{\mathfrak{p}} \frac{1}{\mathbf{N}\mathfrak{p}^s} \sim \sum_{\deg \mathfrak{p}=1} \frac{1}{\mathbf{N}\mathfrak{p}^s}\cdot$$

§3. *The L-series*

Let G be a finite abelian group. The character group $\hat{G}$ consists of all homomorphisms of G into the multiplicative group of roots of unity. If χ is a character of G, then

$$\sum_{x\in G} \chi(x) = \begin{cases} 0 & \text{if } \chi \neq 1 \\ (G:1) & \text{if } \chi = 1. \end{cases}$$

This is trivially seen: If $\chi = 1$, the statement is clear. If $\chi \neq 1$, then for some $y \in G$ we have $\chi(y) \neq 1$. Then

$$\sum_{x\in G} \chi(x) = \sum_{x\in G} \chi(yx) = \chi(y) \sum_{x\in G} \chi(x).$$

Our assertion follows. [We note that the proof applies to a compact abelian group, the sum being replaced by an integral, and the Haar measure being normalized so that $\mu(G) = 1$.]

We shall apply this to the finite abelian group $G = I/P$ of ideal classes in a number field k. More generally, we select a cycle $\mathfrak{c}$, and apply this to the finite group $G(\mathfrak{c}) = I(\mathfrak{c})/P_{\mathfrak{c}}$ of generalized ideal classes. For each character χ of $G(\mathfrak{c})$, we have the value $\chi(\mathfrak{a})$ for any ideal $\mathfrak{a} \in I(\mathfrak{c})$. We define the L-series

$$L_{\mathfrak{c}}(s, \chi) = \prod_{\mathfrak{p}\nmid\mathfrak{c}} \frac{1}{1 - \dfrac{\chi(\mathfrak{p})}{\mathbf{N}\mathfrak{p}^s}}\cdot$$

It is clear that the infinite product converges absolutely and uniformly in the same manner as the product for the zeta function $\zeta_k(s)$, and that we have for $\operatorname{Re}(s) > 1$,

$$\log L_{\mathfrak{c}}(s, \chi) = \sum_{m, \mathfrak{p} \nmid \mathfrak{c}} \frac{\chi(\mathfrak{p})^m}{m\mathbf{N}\mathfrak{p}^{ms}}.$$

As before, from the point of view of convergence to $\operatorname{Re}(s) > 1/2$, we can do away with the terms having $m \geqq 2$, so that

$$\log L_{\mathfrak{c}}(s, \chi) \sim \sum_{\mathfrak{p}} \frac{\chi(\mathfrak{p})}{\mathbf{N}\mathfrak{p}^s},$$

and this holds whether we sum over all $\mathfrak{p}$, or merely over all those $\mathfrak{p}$ such that $\deg \mathfrak{p} = 1$. We also have obviously the Dirichlet series representation

$$L_{\mathfrak{c}}(s, \chi) = \sum_{(\mathfrak{a}, \mathfrak{c}) = 1} \frac{\chi(\mathfrak{a})}{\mathbf{N}\mathfrak{a}^s},$$

and immediately from the definitions, collecting terms,

$$L_{\mathfrak{c}}(s, \chi) = \sum_{\mathfrak{K}} \chi(\mathfrak{K}) \zeta(s, \mathfrak{K}),$$

taking the sum over the classes $\mathfrak{K}$ of $I(\mathfrak{c})/P_{\mathfrak{c}}$.

Using Theorem 3 of Chapter VI, §3, we can now prove one fact about the L-series $L_{\mathfrak{c}}(s, \chi)$ which distinguishes it from the zeta function if $\chi \neq 1$.

Theorem 7. *The Dirichlet series for* $L_{\mathfrak{c}}(s, \chi)$ *is convergent in the half plane* $\operatorname{Re}(s) > 1 - 1/N$ *if* $\chi \neq 1$, *and represents* $L_{\mathfrak{c}}(s, \chi)$, *which is analytic in that half plane.*

Proof. By Theorem 3 loc. cit. we know that the number of ideals $\mathfrak{a}$ in a given class $\mathfrak{K}$ such that $\mathbf{N}\mathfrak{a} \leqq n$ is equal to the same number $\rho_{\mathfrak{c}} n$, with an error term $O(n^{1-1/N})$. Using the remark at the beginning of the section, concerning the sum of a non-trivial character over the elements of a finite abelian group, we conclude that the partial sum of the coefficients of the Dirichlet series satisfies the estimate

$$\sum_{\mathfrak{K}} \sum_{\substack{\mathfrak{a} \in \mathfrak{K} \\ \mathbf{N}\mathfrak{a} \leqq n}} \chi(\mathfrak{a}) = O(n^{1-1/N}).$$

We can therefore apply Theorem 4 of §1 (with $\rho = 0$!) to conclude the proof.

We shall apply the L-series to study the decomposition of primes in abelian extensions. In general, we recall that in a finite extension E/k, a prime $\mathfrak{p}$ of k is said to split completely if there are exactly $[E : k]$ distinct primes $\mathfrak{P}$ of E lying above $\mathfrak{p}$. For each such $\mathfrak{P}$, it follows that the extension of the residue class field has degree $f(\mathfrak{P}|\mathfrak{p}) = 1$. We let $S_{E/k}$ be the set of primes of k which split completely in E.

Let K/k be Galois, and let $\mathfrak{c}$ be a cycle of k divisible by all the ramified primes. (That's all we are going to need for the rest of this section, but what matters is in fact that $\mathfrak{c}$ is admissible in the sense of Chapter VII, §4.) Consider the intermediate group

$$I(\mathfrak{c}) \supset P_{\mathfrak{c}}\mathfrak{N}(\mathfrak{c}) \supset P_{\mathfrak{c}},$$

where $\mathfrak{N}(\mathfrak{c})$ is the group of norms of fractional ideals of K, prime to $\mathfrak{c}$. For any $\mathfrak{p}$ of k and $\mathfrak{P}|\mathfrak{p}$ in K, we have

$$N_k^K\mathfrak{P} = \mathfrak{p}^{f(\mathfrak{P}|\mathfrak{p})}.$$

Thus $\mathfrak{p}$ splits completely in K if and only if $\mathfrak{p}$ is a norm from K, and $\mathfrak{p}$ is unramified.

The factor group

$$I(\mathfrak{c})/P_{\mathfrak{c}}\mathfrak{N}(\mathfrak{c})$$

will be of fundamental importance in class field theory, and we shall use especially its order

$$(I(\mathfrak{c}) : P_{\mathfrak{c}}\mathfrak{N}(\mathfrak{c}))$$

(called the **norm index**) in various technical steps in the proofs of the class field theory. Using what we already know about L-series, we can state and prove a basic result about this order.

Universal Norm Index Inequality. *Let $\mathfrak{c}$ be divisible by the ramified primes of K/k. Then*

$$(I(\mathfrak{c}) : P_{\mathfrak{c}}\mathfrak{N}(\mathfrak{c})) \leqq [K : k].$$

In other words, the norm index is at most equal to the degree of the extension.

Proof. Let $H = P_{\mathfrak{c}}\mathfrak{N}(\mathfrak{c})$ and let $h = (I(\mathfrak{c}) : H)$. Let χ be a non-trivial character of the factor group $I(\mathfrak{c})/H$. Then χ may also be viewed as a character of $I(\mathfrak{c})/P_{\mathfrak{c}}$. Let $m(\chi)$ be the order of the zero of $L_{\mathfrak{c}}(s, \chi)$ at $s = 1$. Then $m(\chi) \geqq 0$. (We shall see in a moment that $m(\chi) = 0$.) Write

$$L_{\mathfrak{c}}(s, \chi) = (s - 1)^{m(\chi)} g(s, \chi).$$

Then

$$\log L_{\mathfrak{c}}(s, \chi) \sim m(\chi) \log (s - 1) \sim -m(\chi) \log \frac{1}{s - 1}\cdot$$

For $\operatorname{Re}(s) > 1$ and any character χ of $I(\mathfrak{c})/H$, we can write

$$\log L_{\mathfrak{c}}(s, \chi) \sim \sum_{\mathfrak{K} \in I(\mathfrak{c})/H} \chi(\mathfrak{K}) \sum_{\mathfrak{p} \in \mathfrak{K}} \frac{1}{\mathbf{N}\mathfrak{p}^s}.$$

Take the sum over all characters χ of $I(\mathfrak{c})/H$. We find

$$\log \zeta_k(s) + \sum_{\chi \neq 1} \log L_{\mathfrak{c}}(s, \chi) \sim \sum_{\chi} \sum_{\mathfrak{K}} \chi(\mathfrak{K}) \sum_{\mathfrak{p} \in \mathfrak{K}} \frac{1}{\mathbf{N}\mathfrak{p}^s}.$$

Consider only real values of $s > 1$, let $s \to 1$, and use the sign $\gtrsim$ to mean that the right-hand side is less than or equal to the left-hand side plus some constant, in a neighborhood of 1. For each $\mathfrak{p} \in S_{K/k}$ there are exactly $N = [K:k]$ primes $\mathfrak{P}$ of K lying above $\mathfrak{p}$. Thus we find:

$$\begin{aligned}
\left[1 - \sum_{\chi \neq 1} m(\chi)\right] \log \frac{1}{s-1} &\sim h \sum_{\mathfrak{p} \in H} \frac{1}{\mathbf{N}\mathfrak{p}^s} \\
&\gtrsim h \sum_{\mathfrak{p} \in S_{K/k}} \frac{1}{\mathbf{N}\mathfrak{p}^s} \\
&\gtrsim \frac{h}{N} \sum_{\deg \mathfrak{P} = 1} \frac{1}{\mathbf{N}\mathfrak{P}^s} \\
&\gtrsim \frac{h}{N} \log \frac{1}{s-1}.
\end{aligned}$$

From this we conclude that $m(\chi) = 0$ for all $\chi \neq 1$, and the inequality

$$h \leqq N$$

falls out at the same time. This concludes the proof.

In view of Theorem 8, Chapter VII, §4 we can formulate our inequality for ideles and idele classes.

Corollary. *Let K/k be a Galois extension of degree N. Then*

$$(J_k : k^* N_k^K J_K) \leqq N \qquad \textit{and} \qquad (C_k : N_k^K C_K) \leqq N.$$

It will be a consequence of class field theory that in fact, the norm index is equal to the degree of the maximal abelian subfield of K.

Assuming results of class field theory, we shall indicate in the next section how the same argument which was used to prove our universal inequality can also be used to prove a more general density statement for primes in certain ideal class groups. Conversely, inserting the next section here also serves as motivation for the theorems of class field theory. In fact, historically, this is precisely how one was led to them.

§4. *Density of primes in arithmetic progressions*

Let $\mathfrak{c}$ be a cycle of k. The class field theory will show that given any intermediate group

$$I(\mathfrak{c}) \supset H \supset P_{\mathfrak{c}},$$

there exists an abelian extension K/k such that

$$H = P_{\mathfrak{c}}\mathfrak{N}(\mathfrak{c}, K/k).$$

In particular, this holds of $P_{\mathfrak{c}}$ itself, and therefore the conclusion that $m(\chi) = 0$ holds for all characters $\chi \neq 1$ of $I(\mathfrak{c})/P_{\mathfrak{c}}$. We state this as a theorem.

Theorem 8. *Let $\mathfrak{c}$ be a cycle of k, and let χ be a character of $I(\mathfrak{c})/P_{\mathfrak{c}}$, $\chi \neq 1$. Then*

$$L_{\mathfrak{c}}(1, \chi) \neq 0.$$

Using the same argument that we did to get our universal inequality, we now obtain a density statement.

Corollary. *Let $h_{\mathfrak{c}} = (I(\mathfrak{c}) : P_{\mathfrak{c}})$ and let $\mathfrak{K}_0$ be a fixed ideal class of $I(\mathfrak{c})$ modulo $P_{\mathfrak{c}}$, in other words an element of $G(\mathfrak{c}) = I(\mathfrak{c})/P_{\mathfrak{c}}$. Then for s real, $s > 1$, $s \to 1$, we have*

$$\log \frac{1}{s-1} \sim h_{\mathfrak{c}} \sum_{\mathfrak{p} \in \mathfrak{K}_0} \frac{1}{\mathbf{N}\mathfrak{p}^s}.$$

Proof. We return to the relation

$$\log L_{\mathfrak{c}}(s, \chi) \sim \sum_{\mathfrak{K} \in G(\mathfrak{c})} \chi(\mathfrak{K}) \sum_{\mathfrak{p} \in \mathfrak{K}} \frac{1}{\mathbf{N}\mathfrak{p}^s}.$$

Multiply the relation by $\chi(\mathfrak{K}_0^{-1})$ and sum over all χ. We get

$$\log \zeta_k(s) \sim \sum_{\mathfrak{K}} \sum_{\chi} \chi(\mathfrak{K}\mathfrak{K}_0^{-1}) \sum_{\mathfrak{p} \in \mathfrak{K}} \frac{1}{\mathbf{N}\mathfrak{p}^s}.$$

The sum over χ yields 0 unless $\mathfrak{K}\mathfrak{K}_0^{-1}$ is the unit class, and therefore

$$\log \frac{1}{s-1} \sim h_{\mathfrak{c}} \sum_{\mathfrak{p} \in \mathfrak{K}_0} \frac{1}{\mathbf{N}\mathfrak{p}^s},$$

as was to be proved.

If M is a set of primes of k, it is convenient to speak of the limit

$$\lim_{s\to 1+} \frac{\displaystyle\sum_{\mathfrak{p}\in M} \frac{1}{\mathbf{N}\mathfrak{p}^s}}{\log \dfrac{1}{s-1}}$$

as the **Dirichlet density** of M (if it exists). The corollary of Theorem 8 shows that an ideal class of $I(\mathfrak{c})/P_{\mathfrak{c}}$ always has such a density, and that this density is precisely $1/h_{\mathfrak{c}}$. We can view this as stating that the primes are equidistributed over the ideal classes.

Example. Without any class field theory, we have proved an equidistribution statement in a special case which is already of interest. Indeed, let $m > 1$ be an integer, and let $\mathfrak{c} = mv_\infty$. Then the field $\mathbf{Q}(\zeta_m) = K$ obtained by adjoining a primitive m-th root of unity to $\mathbf{Q}$ has the property that $P_{\mathfrak{c}}$ is precisely its norm class group, as we already mentioned in Chapter VII, §4. Thus we find Dirichlet's theorem that there are infinitely many primes in an ordinary arithmetic progression as a special case of our corollary. We also have a Dirichlet density for these primes, namely $1/\varphi(m)$, where φ is the Euler function.

It is customary, following Artin, to view classes mod $P_{\mathfrak{c}}$ in an arbitrary number field to be generalizations of arithmetic progressions, whence the title of this section.

Finally, we note that one can define another notion of density (in some sense, the usual one according to probabilistic practice), namely for any set of primes M, it is the limit

$$\lim_{n\to\infty} \frac{\text{Number of } \mathfrak{p} \in M \text{ with } \mathbf{N}\mathfrak{p} \leqq n}{\text{Number of } \mathfrak{p} \text{ with } \mathbf{N}\mathfrak{p} \leqq n}$$

if it exists. It is a simple exercise to show that if the ordinary density exists, then the Dirichlet density also exists and the two densities are equal. (The converse is not always true.) To prove that the ordinary density exists for our ideal classes requires additional arguments. For results without error terms, we shall carry out these arguments in Chapter XV.

We can obtain a characterization of Galois extensions by means of the set of primes splitting completely in the extension. Let S, T be sets of primes in k. We shall write

$$S \prec T$$

if there exists a set of Z of primes of Dirichlet density 0, contained in S, such that $S - Z \subset T$. Thus S is contained in T except for a set of primes of density 0. Observe that we can always take for Z the subset of those primes of S which have degree > 1 (over $\mathbf{Q}$, i.e. the absolute degree).

Let K/k be a Galois extension and let $S_{K/k}$ be the set of primes of k which split completely in K. If $L \supset K$ is another Galois extension of k, then trivially, $S_{L/k} \subset S_{K/k}$. If

$$S_{K/k} \prec S_{L/k},$$

then $L = K$. Indeed, $S_{L/k}$ has density $1/[L:k]$ and hence

$$[L:k] \leqq [K:k],$$

so $L = K$. From this we get:

Theorem 9. *Let K/k be a Galois extension and E a finite extension of k. Then $S_{K/k} \prec S_{E/k}$ if and only if $E \subset K$.*

Proof. A prime $\mathfrak{p}$ of k splits completely in E if and only if it splits completely in the smallest Galois extension L of k containing E, because this condition is equivalent to every conjugate of E over k being contained in the completion $k_{\mathfrak{p}}$. Hence we may assume without loss of generality that $E = L$ is Galois over k. If $L \subset K$, then $S_{K/k} \prec S_{L/k}$ so this direction is obvious. Conversely, assume that $S_{K/k} \prec S_{L/k}$. Then $KL \supset K$ and KL is Galois over k. But

$$S_{KL/k} = S_{L/k} \cap S_{K/k}.$$

Hence

$$S_{K/k} \prec S_{KL/k},$$

and we can apply the remark preceding the theorem to conclude that $KL = K$, whence $L \subset K$, thus proving our theorem.

We conclude this chapter by pointing out a non-abelian generalization of the density statements. We assume that the reader knows the class field theory, and more specifically the Artin reciprocity law, which says that we have an isomorphism

$$I(\mathfrak{c})/H \xrightarrow{\approx} G,$$

where H is a subgroup of ideals containing $P_{\mathfrak{c}}$, and G is the Galois group of an abelian extension K of k, class field to H. This isomorphism is given on primes $\mathfrak{p}$ by the Artin symbol

$$\mathfrak{p} \mapsto (\mathfrak{p}, K/k),$$

and is extended to all fractional ideals by multiplicativity.

Given a Galois extension K/k with group G, and $\sigma \in G$, we ask for the density of those primes $\mathfrak{p}$ in k for which there exists $\mathfrak{P}|\mathfrak{p}$ in K such that

$$\sigma = (\mathfrak{P}, K/k),$$

i.e. σ is the Frobenius automorphism of $\mathfrak{P}$ in K. The prime $\mathfrak{p}$ in k actually determines the conjugacy class of σ in G, since all the primes in K lying above $\mathfrak{p}$ are conjugate.

Theorem 10. (Tchebotarev). *Let K/k be Galois with group G. Let $\sigma \in G$. Let $[K:k] = N$, and let c be the number of elements in the conjugacy class of σ in G. Then those primes $\mathfrak{p}$ of k which are unramified in K and for which there exists $\mathfrak{P}|\mathfrak{p}$ such that*

$$\sigma = (\mathfrak{P}, K/k)$$

have a density, and this density is equal to c/N.

Proof. The simple argument which follows is due to Deuring (*Math. Ann.* 110, 1934). Let σ have order f. Let Z be the fixed field of σ. Then K/Z is cyclic of degree f, and therefore a class field. If $\mathfrak{c}$ is an admissible cycle for K/Z, then we have the Artin isomorphism

$$I(\mathfrak{c})/H \to G(K/Z),$$

where H is a subgroup of $I(\mathfrak{c})$ containing $P_{\mathfrak{c}}$. Let S be the set of primes $\mathfrak{p}$ of k satisfying the condition of the theorem, and prime to $\mathfrak{c}$. Let $S_{K,\sigma}$ be the set of $\mathfrak{P}$ in K such that $\mathfrak{P}|\mathfrak{p}$ for $\mathfrak{p} \in S$, and $(\mathfrak{P}, K/k) = \sigma$. Let $\mathfrak{P}|\mathfrak{q}$ for $\mathfrak{q}$ in Z. Then $S_{K,\sigma}$ is in bijection with the set S_Z of $\mathfrak{q}$ in Z which lie in a given class mod H, and which divide $\mathfrak{p}$ splitting completely in Z. However, the density depends only on those primes of degree 1 over $\mathbf{Q}$. Hence S_Z has density $1/f$, by the density statement for abelian, or even cyclic extensions. On the other hand, for a fixed $\mathfrak{p}$, the number of $\mathfrak{P}$ in K lying above $\mathfrak{p}$ and such that

$$\sigma = (\mathfrak{P}, K/k)$$

is equal to

$$\frac{(G_\sigma : 1)}{(G_{\mathfrak{P}} : 1)},$$

where G_σ is the subgroup of elements of G commuting with σ, and $G_{\mathfrak{P}}$ is the decomposition group of $\mathfrak{P}$. Since $(G : G_\sigma) = c$, we find that this number is equal to N/cf. The density of S is thus equal to $1/f$ divided by N/cf, which gives us c/N, and proves the theorem.

For historical comments on the density theorem, cf. the introductory remarks to the next part. Let us add here only that when one has certain error terms in the density statements, Artin showed, using the formalism of the non-abelian L-series (which we discuss later), how to give the Tchebotarev density with similar error terms, formally using induced characters. We refer the reader to the original paper in Artin's collected works. For our purposes here, the simple argument of Deuring was sufficiently appropriate.

PART TWO

CLASS FIELD THEORY

The fact that there exist relations between ideal class groups and abelian extensions of a number field was observed during the end of the nineteenth century. At first, only the fact that the primes in the unit class are precisely those which split completely in a suitable extension was taken to be the defining relation of a class field by Hilbert, who defined what is now called the Hilbert class field, namely the maximal unramified abelian extension, and conjectured its principal properties. He proved them in special cases, and general proofs were given by Furtwangler.

Weber defined the generalized ideal classes, and proved the uniqueness of the class field corresponding to them, conjecturing the existence, and pointing out that the existence of infinitely many primes in a generalized ideal class would follow from the existence of the class field (precisely the method we have adopted in this book).

Finally, in 1920, Takagi extended the Weber and Hilbert-Furtwangler theorems to the most general case, especially proving the existence theorem for abelian extensions corresponding to generalized ideal class groups, and showing that the Galois group of such an extension was isomorphic to the corresponding ideal class group. However, during all this period, both the splitting laws and the isomorphism were obtained essentially from the numerical invariants, that is the numbers e, f for the splitting case, and the order of the ideal class group for the isomorphism. Since a cyclic group is determined (up to isomorphism) by its order, and since a finite abelian group is a product of cyclic groups, the isomorphism between the Galois group of an abelian extension K/k and the ideal class group $I(\mathfrak{c})/P_{\mathfrak{c}}\mathfrak{N}(\mathfrak{c})$ could be obtained just by counting, and a reduction to the cyclic case.

On the other hand, Frobenius had associated a conjugacy class of elements in the Galois group of a Galois extension to a prime in the ground field, and conjectured that set of primes having a given conjugacy class has the obvious density. He could prove only a weaker result, corresponding to a coarser decomposition of the group into larger classes. In 1923, Artin defined his non-abelian L-series, and conjectured that in the abelian case, the isomorphism of class field theory was induced by the Frobenius automorphism

$$\mathfrak{p} \mapsto (\mathfrak{p}, K/k).$$

In 1926, Tchebotarev proved the Frobenius conjecture by using cyclotomic fields, and Artin, recognizing the connection with his reciprocity law, succeeded in proving his conjecture in 1927, thus completing the basic statements of class field theory. (A more detailed history with references is given in Hasse's Bericht *"Über neuere Untersuchungen und Probleme der algebraischen Zahlkörper"*, reprinted by Physica-Verlag, Wurzburg, Wien, 1965. See also Hasse's talk at the Brighton Conference, [7].)

Thus in this period, from about 1880 to 1927, we see the class field theory developing from three themes: the decomposition of primes, abelian extensions, and ideal class groups.

In 1936, Chevalley introduced the ideles in order to formulate the class field theory for infinite extensions. [Shortly afterwards, Weil introduced adeles, and gave his adelic proof of the Riemann-Roch theorem.] The ideles are very useful technically (among other things) because every generalized ideal class group is a homomorphic image of the idele class group J/k^*. Thus expositions of class field theory making greater use of the ideles were given by Artin in seminars in the late forties. The treatment which I give in this book follows roughly one of these seminars, with some exceptions: I have still made use of the generalized ideal class groups because when the Artin symbol is given for unramified $\mathfrak{p}$, these ideal groups occur naturally and I think it obscures matters deliberately to disregard them. More importantly, I have used the oldest proof for the universal norm inequality (Weber's proof) both because it is more natural than the "purely algebraic" proof of Chevalley (reproduced in Artin-Tate), and also because it motivates the whole approach to class field theory through the density of primes in arithmetic progressions, and the splitting laws. The proof of the reciprocity law is a simplification by Artin himself of his original 1927 proof.

There is another approach to the class field theory, first started in the early thirties by Hasse, namely through the theory of simple algebras, centering around the fundamental theorem that a simple algebra over k splits over k if and only if it splits locally everywhere (Albert-Hasse-Brauer-Noether). Hasse also shows how to associate invariants with a division algebra, and how the reciprocity law has a formulation in terms of the sum of the invariants being equal to 0 (*Math. Ann.*, 1932). Hochschild in 1950 pointed out that one could express the class field theory only in terms of cohomology; the simple algebras were unnecessary if one used only the 2-cocycle used to define them. At about this time, Weil also emphasized the cohomology, by discovering the fundamental 2-cocycle of idele classes. The Artin-Tate notes give a complete systematic treatment from the point of view of cohomology. This approach, which shows that the second cohomology group of the idele classes (for the algebraic closure) is isomorphic to $\mathbf{Q}/\mathbf{Z}$, provides a good background for theories where this result is used to obtain pairings, e.g. some diophantine questions related to abelian varieties over $\mathfrak{p}$-adic fields or number fields as in the work of Tate. In this direction, the simple algebras do not appear. This second cohomology group is used as a receiver of character values.

On the other hand, starting from the functional equation of the zeta function of a division algebra (obtained by Hey, unpublished thesis, Hamburg 1929, cf. Deuring's *Algebren*), Zorn showed how the fundamental theorem on simple algebras over number fields could easily be obtained as a corollary, thus providing still another alternative approach to the class field theory (*Hamburg Abh.*, 1933). After a slumber of thirty years, this approach has again become important because of the recent advances in the arithmetic theory of semisimple Lie groups, and it is the one selected by Weil in his *Basic Number Theory*.

A fourth way of describing the class field theory, and in many ways the most exciting, originated with Kronecker, and consists in giving "natural" generators for class fields as values of transcendental functions, and obtaining an explicit reciprocity law in terms of them. As of now, this program (Kronecker's Jugendtraum) has succeeded only for a limited number of class fields, essentially those over totally imaginary quadratic extensions of totally real fields, in excess of the class fields over the totally real subfield.

The analogy between number fields and function fields in one variable has been a prime source of motivation ever since the nineteenth century (passing through Hensel-Landsberg, Artin's thesis, etc.). Both Artin-Tate and Weil axiomatize the class field theory so that it applies as well to the function fields over finite constant fields. However, once the analogy has been understood, there are some reasons for giving alternative expositions for the two cases. First, certain aspects of number fields are still shrouded in mystery while the corresponding aspects of the function field case are cleared up. Thus a certain emphasis on the peculiarities of number fields is not out of place. Secondly, one can give an exposition of the class field theory in the function field case making use of the generalized Jacobians of Rosenlicht, by a method which was new even in the simplest case of unramified extensions of elliptic function fields, independently of these generalized Jacobians. I did this in two articles (*Annals of Math.*, 1956 and *Bulletin de la Société Mathématique de France*, 1956), as a by-product of showing how to formulate class field theoretic results for higher dimensional varieties. The essential idea is to map the variety into a commutative algebraic group, obtain explicit coverings for the group defined over the finite field with q elements (e.g. the covering defined by the formula $x \mapsto x^{(q)} - x$), verify trivially the reciprocity law for these coverings, and then pull them back to the variety. In the case of curves, Rosenlicht's universal mapping theorem for his generalized Jacobians gives a convenient family of mappings, cofinal with the family of all maps into all commutative algebraic groups. The generalized Jacobians correspond to the generalized ideal class groups of Weber (history comes around full circle). In the "geometric case", this approach allows one to have a much clearer insight into the whole class field theory, since the existence theorem and the reciprocity law become obvious once the machinery of algebraic geometry is available. For these reasons, I have limited myself in the present book to an exposition of the class field theory over number fields. With only minor modifications, though, they are also seen to apply to the function field case. (Only exception: the existence theorem for p-extensions, p equal to the characteristic.)

If there is one moral which deserves emphasis, however, it is that no one piece of insight which has been evolved since the beginning of the subject has ever been "superseded" by subsequent pieces of insight. They may have moved through various stages of fashionability, and various authors may have claimed to give so-called "modern" treatments. You should be warned that acquaintance with only one of the approaches will deprive you of techniques and understandings reflected by the other approaches, and you should not interpret my choosing one method as anything but a means of making easily available an exposition which had fallen out of fashion for twenty years.

The first chapter of this part is quite technical. The reader is advised to read immediately the beginning of Chapter X, i.e. the description of the reciprocity law isomorphism, and the statements of the main results of class field theory in Chapter X, §2 and §3.

CHAPTER IX

Norm Index Computations

§1. *Algebraic preliminaries*

The Herbrand quotient

We begin by considerations of general abelian groups, which will be used both in the local and global case. We recall the index relation

$$(A:B) = (A^f:B^f)(A_f:B_f),$$

if $A \supset B$ are abelian groups, f is a homomorphism of A. This was already used in Chapter II, §3.

Let f, g be homomorphisms of A into itself such that

$$f \circ g = g \circ f = 0.$$

Then we define the **Herbrand quotient**

$$Q(A) = Q_{f,g}(A) = \frac{(A_f:A^g)}{(A_g:A^f)},$$

if the indices in the numerator and denominator are finite.

Lemma 1. *If B is a subgroup of A which is mapped into itself by f and g, so that f, g may be viewed also as endomorphisms of the factor group A/B, then*

$$Q(A) = Q(B)Q(A/B),$$

in the sense that if two of the quotients are defined, so is the third and the relation holds. Furthermore, if A is finite, then

$$Q(A) = 1.$$

Proof. One may view the quotient Q as an Euler-Poincaré characteristic of a complex of length 2 (cf. my book *Algebra*, Chapter IV), and apply a general result, of an elementary nature, to deduce the multiplicativity property. We shall reproduce a sketch of the proof below in our special case. First, we give a proof for the simpler case when B is of finite index in A. We have

$$(A:B) = (A^f:B^f)(A_f:B_f) = (A^f:B^f)\,\frac{(A_f:B^g)}{(B_f:B^g)}$$

$$= (A^f:B^f)(A^g:B^g)\,\frac{(A_f:A^g)}{(B_f:B^g)},$$

whence

$$\frac{(A:B)}{(A^f:B^f)(A^g:B^g)} = \frac{(A_f:A^g)}{(B_f:B^g)}.$$

The left-hand side is symmetric in f and g, so that

$$\frac{(A_f:A^g)}{(B_f:B^g)} = \frac{(A_g:A^f)}{(B_g:B^f)}.$$

This proves that $Q(A) = Q(B)$. The reader can verify for himself that all the steps were legitimate (i.e. under the assumption that $Q(A)$ or $Q(B)$ is finite, then we never divided by zero or infinity.)

Now for the general case. We have a sequence

$$0 \to B \to A \to C \to 0$$

where $C = A/B$. We define

$$H_0(A) = A_f/A^g \qquad \text{and} \qquad H_1(A) = A_g/A^f.$$

And similarly for B and C. We construct a diagram

$$\begin{array}{ccccc} & H_0(A) & \to & H_0(C) & \\ \nearrow & & & & \searrow^{\delta} \\ H_0(B) & & & & H_1(B) \\ {}_{\delta}\nwarrow & & & & \swarrow \\ & H_1(C) & \leftarrow & H_1(A) & \end{array}$$

which is exact, i.e. such that the image of each arrow is the kernel of the next arrow. Going from B to A, and A to C, the arrows are simply the natural homomorphisms induced by the inclusion $B \to A$ and the canonical map $A \to A/B = C$. The maps δ are defined as follows. Let $c \in C_f$ represent an element of $H_0(C)$. Then $fc = 0$. There exists $a \in A$ such that $c = ja$, if $j: A \to C$ is the canonical homomorphism. Then

$$jfa = fja = 0,$$

so that $fa \in B$, and in fact $fa \in B_g$. It is immediate to verify that the association

$$c \mapsto \text{class of } fa \bmod B^f$$

is a well defined homomorphism, whose kernel contains C^g, and hence defines a homomorphism

$$\delta : H_0(C) \to H_1(B).$$

The map from $H_1(C)$ to $H_0(B)$ is defined similarly. It is a routine matter to prove that with these definitions, the hexagon is exact.

If the quotient Q is defined for two out of three of A, B, C we see from the hexagon and the exactness that it must be defined for the third. Under this condition, we order our six groups in the diagram clockwise, starting say with $H_0(A)$, and denote them by M_i ($i = 1, \ldots, 6 \bmod 6$). Let k_i be the order of the kernel of the arrow leaving M_i and let m_i be the order of the image of the arrow arriving at M_i. Then

$$\text{ord } M_i = m_i k_{i+1}.$$

Furthermore $m_i = k_i$ by exactness. Hence

$$m_1 m_3 m_5 k_2 k_4 k_6 = m_2 m_4 m_6 k_1 k_3 k_5.$$

Dividing suitably yields the relation $Q(A) = Q(B)Q(C)$, thus proving the multiplicativity of Q.

We shall next give the proof for the second statement, $Q(A) = 1$ if A is finite. We have the following lattice of subgroups:

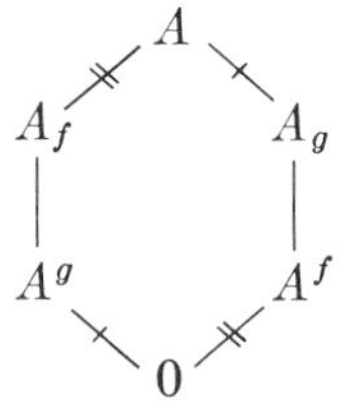

Under the map g we have an isomorphism $A/A_g \approx A^g$ and similarly with f replacing g. Thus opposite slanting sides of the hexagon are equal. It follows that the vertical sides are also equal, thus proving what we want. (Equality here means that the corresponding factor groups have the same order. As an abuse of language, it is very much less obnoxious than the corresponding abuse in plane geometry . . .)

The preceding lemma will be referred to as the **Q-machine.** It will be used in the following context. Let G be a cyclic group operating on an abelian group A. Let σ be a generator of G. Let

$$f = 1 - \sigma \qquad \text{and} \qquad g = 1 + \sigma + \cdots + \sigma^{n-1}$$

where n is the order of G. Let A^G be the subgroup $A_{1-\sigma}$, i.e. the subgroup of A consisting of those elements fixed by G. Note that

$$1 + \sigma + \cdots + \sigma^{n-1} = \mathrm{Tr}_G$$

is a "trace" map, which in multiplicative notation would be denoted by a norm map. Thus our quotient in this case is

$$Q(G, A) = Q(A) = \frac{(A^G : \mathrm{Tr}_G A)}{(A_{\mathrm{Tr}} : (1 - \sigma)A)}.$$

The numerator is the trace index (norm index in multiplicative notation).

If G operates with trivial action on $\mathbf{Z}$ (or any infinite cyclic group, then we have

$$\boxed{Q(G, \mathbf{Z}) = (G : 1)}$$

i.e. the Herbrand quotient is equal to the order of G. This follows because $\mathbf{Z}^G = \mathbf{Z}$, $\mathrm{Tr}(\mathbf{Z}) = n\mathbf{Z}$ (where n is the order of G), and $\mathbf{Z}_{\mathrm{Tr}} = 0$.

Let G be an arbitrary finite group operating on an abelian group A. We associate with (G, A) two abelian groups

$$H^0(G, A) = A^G/\mathrm{Tr}_G A \qquad \text{and} \qquad H^{-1}(G, A) = A_{\mathrm{Tr}}/I_G A,$$

where I_G is the ideal of the group ring $\mathbf{Z}[G]$ generated by all elements $(1 - \sigma)$ for $\sigma \in G$. It is an ideal, because for $\tau \in G$ we have

$$\tau - \tau\sigma = \tau - 1 + 1 - \tau\sigma.$$

Thus $I_G A$ by definition consists of the G-submodule generated by the elements $a - \sigma a$, with $a \in A$ and $\sigma \in G$. If G is cyclic, and σ is a generator of G, then

$$I_G A = (1 - \sigma)A,$$

because $1 - \sigma^i = (1 - \sigma)(1 + \cdots + \sigma^{i-1})$.

In homological terminology, we see that the numerator and denominator of the Herbrand quotient are simply orders of cohomology groups, namely the orders of H^0 and H^{-1} respectively.

Semilocal representations

We shall now prove some lemmas which are useful in computing these orders in a situation which arises all the time. We consider a finite group G operating on the abelian group A. Assume that A is the direct sum of subgroups,

$$A = \prod_{i=1}^{s} A_i,$$

and that G permutes these subgroups A_i transitively. When that occurs, we say that the operation of G is **semilocal.** Let G_1 be the decomposition group of A_1 (i.e. the subgroup of elements $\sigma \in G$ such that $\sigma A_1 = A_1$). We call (G_1, A_1) its local component. Each element $a \in A$ can be written uniquely

$$a = \sum_{i=1}^{s} a_i,$$

with $a_i \in A_i$. Furthermore, let

$$G = \bigcup_{i=1}^{s} \sigma_i G_1 \qquad (\sigma_1 = 1)$$

be a left coset decomposition of G. We can chose the indices i in such a way that $\sigma_i A_1 = A_i$. In that case, each element $a_i \in A_i$ can be written as $\sigma_i a_i'$ for a uniquely determined element $a_i' \in A_1$.

Lemma 2. *The projection $\pi : A \to A_1$ induces an isomorphism*

$$H^0(G, A) \approx H^0(G_1, A_1).$$

Proof. We first observe that A^G consists of all elements of the form

$$\sum_{i=1}^{s} \sigma_i a_1, \qquad \text{with } a_1 \in A_1^{G_1}$$

Namely, it is clear that such an element is fixed under G. On the other hand, if

$$a = \sum_{i=1}^{s} \sigma_i a_i' \qquad (a_i' \in A_1)$$

is fixed under G, then for a fixed index j we apply σ_j^{-1} and see that $a_j' = \sigma_j^{-1}\sigma_j a_j'$ is the A_1-component of $\sigma_j^{-1}a = a$. Hence $a_j' = a_1'$ for all j, thus proving our assertion. In particular, an element of A^G is uniquely determined by its first component, and thus the projection gives an isomorphism

$$A^G \xrightarrow{\approx} A_1^{G_1}.$$

On the other hand, for a fixed j and $a_1 \in A_1$ we have

$$\mathrm{Tr}_G(\sigma_j a_1) = \sum_{\sigma \in G} \sigma a_1 = \sum_{i=1}^{s} \sigma_i \,\mathrm{Tr}_{G_1}(a_1).$$

This shows that $\mathrm{Tr}_G(A)$ consists precisely of those elements of the form

$$\sum_{i=1}^{s} \sigma_i \,\mathrm{Tr}_{G_1}(a_1), \qquad a_1 \in A_1.$$

Thus it is clear that $A^G/\mathrm{Tr}_G A \approx A^{G_1}/\mathrm{Tr}_{G_1}(A_1)$, and the lemma is proved.

Lemma 3. *There is an isomorphism (to be described in the proof)*

$$H^{-1}(G, A) \approx H^{-1}(G_1, A_1).$$

Proof. Let

$$a = \sum_{i=1}^{s} \sigma_i a_i', \qquad a_i' \in A_1.$$

Then

$$\mathrm{Tr}_G(a) = \sum_{j=1}^{s} \sigma_j \,\mathrm{Tr}_{G_1}(a_1' + \cdots + a_s').$$

Hence $\mathrm{Tr}_G(a) = 0$ if and only if $\mathrm{Tr}_{G_1}(a_1' + \cdots + a_s') = 0$. The map

$$a \mapsto a_1' + \cdots + a_s'$$

is therefore a homomorphism

$$\lambda : \mathrm{Ker}\,\mathrm{Tr}_G \to \mathrm{Ker}\,\mathrm{Tr}_{G_1},$$

which is obviously surjective (take $a = a_1$ in $\mathrm{Ker}\,\mathrm{Tr}_{G_1}$). We show that λ maps $I_G A$ into $I_{G_1} A_1$. If $\sigma \in G$, then there is a permutation π of the indices i such that

$$\sigma\sigma_i = \sigma_{\pi(i)}\tau_{\pi(i)}$$

with some $\tau_{\pi(i)} \in G_1$. Hence

$$\lambda(\sigma a - a) = \sum_{i=1}^{s} (\tau_{\pi(i)} a_i' - a_i'),$$

thus proving our assertion. To conclude the proof, it will suffice to show that if $\lambda(a) = 0$ then $a \in I_G A$. But if $a'_1 + \cdots + a'_s = 0$ we can write

$$a = \sum_{i=1}^{s} (\sigma_i a'_i - a'_i),$$

and so $a \in I_G A$. This proves our lemma.

Remark. The two lemmas are frequently used in case $G_1 = \{1\}$, and in that case, we see that $H^0(G, A) = H^{-1}(G, A) = 0$. This occurs in the case of the "regular" representation of G, of which the following is an important case. Let K/k be a Galois extension with group G. It is known from elementary algebra that there exists a normal basis for K/k, i.e. a basis consisting of elements $\{\omega_\sigma\}_{\sigma \in G}$ such that for any $\tau \in G$ we have $\tau\omega_\sigma = \omega_{\tau\sigma}$. In that case, G permutes the 1-dimensional k-spaces $k \cdot \omega_\sigma$ transitively, and each decomposition group is trivial. Thus we get

$$H^0(G, K) = H^{-1}(G, K) = 0.$$

If K/k is cyclic, then we always have

$$H^{-1}(G, K^*) = 1.$$

This is nothing but Hilbert's Theorem 90.

§2. *Exponential and logarithm functions*

Let k be a $\mathfrak{p}$-adic field, and let $| \; | = | \; |_\mathfrak{p}$. The series

$$\log(1 + x) = x - \frac{x^2}{2} + \frac{x^3}{3} - \cdots$$

converges for all $x \in k$ such that $|x| < 1$. To see this, let

$$p^r \leqq n < p^{r+1}.$$

Then

$$\operatorname{ord}_\mathfrak{p} x^n/n = n \cdot \operatorname{ord}_\mathfrak{p} x - \operatorname{ord}_\mathfrak{p} n \geqq n \cdot \operatorname{ord}_\mathfrak{p} x - r,$$

and the right-hand side tends to infinity with n.

For sufficiently small x, we shall see that $\log(1 + x)$ and x have the same order at $\mathfrak{p}$. Precisely, we shall prove that if $n \geqq 2$ and

$$\operatorname{ord}_\mathfrak{p} x > \frac{e}{p - 1}, \qquad \text{or equivalently,} \qquad |x| < p^{-1/(p-1)}$$

then $|x^n/n| < |x|$. Namely, we have

$$\begin{aligned}\log_p |x^n/n| - \log_p |x| &= (n-1)\log_p |x| - \log_p |n| \\ &< -\frac{n-1}{p-1} + r \leqq 0.\end{aligned}$$

This shows that $\log_p |x^n/n| < \log_p |x|$, whence $|x^n/n| < |x|$. Hence for such x, we find that the series of $\log(1+x)$ is dominated by its first term x (remember that the absolute value is non-archimedean!) so that

$$\boxed{\operatorname{ord}_{\mathfrak{p}} \log(1+x) = \operatorname{ord}_{\mathfrak{p}} x}$$

whenever $\operatorname{ord}_{\mathfrak{p}} x > e/(p-1)$.

The functional equation

$$\log(\alpha\beta) = \log \alpha + \log \beta$$

holds whenever α and β are $\equiv 1 \pmod{\mathfrak{p}}$, and we define

$$\log \alpha = \log\big(1 - (1-\alpha)\big).$$

Indeed, it is true as a formal power series relation, and the series involved converge.

The series

$$\exp x = 1 + x + \frac{x^2}{2!} + \frac{x^3}{3!} + \cdots$$

converges for all x such that $\operatorname{ord}_{\mathfrak{p}} x > e/(p-1)$, *that is in the same disc that the log series behaves well, and in that disc, we have the same type of relation as for the log, namely*

$$\operatorname{ord}_{\mathfrak{p}} x = \operatorname{ord}_{\mathfrak{p}}(\exp x - 1).$$

In fact, for $n \geqq 2$, and x in that disc, we have again $|x^n/n!| < |x|$.

To prove this, we meet a slightly more difficult situation than for the log, because the factorials are more divisible and thus tend to zero more strongly than the mere n of the log series. We write

$$n = a_0 + a_1 p + \cdots + a_r p^r$$

with rational integers a_i satisfying $0 \leqq a_i \leqq p-1$. Then

$$\begin{aligned}[n/p] &= a_1 + a_2 p + \cdots + a_r p^{r-1} \\ [n/p^2] &= \qquad\quad a_2 + \cdots + a_r p^{r-2} \\ &\ \,\vdots \qquad\qquad\quad \ddots \qquad\quad \vdots \\ [n/p^r] &= \qquad\qquad\qquad\qquad\quad a_r\end{aligned}$$

Hence

$$\operatorname{ord}_p n! = a_1 + (p+1)a_2 + \cdots + (p^{r-1} + \cdots + 1)a_r,$$

and

$$\begin{aligned}(p-1)\operatorname{ord}_p n! &= (p-1)a_1 + (p^2-1)a_2 + \cdots + (p^r - 1)a_r \\ &= n - (a_0 + \cdots + a_r).\end{aligned}$$

Consequently, we find for $n \geqq 2$,

$$\begin{aligned}\log_p |x^n/n!| &= n \cdot \log_p |x| - \log_p |n!| \\ &< n\left[\log_p |x| + \frac{1}{p-1}\right]\end{aligned}$$

and also

$$\begin{aligned}\log_p |x^n/n!| - \log_p |x| &= (n-1)\log_p |x| - \log_p |n!| \\ &< -\frac{n-1}{p-1} + \frac{1}{p-1}[n - (a_0 + \cdots + a_r)] \leqq 0.\end{aligned}$$

This shows both that $x^n/n! \to 0$ as $n \to \infty$ (for the p-adic topology), and also shows that for $n \geqq 2$, we have $|x^n/n!| < |x|$, thus proving all our assertions.

In the disc $|x| < p^{-1/(p-1)}$, we conclude that

$$\exp \log(1 + x) = 1 + x \qquad \text{and} \qquad \log \exp x = x.$$

Namely, this is a formal power series identity, and all the series converge. In particular, for small $\delta > 0$, and this is all that we shall need in the rest of class field theory, we see that δ-neighborhoods of 1 and 0 are mapped isomorphically onto each other by the log and exp respectively. We shall not need the exact maximal domain in which this is true.

§3. *The local norm index*

Let k be a $\mathfrak{p}$-adic field. Let K/k be a cyclic extension of degree N, with group G, and let σ be a generator. Let U_k be the group of units in k, and U_K the group of units in K. We let e be the ramification index and f the residue class degree as usual.

The Galois group G operates on U_K and K^*. We are interested in

$$H^0(G, K^*) = k^*/N_k^K K^*,$$

or less precisely in the index $(k^*: N_k^K K^*)$. We shall prove:

Lemma 4. *Hypotheses being as above, we have*

$$Q(G, K^*) = (k^*: N_k^K K^*) = [K:k],$$
$$(U_k : N_k^K U_K) = e, \qquad Q(G, U_K) = 1.$$

Proof. We use the Q-machine. By Hilbert's Theorem 90 we know that $H^{-1}(G, K^*) = 1$. Hence

$$Q(K^*) = (k^* : N_k^K K^*)$$

is our norm index. We have $K^*/U_K \approx \mathbf{Z}$ (with trivial action, because $|\sigma\alpha| = |\alpha|$ for all $\alpha \in K^*$), whence

$$[K: k] = Q(\mathbf{Z}) = Q(K^*)/Q(U_K)$$

provided that we can show that $Q(U_K)$ is defined. In fact, we shall prove that it is equal to 1.

Let $\{\omega_\tau\}$ be a normal basis of K over k. After multiplying the elements of this basis by a high power of a prime element π in k, we can assume that they have small absolute value. Let

$$M = \sum_{\tau \in G} \mathfrak{o}\omega_\tau,$$

where $\mathfrak{o}$ is the ring of integers in k. Then G acts on M semilocally, with trivial decomposition group. Furthermore, $\exp M = V$ is G-isomorphic to M (the inverse is given by the log), and V is an open subgroup of the units, whence of finite index in U_K. Therefore we find that

$$1 = Q(V) = Q(U_K)$$

as desired.

Finally, we note that

$$Q(U_K) = \frac{(U_k : N_k^K U_K)}{(H : U_K^{1-\sigma})},$$

where H is the kernel of the norm in U_K. Using Hilbert's Theorem 90 again, together with the fact that $|\sigma\alpha| = |\alpha|$ for all $\alpha \in K^*$, we see that $H = K^{*1-\sigma}$. Hence the denominator of $Q(U_K)$ is given by

$$\begin{aligned}(H : U_K^{1-\sigma}) = (K^{*1-\sigma} : U_K^{1-\sigma}) &= (K^{*1-\sigma} : (k^* U_K)^{1-\sigma}) \\ &= \frac{(K^* : k^* U_K)}{(K^*_{1-\sigma} : (k^* U_K)_{1-\sigma})} \\ &= \frac{e}{(k^* : k^*)} = e.\end{aligned}$$

This shows that $(U_k\colon N_k^K U_K) = e$, and concludes the proof of the lemma.

Observe that we have recovered the result that if K/k is unramified, then every unit in k is a norm of a unit in K, because $e = 1$.

Remark. If k is the real or complex field, then the result of Lemma 4 holds also, and the verification is trivial. We must interpret the "units" then to mean the whole multiplicative group of the field, and $e = [K:k]$ is equal to 2 or 1.

In the local class field theory, we shall see that the factor group $k^*/N_k^K K^*$ is isomorphic to G, and not only in the cyclic case but also in the abelian case.

Finally, we remark that the inequality

$$(k^* : N_k^K K^*) \leqq [K:k]$$

follows easily for an arbitrary abelian extension K/k. To see this, consider a tower

$$K \supset E \supset k.$$

Assume that the inequality is proved for each step of the tower, namely K/E and E/k. We have

$$k^* \supset N_k^E E^* \supset N_k^K K^*$$

because $N_k^K = N_k^E \circ N_E^K$. Therefore

$$(k^* : N_k^K K^*) = (k^* : N_k^E E^*)(N_k^E E^* : N_k^K K^*).$$

But

$$(N_k^E E^* : N_k^E N_E^K K^*) \qquad \text{divides} \qquad (E^* : N_E^K K^*).$$

Since the degree of an extension is multiplicative in towers, we see that if the norm index inequality holds in each step of the tower, then it holds for K/k. This reduces the inequality to cyclic steps, in which case we apply Lemma 4.

Similarly, for any abelian extension K/k we have

$$(U_k : N_k^K U_K) \leqq e.$$

Local class field theory will ultimately show that we have an equality in these index relations.

§4. *A theorem on units*

We turn to the global case, and throughout this section we let k be a number field. Then U_k denotes the group of units in k.

Under a log mapping, we can embed the units (modulo roots of unity) into a Euclidean space $\mathbf{R}^s$. If K/k is a Galois extension with group G, then one can define an operation of G on $\mathbf{R}^s$ which makes this a G-embedding, in a natural way, and allows us to visualize the operation of G on the units somewhat more clearly. This is done as follows.

Let S be a finite set of absolute values on k containing all archimedean ones, and let S_K be the set of absolute values w on K such that $w|v$ for some $v \in S$. For each $w \in S_K$ we select a symbol X_w, and let E^s be the s-dimensional real space having $\{X_w\}$ as basis, for $w \in S_K$. Thus s is the number of elements of S_K. If $\sigma \in G$, we define

$$\sigma X_w = X_{\sigma w},$$

and extend σ to all of E^s by linearity. Then G operates on E^s.

By a lattice in E^s we mean, as usual, a free abelian subgroup of rank s, such that a $\mathbf{Z}$-basis for this subgroup is also an $\mathbf{R}$-basis for E^s. The next theorem is taken from Artin-Tate.

Theorem 1. *Let M be a lattice in E^s which is invariant under G* (i.e. $\sigma M \subset M$ *for all* $\sigma \in G$). *Then there exists a sublattice M' of finite index in M which is invariant under G, and has a $\mathbf{Z}$-basis* $\{Y_w\}$, ($w \in S_K$), *such that*

$$\sigma Y_w = Y_{\sigma w}.$$

Proof. We take the sup norm on E^s with respect to the coordinates relative to the basis $\{X_w\}$. Since M is a lattice, there exists a number b such that for any $X \in E^s$, there exists some $Z \in M$ such that

$$|X - Z| < b.$$

For each $v \in S$, let $\bar{v}$ be a fixed element of S_K such that $\bar{v}|v$. Take t real and large positive, and find some $Z_{\bar{v}} \in M$ such that

$$|tX_{\bar{v}} - Z_{\bar{v}}| < b.$$

For $w|v$, let

$$Y_w = \sum_{\sigma\bar{v}=w} \sigma Z_{\bar{v}}.$$

The sum is taken over all $\sigma \in G$ such that $\sigma\bar{v} = w$. We contend that the family $\{Y_w\}$ is a basis for a sublattice M' satisfying our requirements.

First the action of G is the desired one, because for $\tau \in G$,

$$\tau Y_w = \sum_{\sigma\bar{v}=w} \tau\sigma Z_{\bar{v}} = \sum_{\rho\bar{v}=\tau w} \rho Z_{\bar{v}} = Y_{\tau w}.$$

The second sum is taken over those elements $\rho \in G$ such that $\rho\bar{v} = \tau w$, making the transformation $\rho = \tau\sigma$. This proves our first assertion.

We must now show that the vectors $\{Y_w\}$ are linearly independent over $\mathbf{R}$. Suppose that

$$\sum_w c_w Y_w = 0$$

with real c_w. If not all $c_w = 0$, we may assume that $|c_w| \leqq 1$ for all w, and also $c_w = 1$ for some w. Let

$$Z_{\bar{v}} = tX_{\bar{v}} + B_{\bar{v}}$$

with a vector $B_{\bar{v}}$ such that $|B_{\bar{v}}| < b$. Then

$$Y_w = \sum_{\sigma\bar{v}=w} \sigma Z_{\bar{v}} = t \sum_{\sigma\bar{v}=w} X_{\sigma\bar{v}} + B'_w$$

where $|B'_w| \leqq Nb$, and $N =$ order of G. Hence

$$Y_w = tm_w X_w + B'_w$$

if m_w is the number of $\sigma \in G$ such that $\sigma\bar{v} = w$. Thus we obtain

$$0 = \sum_w c_w Y_w = t \sum_w c_w m_w X_w + B',$$

where $|B'| \leqq sNb$. Looking at that w such that $c_w = 1$, we see that if t was selected sufficiently large then we have a contradiction, thus proving our theorem.

We observe that M' is G-isomorphic to the lattice having $\{X_w\}$ as a basis. We can decompose M' into a direct sum

$$M' = \coprod_{v \in S} \coprod_{w|v} \mathbf{Z} Y_w$$

and each subgroup

$$M'_v = \coprod_{w|v} \mathbf{Z} Y_w$$

is semilocal (i.e. G permutes the factors $\mathbf{Z}Y_w$ transitively), with decomposition group G_w for each w, acting trivially on the local component $\mathbf{Z}Y_w$, which is G_w-isomorphic to $\mathbf{Z}$ itself.

We can now apply the semilocal theory, and the Q-machine.

Corollary 1. *Let G be cyclic of order N. Then*

$$Q(G, M) = Q(G, M') = \prod_{v \in S} N_v,$$

where N_v is the order of the composition group G_w for any $w|v$.

Proof. We have

$$Q(G, M') = \prod_{v \in S} Q(G, M'_v) = \prod_{v \in S} Q(G_{\bar{v}}, \mathbf{Z}Y_{\bar{v}})$$

and $Q(G_w, \mathbf{Z}) = N_w$, so that our corollary follows because $(M : M')$ is finite.

Corollary 2. *Let K/k be cyclic of order N and let K_S be the S-units in K. Then*

$$Q(G, K_S) = \frac{1}{N} \prod_{v \in S} N_v.$$

Proof. The map

$$L : K_S \to E^s$$

given by

$$L(\xi) = \sum_{w \in S_K} \log \|\xi\|_w X_w, \qquad (w \in S_K)$$

is a G-homomorphism of K_S into E^s, whose image is a lattice in a hyperplane of E^s, and whose kernel is finite. Let X_0 be the vector

$$X_0 = \sum_{w \in S_K} X_w.$$

Then X_0 and $L(K_S)$ generate a lattice M in E^s to which we can apply Theorem 1. The Q-machine gives:

$$Q(K_S) = Q\big(L(K_S)\big),$$

and since $\mathbf{Z}X_0$ is G-isomorphic to $\mathbf{Z}$,

$$Q(M') = Q(M) = Q\big(L(K_S)\big)Q(\mathbf{Z}).$$

But $Q(\mathbf{Z}) = N$. This proves our corollary.

§5. *The global cyclic norm index*

In this section, we prove:

If K/k is cyclic of degree N, then

$$(J_k : k^* N_k^K J_K) = (C_k : N_k^K C_K) = N.$$

Remark. The class field theory ultimately shows that the same relation holds if K/k is abelian. However, for an arbitrary finite extension E/k, the group $k^* N_k^E J_E$ is equal to $k^* N_k^K J_K$ where K is the maximal abelian subextension of E. Thus the fact that the index is equal to the degree in the abelian case is a non-trivial global fact, requiring some sort of global argument.

Considering the lemmas proved in the preceding sections, the proof will not be hard. We know by the finiteness of the class number that there exists a set of absolute values S in K such that

$$J_K = K^*J_{K,S} = K^*J_S.$$

We always assume that S contains all the archimedean absolute values, and we enlarge S so that S is invariant under G, i.e. if $\sigma \in G$ and $w \in S$ then $\sigma w \in S$ also. We also enlarge S so that S contains all w which are ramified.

We use the Q-machine, and find:

$$Q(C_K) = Q(J_K/K^*) = Q(K^*J_S/K^*) = Q(J_S/K_S) = Q(J_S)/Q(K_S).$$

We already know of course that $Q(K_S)$ is defined, and we have computed it in the preceding section. It is easy to see that $Q(J_S)$ is also defined and to compute it. Let S_k be the set of absolute values v of k which are induced by elements of $S = S_K$. We can write

$$J_S = \prod_{v \in S_k} \Big(\prod_{w|v} K_w^*\Big) \times \prod_{v \notin S_k} \Big(\prod_{w|v} U_w\Big) \cdot$$

By Lemma 4 of §3, and the assumption that any $v \notin S_k$ is unramified in K, we conclude that

$$H^0(G_w, U_w) = H^{-1}(G_w, U_w) = 1.$$

By the semilocal theory, and the fact that each factor

$$\prod_{w|v} U_w$$

is G-invariant, we conclude that if V denotes the product

$$V = \prod_{v \notin S_k} \prod_{w|v} U_w,$$

then

$$H^0(G, V) = H^{-1}(G, V) = 1,$$

and hence $Q(V) = 1$. Therefore by the semilocal theory, and Lemma 4 of §3,

$$Q(J_S) = \prod_{v \in S_k} Q(G_w, K_w^*) = \prod_{v \in S_k} N_v,$$

where N_v is the local degree $[K_w : k_v]$ for any $w|v$. Combining this with the value of $Q(K_S)$ found in Corollary 2, §4 we see that

$$Q(C_K) = N.$$

But

$$Q(C_K) = \frac{(C_k : N_k^K C_K)}{h_{-1}},$$

where h_{-1} is the order of $H^{-1}(G, C_K)$. Hence $(C_k : N_k^K C_K)$ is divisible by N. In view of the universal norm index inequality, we now conclude that equality must hold, thus proving what we wanted.

Remark. Because of this equality, we also find as a by-product that

$$H^{-1}(G, C_K) = 1.$$

See the next section for an application of this.

As an application of our index result, we can prove:

Let K/k be cyclic of degree > 1. Then infinitely many primes of k do not split completely in K.

Proof. Suppose that all but a finite number of v in k split completely in K. Let S be a finite set of absolute values of k containing those which do not (i.e. for which $K_w \neq k_v$ if $v \notin S$). We shall prove that $J_k = k^* N_k^K J_K$, which will be a contradiction. Let $a \in J_k$. By the approximation theorem, there exists some $\alpha \in k^*$ such that αa is very close to 1 at all $v \in S$, and hence a local norm at all $v \in S$. For $v \notin S$, αa is trivially a local norm since $K_w = k_v$. Hence $\alpha a = N_k^K A$ for some idele $A \in J_K$. Hence

$$J_k \subset k^* N_k^K J_K.$$

This proves our assertion.

This result will be used in the next chapter to show that the reciprocity law mapping is surjective.

§6. *Applications*

This section will not be used in the rest of the book and may be omitted. It deals with cohomological applications of the results obtained so far. We assume that the reader is acquainted with a little bit of cohomology of groups, but nothing worse than H^{-1}, H^0, H^1, H^2 and the exact sequence connecting them. Let K/k be cyclic. Corresponding to the exact sequence

$$0 \to K^* \to J_K \to C_K \to 0$$

we have an exact sequence

$$1 = H^{-1}(G, C_K) \to H^0(G, K^*) \to H^0(G, J_K),$$

whence the map on the right is injective. If the reader looks at the definitions, he will see that this injection is nothing but

Hasse's Theorem. *Let K/k be a cyclic extension. If an element $\alpha \in k^*$ is a local norm everywhere, then it is a global norm.*

Note. This is true in general only in the cyclic case. The variance from this precise relation in, say, abelian extensions, is determined by higher cohomology (3-cohomology, in fact).

Next, consider another piece of the exact sequence,

$$1 = H^1(G, C_K) \to H^2(G, K^*) \to H^2(G, J_K).$$

Again, we have an injective map on the right. But H^2 is nothing but the Brauer group, and the injection is nothing but the fundamental theorem of Albert-Hasse-Brauer-Noether:

A 2-cocycle (or simple algebra) splits globally if and only if it splits locally everywhere.

This last statement has seemingly been proved only in the cyclic case, but it is an easy technical matter to see that it holds for any Galois extension, i.e. that $H^1(G, C_K) = 1$ if K/k is Galois. Our purpose is not to go into this part of theory here, so we let the reader look it up elsewhere (e.g. Artin-Tate).

CHAPTER X

The Artin Symbol, Reciprocity Law, and Class Field Theory

§1. *Formalism of the Artin symbol*

Let K/k be an abelian extension, and let $\mathfrak{p}$ be a prime of k which is unramified in K. We had seen in Chapter I, §5 that there exists a unique element σ of the Galois group G, lying in the decomposition group $G_{\mathfrak{P}}$ (for any $\mathfrak{P}|\mathfrak{p}$, they all coincide in the abelian case) having the effect

$$\sigma\alpha \equiv \alpha^{\mathrm{N}\mathfrak{p}} \pmod{\mathfrak{P}}, \qquad \alpha \in \mathfrak{o}_K.$$

This element σ depends only on $\mathfrak{p}$, is denoted by $(\mathfrak{p}, K/k)$, and will be called the **Artin symbol** of $\mathfrak{p}$ in G.

We extend the map

$$\mathfrak{p} \mapsto (\mathfrak{p}, K/k)$$

to the subgroup $I(\mathfrak{d})$ of fractional ideals prime to the discriminant $\mathfrak{d}$ of K/k, by multiplicativity. In other words, if $\mathfrak{a}$ is prime to $\mathfrak{d}$, and

$$\mathfrak{a} = \prod \mathfrak{p}^{\nu_{\mathfrak{p}}},$$

then we define

$$(\mathfrak{a}, K/k) = \prod (\mathfrak{p}, K/k)^{\nu_{\mathfrak{p}}}.$$

We call again $(\mathfrak{a}, K/k)$ the Artin symbol of $\mathfrak{a}$, and the map

$$\mathfrak{a} \mapsto (\mathfrak{a}, K/k)$$

is a homomorphism

$$\omega : I(\mathfrak{d}) \to G(K/k),$$

which will also be called the **reciprocity law map,** or the **Artin map.** Its kernel will be called the reciprocity law kernel, or **Artin kernel** $\mathfrak{A}$. The Artin symbol satisfies the following formal properties, which are immediate consequences of its definition.

A1. *Let $\sigma: K \to \sigma K$ be an isomorphism (not necessarily equal to the identity on k). Then*

$$(\sigma\mathfrak{a}, \sigma K/\sigma k) = \sigma(\mathfrak{a}, K/k)\sigma^{-1}.$$

Proof. Obvious.

A2. *Let $K' \supset K \supset k$ be a bigger abelian extension. Then*

$$\mathrm{res}_K(\mathfrak{a}, K'/k) = (\mathfrak{a}, K/k).$$

For this statement, any prime entering in the factorization of $\mathfrak{a}$ must be unramified in K'. The statement is obvious for prime ideals, and thus follows for any $\mathfrak{a}$. It is called the **consistency property.**

A3. *Let K/k be abelian and let E/k be finite. Let $\mathfrak{p}$ be a prime in k unramified in K and let $\mathfrak{q}$ be a prime of E lying above $\mathfrak{p}$. Then*

$$\mathrm{res}_K(\mathfrak{q}, KE/E) = (\mathfrak{p}, K/k)^f$$

where f is the residue class degree, $f = [\mathfrak{o}_E/\mathfrak{q} : \mathfrak{o}_k/\mathfrak{p}] = f(\mathfrak{q}|\mathfrak{p})$.

The lattice of fields is as follows:

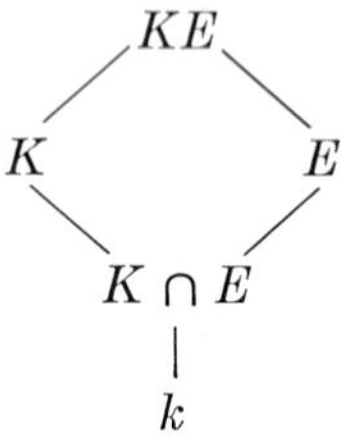

For any $x \in \mathfrak{o}_{KE}/\mathfrak{Q}$ (where $\mathfrak{Q}$ is a prime of KE lying above $\mathfrak{q}$) and $\sigma = (\mathfrak{q}, KE/E)$ we have $\sigma x = x^{\mathbf{N}\mathfrak{q}}$. But $\mathbf{N}\mathfrak{q} = \mathbf{N}\mathfrak{p}^f$. Thus our property is obvious. We also see another formulation, namely:

A4. *Let K, E be as above, and let $\mathfrak{b}$ be a fractional ideal of E such that if $\mathfrak{q}$ occurs in the factorization of $\mathfrak{b}$, and $\mathfrak{q}|\mathfrak{p}$ with $\mathfrak{p}$ in k, then $\mathfrak{p}$ is unramified in K. Then*

$$\mathrm{res}_K\,(\mathfrak{b}, KE/E) = (N_k^E\mathfrak{b}, K/k).$$

In particular, if $K \supset E \supset k$, then

$$(\mathfrak{b}, K/E) = (N_k^E\mathfrak{b}, K/k).$$

The next property is neither trivial nor formal, and is a corollary of the cyclic norm index equality.

Theorem 1. *Let K/k be abelian. Then the reciprocity law map $\mathfrak{a} \mapsto (\mathfrak{a}, K/k)$ is surjective, as a map of $I(\mathfrak{c})$ into the Galois group, for any cycle $\mathfrak{c}$ (divisible by the ramified primes).*

Proof. Let $\mathfrak{c}$ be a fixed cycle of k, divisible by the ramified primes, and let H be the subgroup of G which is the image of the reciprocity law mapping. Let F be the fixed field of H. We must show that $F = k$. Any $\mathfrak{p} \in I(\mathfrak{c})$ must split completely in F, otherwise $(\mathfrak{p}, F/k) \neq 1$, and $(\mathfrak{p}, F/k)$ is the restriction of $(\mathfrak{p}, K/k)$, thus contradicting the fact that F is the fixed field of H. Thus all but a finite number of primes of k split completely in F. If $F \neq k$, then F contains a subfield F_0 which is cyclic over k, of degree > 1, and all but a finite number of primes of k split completely in F_0. This contradicts the result of Chapter IX, §5 (essentially, the global norm index equality), and proves our theorem.

Our main task now is to prove that there exists some admissible cycle $\mathfrak{c}$ such that $P_\mathfrak{c}$ is contained in the kernel of the Artin map. Such $\mathfrak{c}$ is called a **conductor** for the Artin map. This is the crux of the present approach to class field theory, and is a remarkable fact. Indeed, the Artin map is defined for each $\mathfrak{p}$ (unramified) and extended formally to fractional ideals. There is a priori no connection between this definition and the definition of $P_\mathfrak{c}$ (which is very global).

Property **A4** shows that the norm group of ideals is contained in the kernel of the Artin map, that is if $\mathfrak{A}$ is a fractional ideal of K relatively prime to the ramified primes, then

$$(N_k^K \mathfrak{A}, K/k) = 1.$$

Therefore if $\mathfrak{c}$ is a conductor, then the group which we denoted by $P_\mathfrak{c}\mathfrak{N}(\mathfrak{c})$ is contained in the Artin kernel $\mathfrak{A}$. But we know the universal inequality

$$\big(I(\mathfrak{c}) : P_\mathfrak{c}\mathfrak{N}(\mathfrak{c})\big) \leqq [K:k] = (G:1).$$

In view of Theorem 1, the surjectivity of the Artin map, it follows that $P_\mathfrak{c}\mathfrak{N}(\mathfrak{c})$ is the precise kernel, and we get an isomorphism

$$\omega : I(\mathfrak{c})/P_\mathfrak{c}\mathfrak{N}(\mathfrak{c}) \to G$$

from the Artin map. This is the Artin reciprocity law.

Example: Cyclotomic extensions.

We conclude this section by our usual example of cyclotomic extensions, not only because of its special interest, but also because it will be used in the general proofs later.

Let m be an integer > 1. Let $K = \mathbf{Q}(\zeta_m)$ be the extension obtained by adjoining a primitive m-th root of unity to $\mathbf{Q}$. Then only primes p dividing m ramify in K (cf. for instance Proposition 8, Chapter III, §2, together with the fact that ζ_m is a root of $X^m - 1 = 0$). Let p be a prime number, $p \nmid m$. Then the definitions show that $((p), \mathbf{Q}(\zeta_m)/\mathbf{Q})$ has the effect

$$\zeta \mapsto \zeta^p$$

on $\zeta = \zeta_m$. Hence if a is a positive rational number prime to m, and $a \equiv d \pmod{^*\, m}$ for any positive integer d, then

$$((a), \mathbf{Q}(\zeta_m)/\mathbf{Q}) : \zeta \mapsto \zeta^d.$$

In particular, $((a), \mathbf{Q}(\zeta_m)/\mathbf{Q}) = 1$ if and only if $a \equiv 1 \pmod{^*\, m}$.

Next, let k be any number field, and $K \subset k(\zeta_m)$. There exists a cycle $\mathfrak{c}$ of k divisible only by $\mathfrak{p}|m$ and archimedean v such that if $\alpha \in k^*$ and

$$\alpha \equiv 1 \pmod{^*\, \mathfrak{c}},$$

then (α) is in the kernel of the Artin map, i.e. $P_{\mathfrak{c}}$ is contained in $\mathfrak{A}$.

Proof. This follows easily from the formal properties of the Artin symbol. By consistency, it suffices to prove our assertion when $K = k(\zeta_m)$. By the continuity of the local norms, there exists $\mathfrak{c}$ such that if $\alpha \in k^*$ and $\alpha \equiv 1 \pmod{^*\, \mathfrak{c}}$, then $N_{\mathbf{Q}}^k \alpha \equiv 1 \pmod{^*\, m}$ and is positive. At the archimedean absolute values, we simply impose the condition that α is totally positive. Then

$$\operatorname{res}_{\mathbf{Q}(\zeta_m)} ((\alpha), K/k) = (N_{\mathbf{Q}}^k(\alpha), \mathbf{Q}(\zeta_m)/\mathbf{Q}) = 1.$$

The effect of an element of $G(k(\zeta_m)/k)$ is determined by its effect on ζ_m. This concludes the proof that the Artin map has a conductor in cyclotomic extensions, and that we can take this conductor divisible only by $\mathfrak{p}|m$ or archimedean v.

§2. Existence of a conductor for the Artin symbol

We shall need auxiliary cyclotomic fields, and to construct these, we need prime numbers satisfying certain properties. Artin's original proof for the existence of these prime numbers used fancy existence theorems. Van der Waerden observed that one could get them easily and in a very elementary manner, and the proofs of Lemmas 1 and 2 are due to him.

Lemma 1. *Let a, r be integers > 1. Let q be a prime number. Then there exists a prime number p such that a has order q^r (mod p).*

Proof. We consider the positive number

$$T = \frac{a^{q^r} - 1}{a^{q^{r-1}} - 1}.$$

Then

$$T = (a^{q^{r-1}} - 1)^{q-1} + q(a^{q^{r-1}} - 1)^{q-2} + \cdots + q.$$

Let p be a prime dividing T. If p also divides $a^{q^{r-1}} - 1$, then $p = q$. Otherwise, p serves our purposes. If q divides T then q also divides $a^{q^{r-1}} - 1$. If $q > 2$, then $q - 1 > 1$, and hence q^2 does not divide T. But $T > q$, so that there exists a prime $p \neq q$ dividing T and not $a^{q^{r-1}} - 1$, which serves our purposes. Finally, if $q = 2$, then

$$T = (a^{2^{r-1}} - 1) + 2,$$

and is not divisible by 2^2 so that again there exists $p|T$ but p does not divide $a^{2^{r-1}} - 1$, thus concluding the proof.

Let m be an integer > 1. Integers $a, b > 0$ are said to be independent mod m if they generate cyclic groups in $(\mathbf{Z}/m\mathbf{Z})^*$ which are independent, i.e. whose intersection is 1.

Lemma 2. *Let*

$$n = q_1^{r_1} \cdots q_s^{r_s}$$

be a positive integer factorized into powers of primes q_i. Let a be an integer > 1. There exists an integer

$$m = p_1 \cdots p_s p'_1 \cdots p'_s,$$

with distinct primes p_i, p'_i such that a has order (mod m) *divisible by n, and there exists a positive integer b whose order* (mod m) *is divisible by n, and such that a, b are independent* mod m. *The primes p_i, p'_i can be chosen arbitrarily large, satisfying these conditions.*

Proof. By letting $r \to \infty$, we see that in Lemma 1, we can find arbitrarily large primes p such that a has order (mod p) divisible by a fixed power of q. We therefore first find large distinct primes $p_1, \ldots, p_s$ such that a has order $q_i^{r_i^*}$ (mod p_i) with a positive integer $r_i^* > r_i$. Next we find still larger primes $p'_1, \ldots, p'_s$, distinct from $p_1, \ldots, p_s$ and from each other, such that a has order $q_i^{r'_i}$ (mod p'_i) with a positive integer $r'_i > r_i^*$. We let $m = p_1 \cdots p_s p'_1 \cdots p'_s$. Then certainly a has order (mod m)

divisible by n. Let b be a positive integer such that

$$b \equiv a \pmod{p_1 \cdots p_s} \qquad \text{and} \qquad b \equiv 1 \pmod{p'_1 \cdots p'_s}.$$

Then b has order (mod m) divisible by n. Finally, suppose that

$$a^\nu b^\mu \equiv 1 \pmod{m}$$

with positive integers ν, μ. Then $a^\nu \equiv 1 \pmod{p'_1 \cdots p'_s}$, whence

$$q_1^{r'_1} \cdots q_s^{r'_s} \text{ divides } \nu.$$

This implies that $a^\nu \equiv 1 \pmod{p_1 \cdots p_s}$, and hence that $a^\nu \equiv 1 \pmod{m}$. Therefore $b^\mu \equiv 1 \pmod{m}$, thereby finishing the proof of the lemma.

We interpret the lemma in terms of cyclotomic extensions. In an abelian group G, we say that two elements σ, τ are independent if they generate cyclic groups whose intersection is 1.

Lemma 3. *Let K be an abelian extension of the number field k, and let S be a finite set of prime numbers. Let $n = [K:k]$. Let $\mathfrak{p}$ be a prime of k which is unramified in K. Then there exists an integer m relatively prime to the numbers in S and to $\mathfrak{p}$, such that:*

(i) *The Artin symbol $(\mathfrak{p}, k(\zeta_m)/k)$ has order divisible by n.*

(ii) *$K \cap k(\zeta_m) = k$.*

(iii) *There exists an automorphism τ of $k(\zeta_m)$ over k, independent of $(\mathfrak{p}, k(\zeta_m)/k)$, and whose order is divisible by n.*

Proof. We apply Lemma 2 with $a = \mathbf{N}\mathfrak{p}$. We can take m divisible only by arbitrarily large primes, so that $K \cap \mathbf{Q}(\zeta_m) = \mathbf{Q}$ and (ii) is satisfied. Let $\sigma = (\mathfrak{p}, k(\zeta_m)/k)$. Then

$$\sigma\zeta_m = \zeta_m^a,$$

and (i) is satisfied. Finally select b as in Lemma 2, and define τ by $\tau\zeta_m = \zeta_m^b$. Then (iii) is satisfied. This proves the lemma.

Artin's Lemma. *Let k be a number field, K a finite cyclic extension, and S a finite set of prime numbers. Let $\mathfrak{p}$ be a prime of k unramified in K. Then there exists an integer m relatively prime to all numbers in S, and a finite extension E of k such that:*

(1) *$K \cap E = k$.*

(2) *$K(\zeta_m) = E(\zeta_m)$ and $K \cap k(\zeta_m) = k$.*

(3) *$\mathfrak{p}$ splits completely in E.*

Proof. The lattice of fields is as follows:

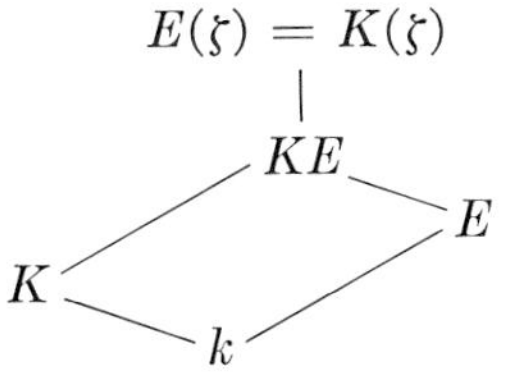

Choose m as in the preceding lemma and let $\zeta = \zeta_m$. The Galois group of $K(\zeta)$ over k is the product of the group G of K over k and the group of $k(\zeta)$ over k. Let σ be a generator of G. Let τ be as in the preceding lemma, and let H be the subgroup of $K(\zeta)$ over k generated by $\sigma \times \tau$ and

$$(\mathfrak{p}, K/k) \times (\mathfrak{p}, k(\zeta)/k).$$

This second condition guarantees that H contains $(\mathfrak{p}, K(\zeta)/k)$, and hence by definition, the decomposition group of $\mathfrak{p}$ in $K(\zeta)$. If E is the fixed field of H, then $\mathfrak{p}$ splits completely in E.

On the other hand, it is clear that the intersection of H and $G \times 1$ is the identity. But $G \times 1$ is the subgroup of $K(\zeta)$ leaving $k(\zeta)$ fixed. Hence $k(\zeta)E = E(\zeta)$ must be all of $K(\zeta)$. This proves Artin's lemma.

The lemma will be applied in a moment to a situation where we deal with a finite number of primes $\mathfrak{p}_1, \ldots, \mathfrak{p}_r$ in k. For each $\mathfrak{p}_i$ $(i = 1, \ldots, r)$ we construct an auxiliary field E_i with a root of unity ζ_{m_i} as in the lemma, selecting successively the integers $m_1, \ldots, m_r$ such that they are divisible by large primes, and are relatively prime to each other. Then

$$K(\zeta_{m_1}, \ldots, \zeta_{m_r})/k \quad \text{has group} \quad G \times G_1 \times \cdots \times G_r,$$

where G_i is the Galois group of $\mathbf{Q}(\zeta_{m_i})/\mathbf{Q}$. Each E_i is the fixed field of the group

$$H_i \times G_1 \times \cdots \times \hat{G}_i \times \cdots \times G_r,$$

where the roof means that G_i is omitted, and H_i is the subgroup of $G \times G_i$ generated by

$$\sigma \times \tau_i \quad \text{and} \quad (\mathfrak{p}_i, K/k) \times (\mathfrak{p}_i, k(\zeta_{m_i})/k).$$

As before, σ is a fixed generator of G.

Contention: The field $E = E_1 \cdots E_r$ (compositum of all E_i) is such that $K \cap E = k$, and hence $G(K/k) \approx G(KE/E)$.

Proof. The field E is the fixed field of the intersection of all groups $G(KE/E_i)$, which contains

$$\sigma \times \tau_1 \times \cdots \times \tau_r.$$

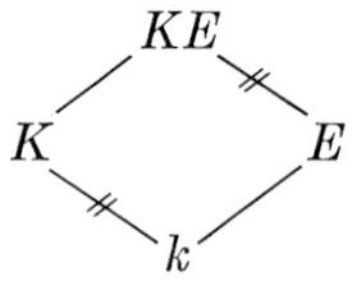

Furthermore, K is left fixed by

$$1 \times \tau_1 \times \cdots \times \tau_r.$$

Hence $K \cap E$ is left fixed by $\sigma \times 1 \times \cdots \times 1$, and is therefore equal to k, thus proving the contention.

Theorem 2. *Let K/k be a cyclic extension. Then there exists an admissible cycle $\mathfrak{c}$ divisible only by ramified $\mathfrak{p}$ in K such that the kernel of the Artin map in $I(\mathfrak{c})$ is equal to $P_{\mathfrak{c}}\mathfrak{N}(\mathfrak{c})$.*

Proof. We shall prove that there exists $\mathfrak{c}$ such that the kernel of the Artin map is contained in $P_{\mathfrak{c}}\mathfrak{N}(\mathfrak{c})$, i.e.

$$\mathfrak{A} \subset P_{\mathfrak{c}}\mathfrak{N}(\mathfrak{c}) \subset I(\mathfrak{c}).$$

By the cyclic norm index inequality, and Theorem 1, which implies

$$(I(\mathfrak{c}) : \mathfrak{A}) = [K : k],$$

we then conclude that $\mathfrak{A} = P_{\mathfrak{c}}\mathfrak{N}(\mathfrak{c})$.

Let $\mathfrak{f}$ be the smallest admissible cycle for K/k, and let $\mathfrak{a} \in I(\mathfrak{f})$ be such that $(\mathfrak{a}, K/k) = 1$. We know that only ramified primes $\mathfrak{p}$ can divide $\mathfrak{f}$. We have to prove that $\mathfrak{a} \in P_{\mathfrak{f}}\mathfrak{N}(\mathfrak{f})$. Factorize $\mathfrak{a}$ into prime powers:

$$\mathfrak{a} = \prod_{i=1}^{r} \mathfrak{p}_i^{\nu_1}.$$

For each $\mathfrak{p}_i$ construct the auxiliary extension E_i by means of a root of unity ζ_{m_i} as described above, and form the compositum

$$E = E_1 \cdots E_r.$$

We have the diagram:

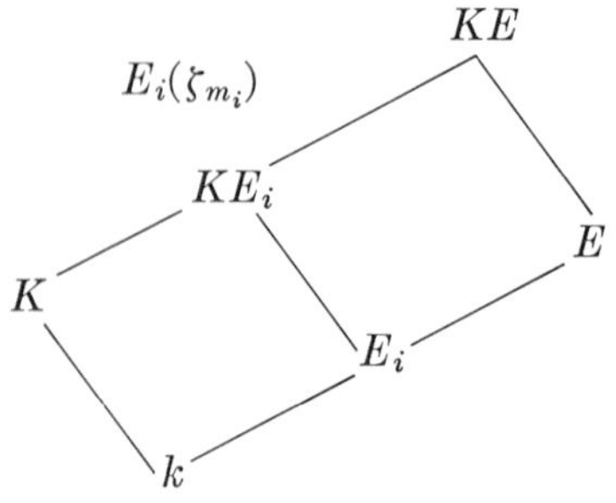

By hypothesis, if we let σ be a generator of G, and

$$(\mathfrak{p}_i^{\nu_i}, K/k) = \sigma^{d_i}$$

for some integer $d_i \geqq 0$, then $(\mathfrak{a}, K/k) = \prod \sigma^{d_i} = \sigma^{\Sigma d_i} = 1$. Hence

$$\sum d_i = dn,$$

where $n = [K:k]$, that is n divides $\sum d_i$. Select a fractional ideal $\mathfrak{b}_E$ in E, prime to $\mathfrak{f}$, and all integers m_i, such that

$$(\mathfrak{b}_E, KE/E) = \sigma.$$

This can be done by Theorem 1. We identify here $G(K/k)$ with $G(KE/E)$. Let $\mathfrak{b}_k = N_k^E \mathfrak{b}_E$. Then

$$(\mathfrak{b}_k, K/k) = \sigma.$$

We note that $\mathfrak{p}_i^{\nu_i}\mathfrak{b}_k^{-d_i}$ is a norm from E_i. This is true of a power of $\mathfrak{p}_i$ because $\mathfrak{p}_i$ splits completely in E_i, and $\mathfrak{b}_k$ is a norm by the transitivity of the norm. Write

$$\mathfrak{p}_i^{\nu_i}\mathfrak{b}_k^{-d_i} = N_k^{E_i}\mathfrak{A}_i$$

with some $\mathfrak{A}_i$ prime to $\mathfrak{f}$ and all m_i. Since $(\mathfrak{p}_i^{\nu_i}\mathfrak{b}_k^{-d_i}, K/k) = 1$, it follows that $(\mathfrak{A}_i, KE_i/E_i) = 1$. But KE_i/E_i is cyclotomic, and we can apply the theorem for cyclotomic extensions. We write

$$\mathfrak{A}_i = (\beta_i) N_{E_i}^{KE_i}\mathfrak{B}_i$$

for some $\mathfrak{B}_i$ prime to $\mathfrak{f}$ and all m_i, and $\beta_i \equiv 1 \pmod{^* m\mathfrak{c}_i'}$ for some cycle $\mathfrak{c}_i'$ in E_i, which we can select highly divisible by all primes dividing $\mathfrak{f}$, and archimedean absolute values. Taking the norm from E_i to k, we get

$$\mathfrak{p}_i^{\nu_i}\mathfrak{b}_k^{-d_i} = (N_k^{E_i}\beta_i) N_k^K (N_K^{KE_i}\mathfrak{B}_i),$$

and $N_k^{E_i}\beta_i \equiv 1 \pmod{^* \mathfrak{f}}$. Taking the product over all i shows that $\mathfrak{a}\mathfrak{b}_k^{-dn} \in P_{\mathfrak{f}}\mathfrak{N}(\mathfrak{f})$. But $n = [K:k]$, so that $\mathfrak{b}_k^{-dn}$ is also a norm. Hence $\mathfrak{a} \in P_{\mathfrak{f}}\mathfrak{N}(\mathfrak{f})$, thereby concluding the proof of the theorem.

Although the next result is a corollary of the cyclic result just proved, we state it as a theorem. It is the central theorem of class field theory.

Theorem 3. *Let K/k be an abelian extension. Let $\mathfrak{c}$ be any admissible cycle for K/k. Then the Artin map*

$$I(\mathfrak{c}) \to G(K/k)$$

has kernel equal to $P_{\mathfrak{c}}\mathfrak{N}(\mathfrak{c})$, *and thus induces an isomorphism*

$$I(\mathfrak{c})/P_{\mathfrak{c}}\mathfrak{N}(\mathfrak{c}) \to G.$$

Proof. Let $\mathfrak{f}$ be the smallest admissible cycle for K/k. If $\mathfrak{c}$ is divisible only by the same v that divide $\mathfrak{f}$, then we know from Theorem 7 of Chapter VII, §4 that $P_{\mathfrak{f}}\mathfrak{N}(\mathfrak{f}) = P_{\mathfrak{c}}\mathfrak{N}(\mathfrak{f})$. We express K/k as a compositum of cyclic extensions. For each such cyclic extension, we can find a conductor divisible only by v such that $v|\mathfrak{f}$, using Theorem 2. An element $\sigma \in G(K/k)$ is equal to 1 if and only if its restriction to each cyclic extension is equal to 1. Hence by Theorem 2, we can find some admissible $\mathfrak{c}$ such that the kernel of the Artin map contains $P_{\mathfrak{c}}$, and we know trivially that the kernel of the Artin map contains $\mathfrak{N}(\mathfrak{f})$. Hence

$$P_{\mathfrak{f}}\mathfrak{N}(\mathfrak{f}) \subset \mathfrak{A}.$$

As pointed out already, using the universal norm index inequality, we obtain $\mathfrak{A} = P_{\mathfrak{f}}\mathfrak{N}(\mathfrak{f})$. For an arbitrary admissible $\mathfrak{c}$, the result follows immediately, because

$$P_{\mathfrak{c}}\mathfrak{N}(\mathfrak{c}) = P_{\mathfrak{f}}\mathfrak{N}(\mathfrak{f}) \cap I(\mathfrak{c}).$$

We have proved the fundamental theorem of class field theory.

We shall formulate the result in terms of ideles in the next section, and prove the other theorems of class field theory, which are now mere corollaries.

§3. *Class fields*

Let K/k be an abelian extension. For any admissible cycle $\mathfrak{c}$, we have an isomorphism

$$J/k^*N_k^K J_K \approx I(\mathfrak{c})/P_{\mathfrak{c}}\mathfrak{N}(\mathfrak{c})$$

described in Chapter VII, §4. This isomorphism allows us therefore to define the Artin map for ideles, and we get a map

$$\omega : J_k \to G(K/k),$$

also denoted by

$$a \mapsto (a, K/k),$$

which we may once more describe explicitly as follows. We select $\alpha \in k^*$ such that $\alpha a \equiv 1 \pmod{^*\ \mathfrak{c}}$. If $\mathfrak{a}$ is the associated ideal of αa, then

$$(a, K/k) = (\mathfrak{a}, K/k).$$

This is well defined. Observe that from our definition, we get

$$(\alpha, K/k) = 1$$

for all $\alpha \in k^*$. Thus the Artin map on ideles may be viewed as defined on the idele classes, and yields an isomorphism

$$C_k/N_k^K C_K \approx G(K/k).$$

If a is an idele, and a_v its v-component for $v \in M_k$, then we identify a_v with the idele whose v-component is a_v, and having component 1 at all $v' \in M_k$, $v' \neq v$. Thus we have the correspondence

$$a_v \leftrightarrow (\ldots, 1, 1, a_v, 1, 1, \ldots)$$

for $a_v \in k_v^*$. If a is an idele, then a_v is a unit for almost all v. Let S be a finite set of absolute values on k containing the archimedean ones and all v which are ramified in K. Let S also contain those v at which a_v is not a unit. If $v \notin S$, then a_v is a local norm, and hence the idele

$$a^S = \prod_{v \notin S} a_v$$

is in $N_k^K J_K$. Hence $(a^S, K/k) = 1$, and

$$(a, K/k) = \prod_{v \in S} (a_v, K/k).$$

Since $(a_v, K/k) = 1$ for all but a finite number of v, we may summarize the preceding discussion in a theorem as follows.

Theorem 4. *Let K/k be abelian. The Artin map $a \mapsto (a, K/k)$ induces an isomorphism*

$$C_k/N_k^K C_K = J_k/k^* N_k^K J_K \xrightarrow{\approx} G(K/k),$$

and for any idele a, we have

$$(a, K/k) = \prod_{v \in M_k} (a_v, K/k).$$

Next we have formal properties of the symbol $(a, K/k)$, similar to the symbol for ideals.

A1. *Let $\sigma : K \to \sigma K$ be an isomorphism (not necessarily equal to the identity on k). Then*

$$(\sigma a, \sigma K/\sigma k) = \sigma(a, K/k)\sigma^{-1}.$$

A2. *Let $K' \supset K \supset k$ be a bigger abelian extension. Then*

$$\mathrm{res}_K\,(a, K'/k) = (a, K/k).$$

A3. *Let K/k be abelian and let E/k be finite. Let $b \in J_E$. Then*

$$\mathrm{res}_K\,(b, KE/E) = (N_k^E b, K/k).$$

These properties are immediate from the corresponding properties for the ideal map.

If E/k is a finite extension, then $N_k^E J_E$ is an open subgroup of J_k. Indeed, if v is unramified in E, then every unit in k_v is a local norm. Even if v is ramified, the group of local norms contains an open neighborhood of 1, which is of finite index in the group of units. Hence the group of local norms is open. Hence $N_k^E J_E$ is open. Thus the group $k^* N_k^E J_E$ is an open subgroup of J_k, containing k^*. There is a bijection between open subgroups of J_k containing k^* and open subgroups of $C_k = J_k/k^*$. If H is an open subgroup of J_k containing k^*, we say that H **belongs to the abelian extension** K/k if $H = k^* N_k^K J_K$. And similarly if H is an open subgroup of C_k, we say that it belongs to K/k if $H = N_k^K C_K$. We shall also say that K is the **class field belonging** to H. We also say that H is the **class group belonging** to K.

If K is the class field belonging to H, and $\sigma : K \to \sigma K$ is an isomorphism (not necessarily identity on k), then it is clear from the basic definitions that σK is class field (over σk) to σH.

Theorem 5. *The map $K \mapsto N_k^K C_K$ (resp. $K \mapsto k^* N_k^K J_K$) establishes a bijection between finite abelian extensions of k and open subgroups of C_k (resp. of J_k, containing k^*). If K belongs to H and K' belongs to H', then $K \subset K'$ if and only if $H \supset H'$. Furthermore, KK' belongs to $H \cap H'$, and $K \cap K'$ belongs to HH'.*

Proof. Suppose that H belongs to K and H' belongs to K'. The kernel of the Artin map

$$C_k \to G(KK'/k)$$

is $H \cap H'$, because of the consistency property **A2.** Hence $H \cap H'$ belongs to KK'. If $K \subset K'$, it follows from the transitivity of the norm that $H \supset H'$. Conversely, if $H \supset H'$, then $H \cap H' = H'$, and

$$(C_k \colon H') = [K' : k] = [KK' : k].$$

Since $k \subset K' \subset KK'$, we conclude that $KK' = K'$, whence $K \subset K'$. This proves our theorem, except for the fact that every open subgroup of C_k belongs to an abelian extension. This will be proved in the next chapter.

Corollary 1. *Let K/k be class field to H and let $H_1 \supset H$. Then H_1 has a class field, which is the fixed field of $(H_1, K/k)$.*

Proof. Let K_1 be the fixed field of $(H_1, K/k)$. By the consistency property of the Artin map, we see at once that H_1 is the kernel of the map $C_k \to G(K_1/k)$, so K_1 is the class field belonging to H_1.

Corollary 2. *Let K/k be an abelian extension and let $\mathfrak{c}$ be a cycle of k, admissible for K/k. Let $W_{\mathfrak{c}}$ be the neighborhood of 1 in J_k defined in Chapter VII, §4. If $k^*W_{\mathfrak{c}}$ belongs to the class field $K_{\mathfrak{c}}/k$, then $K \subset K_{\mathfrak{c}}$.*

Proof. Let H belong to K. As we saw in Chapter VII, §4, we have the inclusion $H \supset k^*W_{\mathfrak{c}}$. Hence our assertion is now obvious.

The class field to $k^*W_{\mathfrak{c}}$ (whose existence will be proved in general in the next chapter) is called a **ray class field** (Strahl Klassenkörper).

Example. Let $K = \mathbf{Q}(\zeta_m)$. We shall prove that K is the ray class field to the cycle mv_∞, thus belonging to $\mathbf{Q}^*W_{mv_\infty}$.

Proof. We first consider the case when $m = p^\nu$ is a prime power. Let u be a local unit at p, i.e. $u \in U_p$. We identify u with the idele

$$u = (\ldots, 1, u, 1, \ldots)$$

having component 1 at all $v \neq v_p$, and component u at p. Let $\mathfrak{c} = p^\mu v_\infty$ be an admissible cycle for $K/\mathbf{Q}$, with $\mu \geqq \nu$. Let a be a positive integer such that

$$au \equiv 1 \pmod{p^\mu}.$$

Then

$$au = (\ldots, a, a, au, a, a, \ldots)$$

is an idele such that

$$au \equiv 1 \ (\text{mod}^*\ p^\mu v_\infty).$$

If

$$\sigma = (u, \mathbf{Q}(\zeta_{p^\nu})/\mathbf{Q}) = (au, \mathbf{Q}(\zeta_{p^\nu})/\mathbf{Q}),$$

then from the definition of the Artin map for ideles, we find that

$$\sigma\zeta = \zeta^a.$$

However, ζ^a depends only on the residue class of $a \pmod{p^\nu}$. We conclude that if $u \in U_p$ and $u \equiv 1 \pmod{p^\nu}$, then

$$(u, \mathbf{Q}(\zeta_{p^\nu})/\mathbf{Q}) = 1.$$

This implies that if $m = p^\nu$, and H_m is the class group belonging to $\mathbf{Q}(\zeta_m)$, then

$$W_{mv_\infty} \subset H_m.$$

For an arbitrary unit u in U_p, we can write symbolically

$$(u, \mathbf{Q}(\zeta_{p^\nu})/\mathbf{Q}) : \zeta \mapsto \zeta^{u^{-1}},$$

exponentiation by u^{-1} meaning exponentiation by any positive integer a such that $au \equiv 1 \pmod{p^\nu}$.

For composite m, we see at once that $W_{mv_\infty} \subset H_m$, using the multiplicativity of the Artin symbol for ideles. However, we have an isomorphism $J/\mathbf{Q}^*W_{mv_\infty} \approx (\mathbf{Z}/m\mathbf{Z})^*$ under the ideal map, as in Chapter VII, §4, and thus the index relation

$$(J : \mathbf{Q}^*W_{mv_\infty}) = [\mathbf{Q}(\zeta_m) : \mathbf{Q}] = (J : H_m).$$

Hence

$$\mathbf{Q}^*W_{mv_\infty} = H_m,$$

thus proving our assertion.

Corollary 3. *Let $K/\mathbf{Q}$ be an abelian extension of the rationals. Then K is cyclotomic,* i.e. *there exists a root of unity ζ such that $K \subset \mathbf{Q}(\zeta)$.*

Proof. Let mv_∞ be an admissible cycle for $K/\mathbf{Q}$, and let H be the class group of K. Then

$$H_m = \mathbf{Q}^*W_{mv_\infty} \subset H,$$

whence $K \subset \mathbf{Q}(\zeta_m)$ by Theorem 5.

Corollary 3 is known as **Kronecker's theorem.** According to some critical modern appraisals, Kronecker stated the theorem, but the first complete proof seems to have been given by Weber. For a proof depending on higher ramification theory, but not on class field theory, cf. Speiser, *J. Reine Angew. Math.*, 1919.

Theorem 6. *Let K/k be the class field of H, and let E/k be finite. Then KE/E is the class field of $N_{E/k}^{-1}(H)$.*

Proof. The kernel of the Artin map

$$C_E \to G(KE/E)$$

is precisely equal to $N_{E/k}^{-1}(H)$ because for $b \in C_E$ we have

$$\mathrm{res}_K\,(b, KE/E) = (N_k^E b, K/k),$$

and an automorphism of KE/E is determined by its effect on K. This proves our theorem.

To prove the next theorem, we shall use the fact that given an open subgroup H of J_k containing k^*, there exists an abelian extension K/k such that $H = k^*N_k^K J_K$. This is the **existence theorem** which will be proved in the next chapter.

Theorem 7. *Let E/k be a finite extension, and let $H = N_k^E C_E$. Then H belongs to the maximal abelian subextension of E.*

Proof. Let K/k be the class field belonging to H. For any $b \in C_E$ we have $N_k^E b \in H$, and hence

$$1 = (N_k^E b, K/k) = \mathrm{res}_K\,(b, KE/E).$$

Hence KE is the class field to all of C_E, whence $KE = E$ and $K \subset E$. It is then clear that K is maximal abelian in E, thus proving the theorem.

Corollary. *We have $[E : k] = (C_k : N_k^E C_E)$ if and only if E/k is abelian.*

Proof. Clear.

From the consistency property, we can define the Artin map for infinite abelian extensions. Let A be the maximal abelian extension of k (i.e. compositum of all finite abelian extensions). Given $a \in C_k$ we define an automorphism (a, k) on A to be $(a, K/k)$ on each subextension K of A, finite over k. The consistency property shows that this is well defined, and from the definition of the (Krull) topology on $G(A/k)$, which is a compact totally disconnected group, we obtain a continuous map

$$C_k \to G(A/k).$$

This map, which we again call the **Artin map,** has an image which is everywhere dense in $G(A/k)$, because of the surjectivity in finite extensions. We can write C_k as a product

$$C_k = \mathbf{R}^+ \times C_k^0,$$

both algebraically and topologically, and the positive reals $\mathbf{R}^+$ are infinitely divisible (i.e. every element is an n-th power for all n). Hence our infinite Artin map is given by its restriction to C_k^0, which is compact (Theorem 4, Chapter VII, §3). Since the continuous image of a compact set is compact, it follows that the Artin map is surjective, i.e. maps C_k^0 *onto* $G(A/k)$.

Similarly, if K is any infinite abelian extension, we obtain a continuous surjective homomorphism

$$\omega_{K/k} : C_k \to G(K/k).$$

An open subgroup H of C_k is of finite index, and hence closed (it is the complement of the union of a finite number of cosets). The kernel of $\omega_{K/k}$ is the intersection

$$H_K = \bigcap_{F \subset K} H_F$$

of all groups H_F belonging to finite subextensions F of K. Actually, it is better to look at $\omega_{K/k}$ as defined on C_k^0, because of the compactness. We can then write the kernel of $\omega_{K/k}$ in C_k^0 as the intersection

$$H_K^0 = \bigcap_{F \subset K} H_F^0,$$

where $H_F^0 = H_F \cap C_F^0$, and H_F^0 is open, of finite index in C_k^0. This kernel is then compact, and we have an algebraic and topological isomorphism

$$C_k^0 / H_K^0 \approx G(K/k).$$

We then obtain a bijection between closed subgroups of C_k containing H_A and (possibly infinite) abelian extensions of k, given by

$$K \mapsto H_K.$$

In the other direction, if H is a closed subgroup of C_k containing H_A, then its class field K is the fixed field of $(H, A/k) = (H, k)$. As in the finite case, the association $K \mapsto H_K$ reverses inclusion relations. We call K the **class field** to H_K as before. The group H_A will be called the group of **universal norms**. It is the intersection of C_k of all the norm groups from finite extensions (or finite abelian extensions, same thing). Using the existence theorem, we shall prove a structure theorem for it later (Theorem 6, in Chapter 11, §6).

CHAPTER XI

The Existence Theorem and Local Class Field Theory

§1. Reduction to Kummer extensions

We must prove that any open subgroup H of J_k containing k^* belongs to some abelian extension. Thus at some point, we have to start exhibiting abelian extensions of k. There are not that many ways of doing this. One general way is to make cyclotomic extensions, and when the n-th roots of unity are in k, to make Kummer extensions, i.e. adjoining n-th roots of elements of k. We shall prove the existence theorem by this method. Deeper methods involving the values of certain transcendental functions are more significant, but lead into directions which require a whole book to themselves. We first start with the reduction lemma.

Lemma. *Let F/k be a cyclic extension, and let H be an open subgroup of J_k containing k^*. Let $H_F = N_{F/k}^{-1}(H)$. If H_F has a class field (over F) then so does H (over k).*

Proof. Let K/F be the class field of H_F. We shall prove that K is Galois over k. Let K' be the smallest Galois extension of k containing K. Let σ be an automorphism of K' over k. Then $\sigma H_F = H_F$. But σK is class field to σH_F. Hence $\sigma K = K$ and K is Galois over k, so $K = K'$. We shall actually prove that K is *abelian* over k. Let σ be an automorphism of K over k whose restriction to F generates $G(F/k)$. Let τ be any automorphism of K/F. It will suffice to prove that σ commutes with τ. Let $b \in J_F$ be such that

$$\begin{array}{c} K' \\ | \\ K \\ | \\ F \\ | \\ k \end{array}$$

$$\tau = (b, K/F).$$

Then

$$\sigma\tau\sigma^{-1} = (\sigma b, \sigma K/\sigma F) = (\sigma b, K/F).$$

However, $N_k^F(\sigma b/b) = 1$, so that $\sigma b/b \in H_F$. Hence

$$(\sigma b, K/F) = (b, K/F),$$

and $\sigma\tau\sigma^{-1} = \tau$, thus proving that K/k is abelian. But then $k^* N_k^K J_K \subset H$, and by the Corollary of Theorem 5, Chapter X, §3, we conclude that H has a class field. This proves the lemma.

The lemma will be applied in the following situation. An abelian extension K/k is said to have **exponent** n if $\sigma^n = 1$ for all $\sigma \in G(K/k)$. We make the same definition for an abelian group A (say multiplicative), and say that A has exponent n if $a^n = 1$ for all $a \in A$. Let H be an open subgroup of J_k containing k^*, such that J_k/H has exponent n. We want to prove that there exists a class field to H. Let $F = k(\zeta_n)$ be the field obtained from k by adjoining a primitive n-th root of unity ζ_n. We can construct a cyclic tower

$$k \subset F_1 \subset F_2 \subset \cdots \subset F_r = F$$

such that each F_{i+1}/F_i is cyclic. Let $H_F = N_{F/k}^{-1}(H)$, and similarly $H_i = N_{F_i/k}^{-1}(H)$. If we can prove that H_F has a class field, then we come down stepwise in the tower applying the lemma, to conclude that H has a class field. When J_k/H has exponent n, this reduces the existence theorem to the case when k contains the n-th roots of unity.

We now recall some easy facts about abelian extensions of k, of exponent n, when ζ_n lies in k. Such extensions correspond to subgroups of k^* containing k^{*n} as follows.

Let $k^* \supset D \supset k^{*n}$, and assume $(D : k^{*n})$ finite for simplicity. Let

$$K_D = k(D^{1/n})$$

be the field obtained from k by adjoining all n-th roots of elements of D. If $\alpha_1, \ldots, \alpha_m$ are representatives in D of the factor group D/k^{*n}, then we clearly have

$$K_D = k(\alpha_1^{1/n}, \ldots, \alpha_m^{1/n}),$$

so that K_D is finite. It is trivial to verify that K_D is abelian over k, of exponent n.

Conversely, let K/k be abelian of exponent n. Then K is a composite of cyclic extensions, and each cyclic extension can be written in the form $k(\alpha^{1/n})$ for some $\alpha \in k$, using Hilbert's Theorem 90, Lagrange resolvants, or whatnot. (Cf. books on Algebra, e.g. mine.) Thus $K = K_D$ for some D.

There is a duality between $G(K/k)$ and D/k^{*n} as follows. Let $K = K_D$. For each $\sigma \in G(K/k) = G$, and each $\alpha \in D$, select $A \in K$ such that $A^n = \alpha$. Then $\sigma A/A$ is independent of the choice of A, and is an n-th root of unity, which we denote by $\langle \sigma, \alpha \rangle$. The map

$$G \times D \to \mathbf{C}^*$$

given by

$$(\sigma, \alpha) \mapsto \langle \sigma, \alpha \rangle = \sigma A/A$$

is then trivially verified to be bimultiplicative, i.e. a pairing. It is clear that this pairing depends only on the class of α modulo k^{*n}, and thus induces a pairing

$$G \times D/k^{*n} \to \mathbf{C}^*.$$

We contend that the orthogonal subgroup to G in D is precisely k^{*n}, and that the orthogonal subgroup to D in G is 1. Proof: Let $\alpha \in D$ be orthogonal to all $\sigma \in G$. Then $\sigma A/A = 1$ for all $\sigma \in G$, whence $\alpha^{1/n} \in k$. Hence $\alpha \in k^{*n}$. On the other side, suppose that $\sigma \in G$ is orthogonal to all of D. For any $\alpha \in D$ and A such that $A^n = \alpha$ we have $\sigma A = A$. Hence σ leaves fixed a set of generators for K_D over k, and hence $\sigma = 1$. This proves our assertion, and we conclude that the pairing

$$G \times D/k^{*n} \to \mathbf{C}^*$$

induces an isomorphism of each one of the groups G, D/k^{*n} with the dual group of the other. In particular, we find:

$$[K_D : k] = (D : k^{*n}).$$

The facts which we have just summarized are referred to as **Kummer theory.** The field K_D is called the **Kummer** field belonging to D. Note that the Kummer theory establishes a *duality* between the Galois group and a certain group associated with the ground field, whereas the class field theory establishes an isomorphism, depending on a much more subtle construction, through the Artin symbol.

§2. *Proof of the existence theorem*

Existence Theorem. *Let H be an open subgroup of J_k containing k^*. Then there exists a class field to H.*

Proof. As mentioned in the preceding section, we are reduced to the case when J_k/H has exponent n, and k *contains all* n-th *roots of unity, which we assume from now on.*

Theorem 1. *Let S be a finite set of absolute values of k containing all the archimedean ones, all $\mathfrak{p}$ such that $\mathfrak{p}|n$, and enough absolute values such that $J_k = k^*J_S$. Let*

$$B = \prod_{v \in S} k_v^{*n} \times \prod_{v \notin S} U_v.$$

Then k^*B has a class field K, which is equal to $k(k_S^{1/n})$, i.e. is obtained by adjoining to k all n-th roots of S-units. If s is the number of elements of S, then $[K : k] = n^s$. Finally, $k^* \cap B = k_S^n$.

Proof. Let $K = k(k_S^{1/n})$. Observe that $k_S \cap k^{*n} = k_S^n$ (trivially), and that we have an isomorphism

$$k_S k^{*n}/k^{*n} \approx k_S/(k_S \cap k^{*n}) = k_S/k_S^n.$$

Thus K is the Kummer field belonging to $k_S k^{*n}$. Since k_S modulo n-th roots of unity is a free abelian group on $s - 1$ generators (where s = number of elements of S), we conclude that

$$\boxed{(k_S : k_S^n) = n^s = [K : k].}$$

Note that K/k is unramified outside S by the usual criterion. Namely, K is obtained by adjoining roots of equations

$$f(X) = X^n - \alpha = 0,$$

with $\alpha \in k_S$. If A is a root, then $f'(A)$ is divisible only by primes of S.

We shall prove that $k^*B = k^*N_k^K J_K$. First we prove the inclusion

$$k^*B \subset k^*N_k^K J_K.$$

Since K/k has exponent n, any element of k_v^{*n} for $v \in S$ (viewed as idele with component 1 outside v) is in the kernel of the Artin map, and hence contained in $k^*N_k^K J_K$. (This could also be proved in a very elementary way, using the approximation theorem.) An element of

$$\prod_{v \in S} U_v$$

is contained in $N_k^K J_K$ because for $v \notin S$, every local unit is a local norm. This proves the first inclusion.

Conversely, it will suffice to prove that $(J_k : k^*B) = n^s$. Let $k_B = k^* \cap B$. We have:

$$\begin{aligned}(J_k : k^*B) &= (k^*J_S : k^*B)\\ &= \frac{(J_S : B)}{(J_S \cap k^* : B \cap k^*)}\\ &= \frac{\prod_{v \in S} (k_v^* : k_v^{*n})}{(k_S : k_B)} = \frac{n^{2s}}{(k_S : k_B)}.\end{aligned}$$

(We used the index computed in Chapter II, §3, and the product formula.) There remains to be proved that $k_B = k_S^n$. It is clear that $k_B \supset k_S^n$. Conversely, let $\alpha \in k_B$. Then α is a local n-th power at all $v \in S$, so that v splits completely in $k(\alpha^{1/n})$ for all $v \in S$. Furthermore, if $v \notin S$, then v

is unramified in $k(\alpha^{1/n})$. Let $K' = k(\alpha^{1/n})$. Then $J_S \subset N_k^{K'} J_{K'}$, whence

$$J = k^* J_S \subset k^* N_k^{K'} J_{K'}.$$

Class field theory shows that $K' = k$, and hence $\alpha \in k_S^n$. This concludes the proof of Theorem 1.

The existence theorem is now only a corollary of Theorem 1. Given an open subgroup H of J_k, containing k^*, such that J/H has exponent n, and assuming that the n-th roots of unity are in k, we find a set S as in the theorem, and enlarge S still further, to contain all those v such that U_v is not contained in H. Then $B \subset H$, and since k^*B has a class field, we conclude by the Corollary of Theorem 5 in the preceding chapter that H has a class field.

Remark. We shall see later that v is unramified in an abelian extension F/k if and only if U_v is contained in the group H to which F belongs. From this, we see that in Theorem 1, the class field to k^*B is the maximal abelian extension of exponent n, unramified outside S, because if F/k is abelian, of exponent n, unramified outside S, and class field to H, then $B \subset H$ whence $F \subset K$, where K is class field to k^*B, as in the theorem.

§3. *The complete splitting theorem*

The decomposition of a given absolute value v in an abelian extension K/k is reflected already in the group H to which K belongs.

Theorem 2. *Let K/k be class field to H. Let v be an absolute value on k. Then v splits completely in K if and only if $k_v^* \subset H$.*

Proof. If v splits completely, then $k_v^* \subset H$ because every element of k_v^* is a local norm. We shall prove the converse. In this section, we prove it only when J_k/H has exponent n, and the n-th roots of unity are contained in k. We shall complete the proof in the next section.

Let therefore v_0 be a fixed absolute value on k such that $k_{v_0}^* \subset H$, and let S be a finite set of absolute values containing v_0, satisfying the conditions of Theorem 1, that is containing all archimedean v, all $\mathfrak{p}|n$, and enough v such that $J = k^* J_S$. Assume also that S contains all v which are ramified in K. Let:

$$B_1 = k_{v_0}^* \times \prod_{\substack{v \in S \\ v \neq v_0}} k_v^{*n} \times \prod_{v \notin S} U_v$$

$$B_2 = k_{v_0}^{*n} \times \prod_{\substack{v \in S \\ v \neq v_0}} k_v^* \times \prod_{v \notin S} U_v.$$

Then $B_1 \cap B_2 = B$, where B is the group mentioned in Theorem 1. Also $B_1 \subset H$. We shall construct the class field K_1 to k^*B_1, and we shall see that v_0 splits completely in this class field. It then follows that v_0 splits completely in K, because $K \subset K_1$.

Let $D_1 = k^* \cap B_1$ and $D_2 = k^* \cap B_2$. Then

$$k_S^n \subset D_1 \cap k^{*n} \subset B \cap k^{*n} = k_S^n$$

by what we proved in §3. Hence $D_1 \cap k^{*^n} = k_S^n$, and similarly,

$$D_2 \cap k^{*n} = k_S^n.$$

Let $K_1 = k(D_2^{1/n})$ and $K_2 = k(D_1^{1/n})$. (The reversal of indices is not accidental.) Then by Kummer theory,

$$[K_1 : k] = (D_2 k^{*n} : k^{*n}) = (D_2 : D_2 \cap k^{*n}) = (D_2 : k_S^n),$$

and similarly, reversing 1 and 2.

$$[K_2 : k] = (D_1 k^{*n} : k^{*n}) = (D_1 : D_1 \cap k^{*n}) = (D_1 : k_S^n).$$

Let K_1 and K_2 be class fields to H_1 and H_2 respectively. Then K_1, K_2 are unramified outside S, and if $v \in S$, $v \neq v_0$ then v splits completely in K_2, while v_0 splits completely in K_1. Hence

$$B_1 \subset H_1 \quad \text{and} \quad B_2 \subset H_2.$$

Therefore we obtain inequalities:

$$\begin{aligned}
[K_1 : k] \leqq (J : k^*B_1) &= (k^*J_S : k^*B_1) \\
&= \frac{(J_S : B_1)}{(k_S : k^*B_1)} \\
&= \frac{\prod_{\substack{v \in S \\ v \neq v_0}} (k_v^* : k_v^{*n})}{(k_S : k_S^n)} (k^* \cap B_1 : k_S^n) \\
&= \frac{\prod_{\substack{v \in S \\ v \neq v_0}} (k_v^* : k_v^{*n})}{n^s} [K_2 : k].
\end{aligned}$$

Similarly, we find

$$[K_2 : k] \leqq (J : k^*B_2) = \frac{(k_{v_0}^* : k_{v_0}^{*n})}{n^s} [K_1 : k].$$

Multiplying on the right and on the left, we get

$$[K_1:k][K_2:k] = (J:k^*B_1)(J:k^*B_2) \leqq [K_1:k][K_2:k].$$

Hence equality must hold everywhere in what precedes. In particular, we find that $k^*B_1 = H_1$. We know by construction that v_0 splits completely in K_1, and thus finally, we conclude that v_0 splits completely in K, thus proving what we wanted in the Kummer case.

Remark 1. The technique used here (due to Herbrand) can also be used to give the "algebraic proof" of the universal norm index inequality, as was done by Chevalley. Cf. Artin-Tate.

Remark 2. It did not really matter that we selected one v_0 from S. We could split S into two disjoint sets S_1 and S_2, and argue in a similar way. For the present application, however, what we needed was just for the study of a single v_0.

§4. *Local class field theory and the ramification theorem*

In this section, we conclude the proof of the complete splitting theorem, and derive local class field theory, describing the effect of the Artin map on the local component k_v^* for a fixed v.

Theorem 3. *Let K/k be abelian. The Artin map restricted to k_v^*, namely*

$$a \mapsto (a, K/k), \qquad a \in k_v^*$$

maps k_v^* into the decomposition group G_v ($= G_w$ for any $w|v$), has kernel $N_wK_w^*$, and induces an isomorphism

$$k_v^*/N_wK_w^* \approx G_v,$$

where N_w is the local norm from K_w to k_v.

Proof. We know that the group of local norms is contained in the kernel, since it lies in $N_k^KJ_K$. Hence our theorem follows from the local norm index inequality, Chapter IX, §3, once we have proved that the image of k_v^* is contained in the decomposition group G_v, and is equal to the whole decomposition group (this being the local analogue to the global surjectivity theorem of the Artin map).

Let Z be the fixed field of G_v. Then v splits completely in Z, and hence $k_v^* \subset N_k^ZJ_Z$. If $a \in k_v^*$, then $a = N_k^Zb$ for some local idele $b \in Z_w$, so that

$$(a, K/k) = (b, K/Z),$$

whence $(a, K/k)$ lies in G_v. This proves that the image of k_v^* under the Artin map is contained in G_v.

Next we prove that the map is surjective. Without loss of generality, we may assume that $k = Z$. Let $S = (k_v^*, K/k)$ be the image of k_v^* and let E be the fixed field of S. If $E \neq k$, then E contains a subfield F which is cyclic over k, of prime degree p. Let $k' = k(\zeta_p)$ where ζ_p is a primitive p-th root of unity, and let

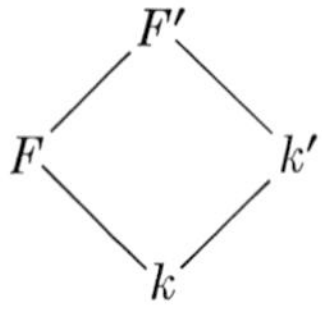

$$F' = Fk' = F(\zeta_p).$$

Let v' be an absolute value of k' such that $v'|v$. The whole local group k_v^* is contained in the kernel of the Artin map

$$k_v^* \to G_v(F/k),$$

and hence $k_{v'}'^*$ is contained in the kernel of the Artin map

$$k_{v'}'^* \to G_{v'}(F'/k').$$

By the Kummer result of the preceding section, this implies that v' splits completely in F'. However, $[k' : k]$ divides $p - 1$, and is relatively prime to $p = [F : k]$. Since the ramification index and residue class degree are multiplicative in towers, it follows that v splits completely in F. Since we assumed that $k = Z$, this gives a contradiction which proves our theorem.

The argument which we have just given also concludes the proof of Theorem 2. Indeed, let K be class field to H, and assume that $k_v^* \subset H$. Then $(k_v^*, K/k) = 1$, and we know that

$$(k_v^*, K/k) = G_v.$$

It follows that $G_v = 1$, i.e. v splits completely.

Corollary. *Let K/k be class field to H. Then*

$$H \cap k_v^* = N_w K_w^* \qquad \text{and} \qquad H \cap U_v = N_w U_w.$$

Theorem 4. *Let K/k be abelian, class field to H. An absolute value v on k is unramified in K if and only if $U_v \subset H$. More generally, $(U_v, K/k)$ is equal to the inertia group T_v ($= T_w$ for any $w|v$).*

Proof. If v is unramified in K, then every local unit is a local norm, so $U_v \subset H$. Conversely, assume that $U_v \subset H$. By the preceding corollary, we know that every unit in U_v is a local norm. By Chapter IX, §3, it follows that v is unramified in every cyclic subfield of K, and hence is unramified in K. To see that $(U_v, K/k) = T_v$ in general, we may assume without loss of generality that the Galois group $G(K/k)$ is equal to the decomposition group G_v. (If Z is the fixed field of G_v, then v splits completely in Z, and so we may use Z as ground field instead of k.) Let F be the maximal subfield of K in which v is unramified. Then T_v is the Galois group of K/F. If $w|v$ in F, then by the norm property of the Artin symbol, we have $(U_w, K/F) = (U_v, K/k)$. In the non-archimedean case, there exists a prime element π in F_w which is a local norm from K. Hence $(\pi, K/F) = 1$. But

$$F_w^* = \{\pi\} \times U_w$$

(where $\{\pi\}$ is the cyclic group generated by π), and $(F_w^*, K/F) = T_v$. Hence $(U_w, K/F) = T_v$, thus proving our result in general. The archimedean case is equally clear.

In view of Theorem 4, it is natural to define v **unramified** in H if $U_v \subset H$. With this terminology, we see that v is unramified in H if and only if v is unramified in the class field belonging to H. Furthermore, if K is class field to H, then the class field to HU_v is the maximal subextension of K in which v is unramified.

Corollary. *Let K/k be an abelian extension. For any v on k, and $w|v$ in K, we have*

$$(U_v : N_w U_w) = e,$$

and the Artin map induces an isomorphism $U_v/N_w U_w \approx T_v$.

Proof. Immediate from the corollary of Theorem 3.

Theorem 5. *Let k_v be a local field. The Artin map defined for abelian extensions K of k_v satisfies the same formalism as the global map, when viewed as defined on the multiplicative group of the local field. The association*

$$K \mapsto N_{k_v}^K K^*$$

establishes a bijection between finite abelian extensions of k_v, and open subgroups of k_v^*, which reverses the inclusion relations.

Proof. Same as in the global case. We should observe in addition that given any abelian extension k'_v of k_v, there exists an abelian extension K of k such that $Kk_v = k'$. To see this, note that k_v^* is embedded in C_k, and hence that any open subgroup H_v of k_v^* can be written as an intersection

$$H_v = H \cap k_v^*$$

for some open subgroup H of C_k. All we have to do is let K be the class field of H.

Note that the local Artin map $k_v^* \to G(k'/k_v)$ is induced by the global map. The consistency property of the global symbol implies that the local map is independent of the global extension K chosen such that $Kk_v = k'$. It becomes a problem to define this local map purely locally in the ramified case (in the unramified case, the Artin symbol locally can be defined in the same manner as the global one). Chevalley was the first to do it, using the simple algebras. What mattered, however, were the cocycles defining the algebras, so that a purely cohomological treatment could be given as was done first by Hochschild. In fact, the local and global cohomology for this can be axiomatized into the "class formations", for which we refer to Artin-Tate.

When asking for a global abelian extension K of k such that $Kk_v = k'$ is a given local abelian extension, one can ask if K can be so chosen that $[K:k] = [k':k_v]$, especially in the cyclic case. The answer is yes, except in one special case. This is the Grunwald-Wang theorem, which even does this for a finite set S of absolute values. Observe that for such a set, the finite product

$$\prod_{v \in S} k_v^*$$

is embedded algebraically in the idele classes C_k (that is the natural map into C_k is injective), but not topologically, in distinction to the case when S has only one element. For a complete treatment of the Grunwald-Wang theorem, which has nothing to do with cohomology, we refer to Artin-Tate.

A related question is the following: If $\alpha \in k^*$ is an n-th power locally at every $v \in M_k$, is α also an n-th power in k? The answer is yes, except in a special case which can be described completely. Cf. Artin-Tate for that too.

As in the global case, the local existence theorem allows us to see that if E/k_v is a finite extension, then $N_{k_v}^E E^*$ is the local norm group to the maximal abelian subextension of E. The proof is the same as in the global case.

Using the consistency property, we can define the local Artin map for the maximal abelian extension A of k_v, thus obtaining a homomorphism

$$\omega_v : k_v \to G(A/k_v),$$

whose image is everywhere dense. Let us assume that v is $\mathfrak{p}$-adic. Since the intersection of all open subgroups of k_v^* is obviously equal to 1 (this is now different from the global situation), we conclude that the kernel of the infinite map is trivial. In the local case, however, the map is not surjective any more. In fact, we can write k_v^* as a product

$$k_v^* = \{\pi\} \times U_v \approx \mathbf{Z} \times U_v,$$

where $\{\pi\}$ is the cyclic group generated by a prime element π in k_v. The map ω_v is not continuous for the product topology, but is continuous for the topology in which subgroups of finite index form a fundamental system of neighborhoods of 1 in k_v^*. The restriction of this topology to $\mathbf{Z}$ is the "ideal topology". Following Artin, we can then complete $\mathbf{Z}$ under this topology, and using the Chinese remainder theorem we see that the completion $\overline{\mathbf{Z}}$ is the compact group equal to the direct product of all p-adic integers for all p. Extending the map ω_v by continuity, we obtain an isomorphism,

$$\overline{k_v^*} = \overline{\mathbf{Z}} \times U_v \xrightarrow{\approx} G(A/k_v)$$

which is both algebraic and topological. This gives a rather good model for the Galois group $G(A/k_v)$. For instance, we see that $G(A/k_v)$ has a unique subgroup of order 2 (which one?), and hence that there exists a unique subfield of A containing k_v, which is of degree 2 under A.

Finally, we mention that Theorem 4 admits a substantial refinement. Let k denote a p-adic field until the end of the section. Then k has a filtration

$$k^* = U_{-1} \supset U_0 \supset U_1 \supset U_2 \supset \cdots \supset U_i \supset \cdots,$$

where $U_0 = U$, and U_i consists of those elements $x \in U$ such that

$$x \equiv 1 \pmod{\mathfrak{p}^i}.$$

Correspondingly, let K/k be a Galois extension with group G (equal to the decomposition group since we assumed that k is local), inertial group T. We can define a sequence of subgroups V_i (called the higher ramification groups) by the condition that $\sigma \in V_i$ if and only if

$$\sigma\alpha \equiv \alpha \pmod{\mathfrak{P}^{i+1}}$$

for all $\alpha \in \mathfrak{o}_K$. Thus $V_0 = T$.

Theorem. *If K/k is abelian, and k is p-adic, then the reciprocity law map $k^* \to G(K/k)$ maps U_i onto $V_{i'}$ (i' depending on i).*

The proof requires a refined look at the higher ramification, and is carried out in detail, for instance in Artin-Tate. Our purpose is not to rewrite or copy Artin-Tate here, and we refer the reader to it. The discussion is arithmetic, and independent of cohomology. The local theory thus obtained also yields a description of the local conductor in terms of the higher ramification groups, and into a description of the precise relations existing between the (local) different and the conductor.

§5. *The Hilbert class field and the principal ideal theorem*

The ramification theorem (Theorem 4) and the existence theorem have an interesting global application. The group

$$H = k^*J_{S_\infty}$$

has a class field K which by Theorem 4 is unramified everywhere (including the archimedean absolute values). Furthermore

$$J/k^*J_{S_\infty} \approx I/P$$

is isomorphic to the ideal class group of k, under the ideal map. This class field K is called the **Hilbert class field.** We see that its Galois group is isomorphic under the Artin map to the ordinary ideal class group. It becomes a problem to exhibit K explicitly. Complex multiplication and its generalizations do this in special cases, by transcendental methods, outside the scope of this book.

Hilbert had conjectured that *an ideal of k becomes principal in the Hilbert class field.* This was reduced by Artin to a statement of finite group theory by means of the reciprocity law as follows.

Let k be the number field, K the Hilbert class field over k, and L the Hilbert class field over K. It is clear that L is Galois over k: If λ is any isomorphism of L over k, then $\lambda K = K$ and λL is unramified over λK, whence $\lambda L \subset L$, so $\lambda L = L$. Let G be the Galois group of L/k and S the Galois group of L/K. Then G/S is the Galois group of K/k. From the definition of the Hilbert class field, it is clear that K is maximal abelian in L, and hence translating this in terms of the Galois groups, we conclude that G/S is the maximal abelian factor group of G, whence $S = G^c$ is the commutator subgroup of G.

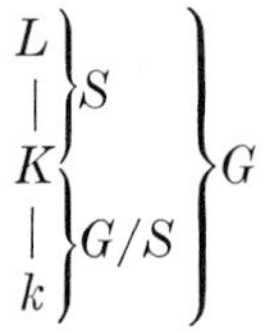

Let $\mathfrak{p}$ be a prime of k. We must prove that $(\mathfrak{p}, L/K) = 1$, identifying $\mathfrak{p}$ with $\mathfrak{p}\mathfrak{o}_k$. Let

$$\mathfrak{p} = \mathfrak{q}_1 \cdots \mathfrak{q}_r$$

be the factorization of $\mathfrak{p}$ in distinct primes of K. Then

$$(\mathfrak{p}, L/K) = \prod_{i=1}^{r} (\mathfrak{q}_i, L/K).$$

Let $\mathfrak{q}$ be any one of the primes of K dividing $\mathfrak{p}$, and let $\sigma_i \in G/S$ be one of the automorphisms of K/k such that $\sigma_i\mathfrak{q} = \mathfrak{q}_i$. Extend σ_i to all of L.

Then

$$(\mathfrak{q}_i, L/K) = (\sigma_i\mathfrak{q}, L/K) = (\sigma_i\mathfrak{q}, \sigma_i L/\sigma_i K) = \sigma_i(\mathfrak{q}, L/K)\sigma_i^{-1}.$$

Thus we obtain

$$(\mathfrak{p}, L/K) = \prod_{i=1}^{r} \sigma_i(\mathfrak{q}, L/K)\sigma_i^{-1}.$$

If we can prove that the product on the right is equal to 1, then we conclude that $\mathfrak{p}$ is principal, by the reciprocity law!

A complicated group theoretic proof was given by Furtwangler. A much simpler proof was given shortly thereafter by Iyanaga, following a suggestion of Artin concerning a group-theoretical map, the transfer, which shows that a product like the above is always equal to 1. We refer the reader to Artin-Tate, Chapter XIII, §4, for the self-contained proof (and definition of the transfer in general), having to do only with group theory, but nothing to do with ideal theory. In this connection, it had been an unsolved problem for a long time whether the tower which is constructed by taking successive Hilbert class fields can ever become infinite. In his talk at the International Congress in 1962, Shafarevich showed how this question could be reduced to a group theoretic statement, involving certain bounds for the number of generators of certain groups. Shortly afterwards, he and Golod succeeded in giving examples when the tower is infinite, and showing that in some sense, this is a very frequent occurrence. For this we refer the reader to the original paper of Golod and Shafarevich (*On class field towers*, AMS translations 48) or the exposition by Roquette in [7].

§6. *Infinite divisibility of the universal norms*

Theorem 6. *The group of universal norms in C_k is infinitely divisible. In other words, if $a \in C_k$ is a universal norm, and n is a positive integer, then there exists a universal norm b such that $a = b^n$.*

Proof. We shall first need a lemma, whose proof goes back to the technique of the existence theorem.

Lemma. *Let n be a positive integer, assume that the n-th roots of unity lie in k, and let a be a universal norm. Then $a \in C_k^n$.*

Proof. We construct a large set S as in Theorem 1, §2, and also we construct the group

$$B = \prod_{v \in S} k_v^{*^n} \times \prod_{v \notin S} U_v.$$

Let K be the class field belonging to k^*B. Then a is a norm from K, so there exists $b \in B$ in the same idele class as a. Let S' be any set of absolute values such that $S' \supset S$, and form the group

$$B' = \prod_{v \in S} k_v^{*^n} \times \prod_{\substack{v \in S' \\ v \notin S}} U_v^n \times \prod_{v \notin S'} U_v.$$

Then a also has a representative idele b' in B', and there exists $\beta \in k^*$ such that $b = \beta b'$. Then $\beta \in k^* \cap B = k_S^n$ by Theorem 1, §2. Hence b_v is an n-th power for all $v \in S'$. We can take S' arbitrarily large. This proves that b_v is an n-th power for all v, i.e. $b = c^n$ for some idele c, thus proving our lemma.

We shall now prove Theorem 6, as in Artin-Tate. We let D_k be the group of universal norms in C_k. We first prove that for any finite extension E/k we have

$$D_k = N_k^E D_E.$$

From the transitivity of the norm, one has trivially $N_k^E D_E \subset D_k$. Conversely, let $a \in D_k$. For each finite extension K containing E let

$$X_K = N_E^K C_K \cap N_{E/k}^{-1}(a).$$

By Theorem 4 of Chapter VII, §3, it follows at once that $N_{E/k}^{-1}(a)$ is compact. Hence X_K is compact, and is not empty by the transitivity of the norm. The family $\{X_K\}$ for all finite extensions K containing E has the finite intersection property, because if $K_1, \ldots, K_r$ is a finite number of such extensions, and K contains each K_i $(i = 1, \ldots, r)$ then $X_K \subset X_{K_i}$ for all i. It follows that there exists $b \in X_K$ for all K. Then $a = N_k^E b$ and b is a universal norm in C_E. This proves that $D_k = N_k^E D_E$.

Given an integer n, and $a \in D_k$, to prove that $a \in D_k^n$ we let $E = k(\zeta_n)$. Let $a = N_k^E b$ with $b \in D_E$. It will suffice to prove that $b \in D_E^n$. This reduces our proof to the case when k contains the n-th roots of unity, which we assume for the rest of the proof.

By the lemma, we have for each finite (Galois, if you wish) K,

$$D_k = N_k^K D_K \subset N_k^K(C_K^n) = (N_k^K C_K)^n.$$

Let

$$Y_K = N_k^K C_K \cap a^{1/n},$$

where $a^{1/n}$ means the set of all $b \in C_k$ such that $b^n = a$. Then $a^{1/n}$ is closed in C_k, and is compact by the same Theorem 4 of Chapter VII, §3. We have just seen that Y_K is not empty, and the transitivity of the norm shows that the family $\{Y_K\}$ for all finite K/k has the finite intersection property. Hence there exists $b \in Y_K$ for all K. This b is a universal norm, and $b^n = a$, thereby concluding the proof of Theorem 6.

We refer to Artin-Tate for the proof that D_k is the connected component of C_k.

CHAPTER XII

L-Series Again

§1. The proper abelian L-series

Let χ be a character of the idele classes C_k (or equivalently, of J_k, vanishing on k^*), that is a continuous homomorphism

$$J_k/k^* \to \mathbf{C}^*,$$

and assume in addition throughout this section that χ *has finite period.* Then the kernel H_χ of χ is a closed subgroup of finite index, which is therefore open, and has a class field denoted by K_χ.

A prime $\mathfrak{p}$ is said to be **unramified** for χ, or χ is said to be *unramified at* $\mathfrak{p}$, if the group of local units $U_\mathfrak{p}$ is contained in H_χ. (Cf. Theorem 4 of Chapter XI, §4.) If that is the case, and π is an element of order 1 in $k_\mathfrak{p}$, we view π as an idele,

$$\pi = (\ldots, 1, \pi, 1, \ldots)$$

as usual, corresponding to the embedding of $k_\mathfrak{p}$ in J, and we define

$$\chi(\mathfrak{p}) = \chi(\pi).$$

This is well defined, and is independent of the choice of π, since any other element π_1 of order 1 differs from π by a unit, i.e. $\pi_1 = u\pi$, $u \in U_\mathfrak{p}$, and $\chi(u) = 1$ since $U_\mathfrak{p} \subset H$. If χ is ramified at $\mathfrak{p}$, we *define* $\chi(\mathfrak{p}) = 0$.

If $\mathfrak{c}$ is an admissible cycle for K_χ/k, then we could interpret J/H as an ideal class group, we could interpret χ as a character of this group, and $\chi(\mathfrak{p})$ would be the value of this character, viewing $\mathfrak{p}$ as an element of an ideal class as in Chapter VII, §4.

Let H be an open subgroup of J_k containing k^*. By the **conductor** for H we shall mean the smallest cycle $\mathfrak{f}$ such that the group $W_\mathfrak{f}$ of Chapter VII, §4 is contained in H. The conductor of H_χ will also be called the **conductor** of χ, and will be denoted by $\mathfrak{f}_\chi$. In general, a cycle $\mathfrak{c}$ is said to be **admissible** for H if $W_\mathfrak{c} \subset H$. The conductor for H is thus its smallest admissible cycle. The ramification theorem (Theorem 4 of Chapter XI,

§4) shows that the conductor for χ is divisible precisely by those primes $\mathfrak{p}$ which are ramified in K_χ.

Let χ be a character as above. We define the L-series

$$L(s, \chi) = \prod_{\mathfrak{p} \nmid \mathfrak{f}_\chi} \frac{1}{1 - \dfrac{\chi(\mathfrak{p})}{\mathbf{N}\mathfrak{p}^s}} = \prod_{\text{all } \mathfrak{p}} \frac{1}{1 - \dfrac{\chi(\mathfrak{p})}{\mathbf{N}\mathfrak{p}^s}}.$$

The convergence theorems proved in Chapter VIII, §3, apply to this L-series, which differs from $L_{\mathfrak{c}}(s, \chi)$ only by a finite number of factors, if $\mathfrak{f}|\mathfrak{c}$. It is clear that

$$L(s, 1) = \zeta_k(s).$$

Theorem 1. *Let K/k be an abelian extension, class field to the class group $H \subset J_k$. Then*

$$\zeta_K(s) = \prod_{\chi(H)=1} L(s, \chi) = \zeta_k(s) \prod_{\chi \neq 1} L(s, \chi)$$

where the second product is taken over those characters χ which are trivial on H, but $\chi \neq 1$.

Proof. It suffices to prove that for each prime $\mathfrak{p}$ of k, we have

$$\prod_{\mathfrak{P}|\mathfrak{p}} \left(1 - \frac{1}{\mathbf{N}\mathfrak{P}^s}\right) = \prod_{\chi(H)=1} \left(1 - \frac{\chi(\mathfrak{p})}{\mathbf{N}\mathfrak{p}^s}\right).$$

Let $\mathfrak{p}$ split in K as

$$\mathfrak{p} = (\mathfrak{P}_1 \cdots \mathfrak{P}_r)^e.$$

Then $efr = N = [K:k]$, and $\mathbf{N}\mathfrak{P} = \mathbf{N}\mathfrak{p}^f$. Change variable, let $u = \mathbf{N}\mathfrak{p}^{-s}$. It suffices to prove that

$$(*) \qquad (1 - u^f)^r = \prod_{\chi(H)=1} (1 - \chi(\mathfrak{p})u).$$

We have a trivial identity

$$1 - u^f = \prod_{\zeta} (1 - \zeta u),$$

where the product is taken over all f-th roots of unity ζ. We shall first prove formula (*) under the assumption that $\mathfrak{p}$ is unramified, i.e. $e = 1$. We then have to show that the values $\chi(\mathfrak{p})$ are simply the values $1, \zeta_f, \ldots, \zeta_f^{f-1}$ repeated r times.

Let $Hk_{\mathfrak{p}}^* = H_{\mathfrak{p}} \supset H$. By the complete splitting theorem, $H_{\mathfrak{p}}$ is the class group to the maximal subfield of K in which $\mathfrak{p}$ splits completely, i.e. the fixed field of the decomposition group $G_{\mathfrak{P}}$. Hence

$$(H_{\mathfrak{p}} : H) = f.$$

Let $1 = \psi_1, \ldots, \psi_f$ be the distinct characters of $H_{\mathfrak{p}}/H$, which is cyclic, generated by a prime element π. Extend these characters to characters of J/H, denoted by the same letters. Let $1 = \chi_1, \ldots, \chi_r$ be the distinct characteristics of $J/H_{\mathfrak{p}}$. Then

$$\{\chi_i\psi_j\} \qquad (i = 1, \ldots, r;\, j = 1, \ldots, f)$$

are the characters of J/H. But π has order f mod H. Hence the values

$$\psi_1(\pi), \ldots, \psi_f(\pi)$$

are precisely the values $1, \zeta_f, \ldots, \zeta_f^{f-1}$. This proves what we wanted if χ is unramified at $\mathfrak{p}$.

We now deal with the general case, where $\mathfrak{p}$ may be ramified. We have

$$(HU_{\mathfrak{p}} : H) = (U_{\mathfrak{p}} : U_{\mathfrak{p}} \cap H) = e$$

by Theorem 4 of Chapter XI, §4, and its corollary. Let $1 = \psi_1, \ldots, \psi_e$ be the distinct characters of $HU_{\mathfrak{p}}/H$, and extend them to characters of J/H. Let $1 = \chi_1, \ldots, \chi_{fr}$ be the characters of $J/HU_{\mathfrak{p}}$. Then $\mathfrak{p}$ is unramified for all χ_i, $i = 1, \ldots, fr$, and the characters

$$\{\chi_i\psi_j\} \qquad (i = 1, \ldots, fr;\, j = 1, \ldots, e)$$

are all the characters of J/H. If $j \neq 1$, so $\psi_j \neq 1$, then $\psi_j(\mathfrak{p}) = 0$ by definition. Hence the only characters χ of J/H which are not 0 on $\mathfrak{p}$ are precisely the characters χ_i for which $\mathfrak{p}$ is unramified. This reduces the general case to the unramified case, which has already been dealt with, and concludes the proof of our theorem.

From the factorization of the zeta function into a product of L-series, and the evaluation at $s = 1$, one gets a formula relating the class number, regulator, and discriminant. We don't go into this here, but refer the reader to Borevich-Shafarevich [4], or Hasse's *Über die Klassenzahl abelscher Zahlkörper*, Akademie Verlag, Berlin, 1952. The reader should also look at Leopoldt's results on the p-adic analogue, for instance his paper *Über Fermatquotienten von Kreiseinheiten und Klassenzahlformeln modulo p*, Rendiconti del Circolo di Palermo, 1960, pp. 1–12.

§2. *Artin* (*non-abelian*) *L-series*

All results used here from the elementary theory of group representations and characters can be found in the last chapter of my book *Algebra*.

Throughout this section and the next, I follow Artin (cf. his collected works).

Let K/k be a Galois extension with group G. If $\mathfrak{p}$ is a prime of k, then $\mathfrak{p}$ splits in K into a product

$$\mathfrak{p} = (\mathfrak{P}_1 \cdots \mathfrak{P}_r)^e,$$

and $efr = [K:k]$, where f is the degree of the residue class field extension. For any $\mathfrak{P}|\mathfrak{p}$ in K, we have $\mathbf{N}\mathfrak{P} = \mathbf{N}\mathfrak{p}^f$. We have a Frobenius automorphism $\sigma = (\mathfrak{P}, K/k)$ in the decomposition group $G_{\mathfrak{P}}$ characterized by the fact that

$$\sigma\alpha \equiv \alpha^{\mathbf{N}\mathfrak{p}} \pmod{\mathfrak{P}}$$

for $\alpha \in \mathfrak{o}_K$. This σ is determined only in the coset of the inertia group $T_{\mathfrak{P}}$, which consists of all $\tau \in G_{\mathfrak{P}}$ inducing the identity automorphism on the residue class field extension.

If S is a subset of G and χ is the character of a representation of G (in a finite dimensional space over an algebraically closed field of characteristic zero), we define

$$\chi(S) = \sum_{\tau \in S} \chi(\tau).$$

We may therefore view S as the element in the group ring equal to the sum of all elements of S.

Let m be an integer $\geqq 1$. If $\sigma = (\mathfrak{P}, K/k)$, we define

$$\chi(\mathfrak{p}^m) = \frac{1}{e}\,\chi(\sigma^m T_{\mathfrak{P}}).$$

This can also be viewed as the value of χ on the element

$$\frac{1}{e} \sum_{\tau \in T_{\mathfrak{P}}} \sigma^m \tau.$$

Since $T_{\mathfrak{P}}$ is normal in $G_{\mathfrak{P}}$, it follows that our value for $\chi(\mathfrak{p}^m)$ is independent of the choice of σ in the coset of $T_{\mathfrak{P}}$. Since Frobenius automorphisms corresponding to different $\mathfrak{P}_i|\mathfrak{p}$ are conjugate in G, and since the inertia groups $T_{\mathfrak{P}_i}$ are also conjugate in G, it follows that this value is independent of the choice of $\mathfrak{P}|\mathfrak{p}$, and that our notation involving only $\mathfrak{p}$ in $\chi(\mathfrak{p}^m)$ is justified.

We now define the L-series $L(s, \chi, K/k)$ by its logarithm, namely

$$\log L(s, \chi, K/k) = \sum_{\mathfrak{p},m} \frac{\chi(\mathfrak{p}^m)}{m\mathbf{N}\mathfrak{p}^{ms}}\cdot$$

The L-series is then the exponent of this logarithm. Trivial bounds in terms of the degree of the representation, and the order of G, show that this series converges absolutely and uniformly for the usual

$$\mathrm{Re}(s) \geqq 1 + \delta, \qquad \delta > 0$$

by comparison with the ordinary zeta function.

The L-series satisfy the following formalism.

L1. *We have* $L(s, 1, K/k) = \zeta_k(s)$.

L2. *If* χ_1, χ_2 *are characters of* G, *then*

$$L(s, \chi_1 + \chi_2, K/k) = L(s, \chi_1, K/k)L(s, \chi_2, K/k).$$

L3. *If* $K' \supset K \supset k$ *is a bigger Galois extension, and* χ *is a character of* $G(K/k)$, *also viewed as character of* $G(K'/k)$, *then*

$$L(s, \chi, K/k) = L(s, \chi, K'/k).$$

L4. *Let* $k \subset F \subset K$ *be an intermediate field, and let* ψ *be a character of* $G(K/F)$. *Let* χ_ψ *be the induced character of* $G(K/k)$. *(We recall the definition below.) Then*

$$L(s, \psi, K/F) = L(s, \chi_\psi, K/k).$$

Of these properties, only the fourth one requires a non-trivial proof. Indeed, the first is obvious, and so is the second since the character χ appears linearly in the definition of $\log L(s, \chi, K/k)$.

The third is also easy to see. Let $\mathfrak{P}'|\mathfrak{p}$ in K', and $\mathfrak{P}'|\mathfrak{P}$ for $\mathfrak{P}$ in K. Let $S = G(K'/K)$ and let $G' = G(K'/k)$. Let $G_{\mathfrak{P}'}$ be the decomposition group of $\mathfrak{P}'$ in G', and let $T_{\mathfrak{P}'}$ be the inertia group of $\mathfrak{P}'$ in G'. We first contend that we have natural isomorphisms

$$G'\left\{\begin{array}{c} K' \\ | \\ K \\ | \\ k \end{array}\right. \quad \begin{array}{l} \}S \\ \\ \}G \end{array}$$

$$G_{\mathfrak{P}} \approx G_{\mathfrak{P}'}S/S$$

and

$$T_{\mathfrak{P}} \approx T_{\mathfrak{P}'}S/S.$$

Proof. It is clear that the restriction to K of an element in $G_{\mathfrak{P}'}S$ leaves $\mathfrak{P}$ fixed, and so lies in $G_{\mathfrak{P}}$. Conversely, if λ is an element of G' which restricts to an element of $G_{\mathfrak{P}}$, then there exists some $\gamma \in S$ such that $\lambda\gamma \in G_{\mathfrak{P}'}$ (because λ maps $\mathfrak{P}'$ on another divisor of $\mathfrak{P}$ and S permutes such divisors transitively). Hence $\lambda \in G_{\mathfrak{P}'}S$, thus proving that

$$G_{\mathfrak{P}} \approx G_{\mathfrak{P}'}S/S.$$

A similar argument shows that $T_{\mathfrak{P}} \approx T_{\mathfrak{P}'}S/S$.

We can also phrase our isomorphisms by saying that the restriction homomorphisms

$$G_{\mathfrak{P}'} \to G_{\mathfrak{P}} \qquad \text{and} \qquad T_{\mathfrak{P}'} \to T_{\mathfrak{P}}$$

from K' to K are surjective, and hence that

$$G_{\mathfrak{P}} \approx G_{\mathfrak{P}'}/(G_{\mathfrak{P}'} \cap S) \qquad \text{and} \qquad T_{\mathfrak{P}} \approx T_{\mathfrak{P}'}/(T_{\mathfrak{P}'} \cap S).$$

The value of χ on an element of G' depends only on its class mod S, i.e. on its restriction to K', by definition of the extension of χ from G to G'. Finally, if $\sigma' = (\mathfrak{P}', K'/k)$ is a Frobenius automorphism of $\mathfrak{P}'$ in $G_{\mathfrak{P}'}$, then its restriction to K is a Frobenius automorphism of $\mathfrak{P}$ in $G_{\mathfrak{P}}$. From this it follows that

$$\frac{1}{e} \sum_{\tau \in T_{\mathfrak{P}}} \chi(\sigma^m \tau) = \frac{1}{e'} \sum_{\tau \in T_{\mathfrak{P}'}} \chi(\sigma'^m \tau)$$

and hence that the value

$$\chi(\mathfrak{p}^m)$$

does not depend on the field K'. This is precisely property **L3.**

The fourth property is slightly harder to prove, and depends on a more accurate analysis of the decomposition groups and inertia groups at the various levels. We do this in the next section. Here, we conclude with still a simple statement.

Theorem 2. *If K/k is abelian, class field to H, and if we identify $G(K/k)$ with the idele class group C_k/H under the Artin map, and χ is a simple character, then*

$$L(s, \chi, K/k) = L(s, \chi),$$

interpreting the character χ on the right as a character on C_k/H, and the L-series on the right being the proper abelian L-series of §1.

Proof. If $\mathfrak{p}$ is unramified in K, then the Artin map is given by means of the Frobenius automorphism, which depends only on $\mathfrak{p}$, and so the $\mathfrak{p}$-contribution to the L-series is the same no matter which L-series we deal with. Let S be the kernel of χ in G, and let K_χ be the fixed field of S. By property **L3,** we may view χ as a character on $G(K_\chi/k)$, and

$$L(s, \chi, K_\chi/k) = L(s, \chi, K/k).$$

Hence it suffices to prove our result when $K = K_\chi$, which we assume. In that case, $\mathfrak{p}$ is ramified in K if and only if it is ramified for χ, i.e. ramified in H, and χ is a non-trivial character on the inertia group $T_\mathfrak{P}$. The Galois group definition of the L-series yields

$$\chi(\mathfrak{p}^m) = \frac{1}{e} \sum_{\tau \in T_\mathfrak{P}} \chi(\sigma^m \tau) = \frac{1}{e} \chi(\sigma^m) \sum_{\tau \in T_\mathfrak{P}} \chi(\tau) = 0,$$

because the sum of a non-trivial character over an abelian group is 0. Hence the $\mathfrak{p}$-contribution to the L-series $L(s, \chi, K/k)$ is equal to 0. By definition, it is also equal to 0 in the abelian definition of L-series. This proves the theorem.

We conclude this section by the expression of the L-series as a product over the primes, again as in Artin. Let $A: \sigma \mapsto A(\sigma)$ be a representation of G in terms of endomorphisms of the vector space V, so $A(\sigma) \in \mathrm{End}(V)$. Then

$$\frac{1}{e} A(T_\mathfrak{P}) = \frac{1}{e} \sum_{\tau \in T_\mathfrak{P}} A(\tau)$$

is idempotent in $\mathrm{End}(V)$. If $\sigma = (\mathfrak{P}, K/k)$ as before, we define

$$A(\mathfrak{p}^m) = A(\sigma^m) \frac{1}{e} A(T_\mathfrak{P}).$$

We can then form the series

$$\log L(s, A, K/k) = \sum_{\mathfrak{p}, m} \frac{A(\mathfrak{p}^m)}{m \mathbf{N}\mathfrak{p}^{ms}},$$

which converges uniformly and absolutely for $\mathrm{Re}(s) \geqq 1 + \delta$, as usual, but has its values in $\mathrm{End}(V)$, assuming that V is a vector space over the complex numbers. Because of the non-commutativity, it appears to be a mess to exponentiate this series in $\mathrm{End}(V)$, although I cannot escape the idea that there may be something in doing so. However, as in Artin, one has

$$\operatorname{trace} \sum_{m=1}^{\infty} \frac{A(\mathfrak{p}^m)}{m \mathbf{N}\mathfrak{p}^{ms}} = -\log |I - \mathbf{N}\mathfrak{p}^{-s} A(\mathfrak{p})|,$$

where I is the identity in $\mathrm{End}(V)$, and consequently, one finds the product representation

$$L(s, \chi, K/k) = \sum_{\mathfrak{p}} \frac{1}{|I - \mathbf{N}\mathfrak{p}^{-s}A(\mathfrak{p})|},$$

valid for $\mathrm{Re}(s) > 1$.

For purposes of functional equations, to have neat formulas, it is necessary to multiply zeta functions and L-series by suitable factors, corresponding to the archimedean absolute values, namely Γ-factors. We shall see this later for abelian L-series. For the non-abelian ones, we refer to Artin's original paper for the description of these factors.

§3. *Induced characters and L-series contributions*

In this section, we relate induced characters with the decomposition and inertia groups. Let S be a subgroup of $G = G(K/k)$, and let ψ be a character of S. If $\{c\}$ denotes the collection of right cosets of S in G, and for each coset c we let $\bar{c}$ be a coset representative, so that

$$G = \bigcup_{\bar{c}} S\bar{c},$$

then the induced character χ_ψ can be defined by the formula

$$\chi_\psi(\lambda) = \sum_{c} \psi(\bar{c}\lambda\bar{c}^{-1}).$$

(For all properties concerning characters used here, cf. for instance the last chapter of my book *Algebra*.) It is understood that ψ is extended to a function on G by letting $\psi(x) = 0$ if $x \in G$, $x \notin S$.

We shall find suitable coset representatives in terms of the splitting of the prime $\mathfrak{p}$. We let F be the fixed field of S. Let

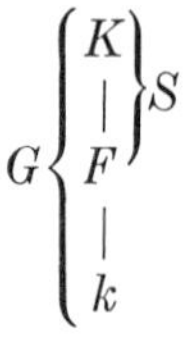

$$\mathfrak{p} = \mathfrak{q}_1^{e_1} \cdots \mathfrak{q}_s^{e_s}$$

be the splitting of $\mathfrak{p}$ into distinct prime powers in F. For each $i = 1, \ldots, s$ let $\mathfrak{P}_i$ be a prime of K lying above $\mathfrak{q}_i$. Let $\eta_i \in G$ be such that

$$\eta_i \mathfrak{P}_1 = \mathfrak{P}_i.$$

Let $G_i = G_{\mathfrak{P}_i}$ be the decomposition group of $\mathfrak{P}_i$ in G, and T_i its inertia group. Then

$$G_i = \eta_i G_1 \eta_i^{-1} \qquad \text{and} \qquad T_i = \eta_i T_1 \eta_i^{-1}.$$

If $\sigma_i = (\mathfrak{P}_i, K/k)$ is a Frobenius automorphism of $\mathfrak{P}_i$ in G_i (well defined modulo T_i), then we can choose σ_i such that

$$\sigma_i = \eta_i \sigma_1 \eta_i^{-1}.$$

We let e_i, f_i and e_i', f_i' denote the usual indices at the levels indicated on the following diagram.

$$e, f\left\{\begin{array}{c} \mathfrak{P}_i \\ | \\ \mathfrak{q}_i \\ | \\ \mathfrak{p} \end{array}\right. \begin{array}{l} \left.\right\} e_i', f_i' \\ \\ \left.\right\} e_i, f_i \end{array}$$

Thus

$$e = e_i e_i' \qquad \text{and} \qquad f = f_i f_i'.$$

We have

$$\sum_{i=1}^{s} e_i f_i = [F:k].$$

Note that the order of G_i is ef, and the order of $G_i \cap S$ (which is the decomposition group of $\mathfrak{P}_i$ in S) is $e_i' f_i'$. Hence

$$(G_i : G_i \cap S) = e_i f_i.$$

Let

$$\{\gamma_{i,\nu}\} \qquad (i = 1, \ldots, s;\ v = 1, \ldots, e_i f_i)$$

be right coset representatives of $G_i \cap S$ in G_i.

Lemma 1. *We contend that $\{\gamma_{i,\nu}\eta_i\}$ is a system of distinct right coset representatives of S in G.*

Proof. We first prove that they represent distinct cosets. Suppose that

$$S\gamma_{i,\nu}\eta_i = S\gamma_{j,\mu}\eta_j.$$

Then

$$\gamma_{i,\nu}\eta_i\eta_j^{-1}\gamma_{j,\mu}^{-1} \in S.$$

Looking at the effect of this element on $\mathfrak{P}_j$, we see that it maps $\mathfrak{P}_j$ on $\mathfrak{P}_i$. But an element of S leaves $\mathfrak{q}_j$ fixed, and $\mathfrak{P}_j | \mathfrak{q}_j$. Hence $i = j$. Canceling $\eta_i = \eta_j$ we now conclude immediately that $\nu = \mu$, thus proving our first assertion. Our contention follows because the index of S in G is equal to $[F:k] = \sum e_i f_i$.

Having found coset representatives of S in G, we can write down the value of the induced character in terms of these, and find

$$\chi_\psi(\lambda) = \sum_{i=1}^{s} \sum_{\nu=1}^{e_i f_i} \psi(\gamma_{i,\nu}\eta_i\lambda\eta_i^{-1}\gamma_{i,\nu}^{-1}). \tag{1}$$

This formula applies whether λ is an element of G, or represents a sum of elements of G. In the applications, of course, we use sums of elements of G, namely $\lambda = \sigma_1^m T_1$. If we conjugate $\sigma_1^m T_1$ by η_i, then we obtain $\sigma_i^m T_i$. Furthermore, T_i is normal in G_i, hence further conjugation by $\gamma_{i,\nu}$ does not change $\sigma_i^m T_i$. Consequently, we find an expression for the value of χ_ψ appearing in the L-series, namely

$$\boxed{\chi_\psi(\sigma_1^m T_1) = \sum_{i=1}^{s} e_i f_i \psi(\sigma_i^m T_i).} \tag{2}$$

We must therefore determine the intersection of $\sigma_i^m T_i$ with S, because outside of this intersection, the value of ψ is 0.

Lemma 2. *The intersection $\sigma_i^m T_i \cap S$ is not empty if and only if $f_i | m$. In that case,*

$$\sigma_i^m T_i \cap S = \varphi_i^{m/f_i}(T_i \cap S) = \varphi_i^{m/f_i} T_i'$$

where $\varphi_i = (\mathfrak{P}_i, K/F)$, and $T_i' = T_i \cap S$ is the inertia group of $\mathfrak{P}_i$ in S.

Proof. Suppose that $\sigma_i^m T_i$ contains an element $\sigma_i^m \tau \in S$, with $\tau \in T_i$. Then on the residue class field $\mathfrak{o}_K/\mathfrak{P}_i$ the effect of $\sigma_i^m \tau$ is the same as that of σ_i^m, and it also leaves $\mathfrak{o}_F/\mathfrak{q}_i$ fixed. This effect is that of

$$x \mapsto x^{\mathbf{N}\mathfrak{p}^m},$$

and $\mathfrak{o}_F/\mathfrak{q}_i$ has $\mathbf{N}\mathfrak{p}^{f_i}$ elements. For $\mathfrak{o}_F/\mathfrak{q}_i$ to be fixed, we must therefore have $f_i | m$.

Suppose now that this is the case. The effect of φ_i on $\mathfrak{o}_K/\mathfrak{P}_i$ is

$$x \mapsto x^{\mathbf{N}\mathfrak{q}_i},$$

with $\mathbf{N}\mathfrak{q}_i = \mathbf{N}\mathfrak{p}^{f_i}$. Hence $\sigma_i^m \tau$ and φ_i^{m/f_i} have the same effect on $\mathfrak{o}_K/\mathfrak{P}_i$. They both lie in $G_i \cap S$, which is the decomposition group of $\mathfrak{P}_i$ in S. Hence they lie in the same coset of T_i. This shows that

$$\sigma_i^m T_i \cap S \subset \varphi_i^{m/f_i}(T_i \cap S).$$

The converse is also clear, and this proves the lemma.

The desired relationship **L4** for L-series is now immediate from this last formula. We have for fixed $\mathfrak{p}$,

$$\sum_m \frac{\chi_\psi(\mathfrak{p}^m)}{m\mathbf{N}\mathfrak{p}^{ms}} = \sum_m \sum_{i=1}^{s} \frac{1}{e} \frac{e_i f_i \psi(\sigma_i^m T_i)}{m\mathbf{N}\mathfrak{p}^{ms}}$$

$$= \sum_{i=1}^{s} \sum_m \frac{1}{e} \frac{e_i f_i \psi(\sigma_i^m T_i)}{m\mathbf{N}\mathfrak{p}^{ms}}.$$

For each i, write $m = nf_i$. Only such m divisible by f_i give a non-zero contribution to the i-th sum. We have $e_i/e = e_i'$. Hence we get

$$\sum_m \frac{\chi_\psi(\mathfrak{p}^m)}{m\mathbf{N}\mathfrak{p}^{ms}} = \sum_{i=1}^{s} \sum_n \frac{\psi(\mathfrak{q}_i^n)}{n\mathbf{N}\mathfrak{p}^{ns}}$$

$$= \sum_{\mathfrak{q}|\mathfrak{p}} \sum_n \frac{\psi(\mathfrak{q}^n)}{n\mathbf{N}\mathfrak{p}^{ns}}.$$

This proves **L4,** because it proves that

$$\log L(s, \chi_\psi, K/k) = \log L(s, \psi, K/F).$$

PART THREE

ANALYTIC THEORY

The simple analytic results obtained in Chapter VIII were used up to now only incidentally in basically algebraic results, especially in the class field theory. We shall concentrate more on the analytic aspects for the rest of the book. We give two proofs for the functional equation, one following Hecke, and the other following Tate. The reader will profitably compare both techniques. Hecke's proof makes use of the general Poisson summation formula for the integral lattice in Euclidean space. Tate's proof uses the adelic form of the Poisson formula. We give the functional equation for the L-series with characters only in Tate's version, which in this case I find slightly easier to keep track of the computations. If the character is of finite period, then there would still not be too much difference with the functional equation as given in Chapter XIII.

The chapter on densities, using the Tauberian theorem, is misleading. Statements on the distribution of primes depend essentially on the explicit formulas, which give much better insight (especially when one will have better results in the direction of the Riemann Hypothesis). The reader can refer to Landau [11], or also Hooley's paper "On Artin's conjecture," *J. Reine Angew, Math.*, 225, 1967, pp. 209–220. Again, the Brauer-Siegel theorem on $\log hR \sim \log d^{1/2}$ really depends on a weak result on the zeros of the zeta function to have a neat proof. Siegel and Brauer had to surmount considerable technical difficulties to go around the non-availability of such results at this time. I have reproduced Siegel's argument for this in Chapter XIII.

CHAPTER XIII

Functional Equation of the Zeta Function, Hecke's Proof

§1. *The Poisson summation formula*

Let f be a function on $\mathbf{R}^n$. We shall say that f **tends to 0 rapidly at infinity** if for each positive integer m the function

$$x \mapsto (1 + |x|)^m f(x), \qquad x \in \mathbf{R}^n,$$

is bounded for $|x|$ sufficiently large. Here as in the rest of this chapter, $|x|$ is the Euclidean norm of x. Equivalently, the preceding condition can be formulated by saying that for every polynomial P (in n variables) the function Pf is bounded, or that the function

$$x \mapsto |x|^m f(x)$$

is bounded, for x sufficiently large (i.e. $|x|$ sufficiently large).

We define the **Schwartz space** to be the set of functions on $\mathbf{R}^n$ which are infinitely differentiable (i.e. partial derivatives of all orders exist and are continuous), and which tend to 0 rapidly at infinity, as well as their partial derivatives of all orders.

Example of such functions. In one variable, e^{-x^2} is one, and similarly in n variables if we interpret x^2 as the dot product $x \cdot x$, which we also write x^2. As a matter of notation, we shall write xy instead of $x \cdot y$ if x, y are elements of $\mathbf{R}^n$.

If f is a C^∞ function of one variable which is 0 outside some bounded interval, then f is in the Schwartz space. As an example, one can take the function

$$f(x) = \begin{cases} e^{-\frac{1}{(x-a)(b-x)}} & \text{if } a < x < b \\ 0 & \text{otherwise.} \end{cases}$$

An analogous function in n variables can be obtained by taking the product

$$f(x_1) \cdots f(x_n).$$

It is clear that the Schwartz space is a vector space, which we denote by S. We take all our functions to be complex valued, so S is a space over **C**.

We let D_j be the partial derivative with respect to the j-th variable. For each n-tuple of integers $\geqq 0$, $p = (p_1, \ldots, p_n)$, we write

$$D^p = D_1^{p_1} \cdots D_n^{p_1},$$

so that D^p is a partial differential operator, which maps S into itself. As a matter of notation, we write

$$|p| = p_1 + \cdots + p_n.$$

It is also convenient to use the notation $M_j f$ for the function such that

$$(M_j f)(x) = x_j f(x).$$

Thus M_j is multiplication by the j-th variable. Also

$$M^p f = M_1^{p_1} \cdots M_n^{p_n} f,$$

so that

$$(M^p f)(x) = x_1^{p_1} \cdots x_n^{p_n} f(x).$$

In what follows, we shall take the integral of certain functions over $\mathbf{R}^n$, and we use the following notation:

$$\int f(x)\,dx = \int_{\mathbf{R}^n} f(x)\,dx = \int_{-\infty}^{\infty} \cdots \int_{-\infty}^{\infty} f(x_1, \ldots, x_n)\,dx_1 \cdots dx_n.$$

Since our functions will be taken from S, there is no convergence problem, because for x sufficiently large, we have for some constant C:

$$|f(x)| \leqq \frac{C}{(1 + x_1^2) \cdots (1 + x_n^2)},$$

and we can view the integral as a repeated integral, the order of integration being arbitrary. The justification is at the level of elementary calculus. Furthermore, we differentiate under the integral sign, using the formula

$$\frac{\partial}{\partial y_j} \int K(x, y)\,dx = \int \frac{\partial}{\partial y_j} K(x, y)\,dx$$

for suitable functions K in situations where this is obviously permissible (justification loc. cit.), namely when the partial derivatives of K exist, are continuous and bounded by an absolutely integrable function of x over $\mathbf{R}^n$, independent of y. The trivial argument runs as follows, say when x and y each consist of one variable:

$$\left|\int_{-\infty}^{\infty}\left[\frac{K(x, y+h) - K(x, y)}{h} - D_2K(x, y)\right]dx\right|$$
$$\leqq \int_{-\infty}^{\infty}\left|\frac{K(x, y+h) - K(x, y)}{h} - D_2K(x, y)\right| dx.$$

But by the mean value theorem,

$$\frac{K(x, y+h) - K(x, y)}{h} - D_2K(x, y) = D_2K(x, c) - D_2K(x, y),$$

where c lies between y and $y + h$, and c depends on x, y, h. Now we split the integral into a finite integral and a tail end, so that the tail end is very small because of the absolute integrability of D_2K, and then take h small and use uniform continuity of D_2K on the finite part to get our expression less than ϵ, for given ϵ.

A similar argument which is even simpler works to show that similar integrals depend continuously on parameters.

We shall also change variables in an integral. For instance,

$$\int f(x - y)\, dx = \int f(x)\, dx, \qquad \int f(-x)\, dx = \int f(x)\, dx.$$

$$\textit{If } c > 0, \textit{ then } \int f(cx)\, dx = \frac{1}{c^n}\int f(x)\, dx.$$

We now define the **Fourier transform** of a function $f \in S$ by

$$\hat{f}(y) = \int f(x)e^{-2\pi ixy}\, dx.$$

Remember that $xy = x \cdot y$.

We shall now see that the Fourier transform interchanges the maps D_j and M_j.

Since

$$\frac{\partial}{\partial y_j} f(x)e^{-2\pi ixy} = f(x)(-2\pi i)x_je^{-2\pi ixy},$$

we see that we can differentiate under the integral sign, and that

$$D_j\hat{f} = (-2\pi i)(M_jf)^\wedge.$$

By induction, we get

$$\boxed{D^p\hat{f} = (-2\pi i)^{|p|}(M^p f)^\wedge.}$$

The analogous formula reversing the roles of D^p and M^p is also true, namely:

$$\boxed{M^p\hat{f} = (-2\pi i)^{|p|}(D^p f)^\wedge.}$$

To see this, we consider

$$y_j\hat{f}(y) = \int f(x)y_j e^{-2\pi ixy}\,dx$$

and integrate by parts with respect to the j-th variable first. We let

$$u = f(x) \qquad \text{and} \qquad dv = y_j e^{-2\pi ixy}.$$

Then $v = ie^{-2\pi ixy}$ and the term uv between $-\infty$ and $+\infty$ gives zero contribution because f tends to 0 at infinity. Hence

$$M_j\hat{f}(y) = (-2\pi i)\int D_j f(x)e^{-2\pi ixy}\,dx = (-2\pi i)(D_j f)^\wedge(y).$$

Induction now yields our formula.

Lemma. *The Fourier transform $f \mapsto \hat{f}$ is a linear map of the Schwartz space into itself.*

Proof. If $f \in S$, then it is clear that $\hat{f}$ is bounded, in fact by

$$|\hat{f}(y)| \leqq \int |f(x)|\,dx.$$

The expression for $M^p\hat{f}$ in terms of the Fourier transform of $D^p f$, which is in S, shows that $M^p\hat{f}$ is bounded, so that $\hat{f}$ tends rapidly to zero at infinity. Similarly, one sees that $M^pD^q\hat{f}$ is bounded, because we let $g = D^q f$, $g \in S$, and

$$M^pD^q\hat{f} = (-2\pi i)^{|p|}M^p\hat{g}$$

is bounded. This proves our theorem.

A function g on $\mathbf{R}^n$ will be called **periodic** if $g(x + k) = g(x)$ for all $k \in \mathbf{Z}^n$. We let $T^n = \mathbf{R}^n/\mathbf{Z}^n$ be the n-torus. Let g be a periodic C^∞ function. We define its k-th Fourier coefficient for $k \in \mathbf{Z}^n$ by

$$c_k = \int_{T^n} g(x)e^{-2\pi ikx}\,dx.$$

The integral on T^n is by definition the n-fold integral with the variables $(x_1, \ldots, x_n)$ ranging from 0 to 1. Integrating by parts d times for any integer $d > 0$, and using the fact that the partial derivatives of g are bounded, we conclude at once that there is some number $C = C(d, g)$ such that for all $k \in \mathbf{Z}^n$ we have $|c_k| \leqq C/\|k\|^d$, where $\|k\|$ is the sup norm. Hence the Fourier series

$$g(x) = \sum_{k \in \mathbf{Z}^n} c_k e^{2\pi i k x}$$

converges to g uniformly.

Poisson summation formula. *Let f be in the Schwartz space. Then*

$$\sum_{m \in \mathbf{Z}^n} f(m) = \sum_{m \in \mathbf{Z}^n} \hat{f}(m).$$

Proof. Let

$$g(x) = \sum_{k \in \mathbf{Z}^n} f(x + k).$$

Then g is periodic and C^∞. If c_m is its m-th Fourier coefficient, then

$$\sum_{m \in \mathbf{Z}^n} c_m = g(0) = \sum_{k \in \mathbf{Z}^n} f(k).$$

On the other hand, interchanging a sum and integral, we get

$$\begin{aligned} c_m = \int_{T^n} g(x) e^{-2\pi i m x}\, dx &= \sum_{k \in \mathbf{Z}^n} \int_{T^n} f(x + k) e^{-2\pi i m x}\, dx \\ &= \sum_{k \in \mathbf{Z}^n} \int_{T^n} f(x + k) e^{-2\pi i m (x+k)}\, dx \\ &= \int_{\mathbf{R}^n} f(x) e^{-2\pi i m x}\, dx = \hat{f}(m). \end{aligned}$$

This proves the Poisson summation formula.

In preparation for the n-dimensional theorems of the next section, we treat here the one dimensional case as an example. Let θ be the function defined for $y > 0$ by

$$\theta(y) = \sum_{-\infty}^{\infty} e^{-n^2 \pi y}.$$

It is easy to see that if $h(y) = e^{-\pi y^2}$, then $\hat{h} = h$. (We shall recall the proof briefly in the next section.) Furthermore, if f is in the Schwartz space, and $b > 0$, and $f_b(y) = f(by)$, then

$$\hat{f}_b(y) = \frac{1}{b} f(b^{-1} y).$$

From this and the Poisson formula in one variable, we find at once the functional equation of the theta function, namely

$$\theta(y^{-1}) = y^{1/2}\theta(y).$$

Let $s = \sigma + it$ with σ, t real. We have by definition

$$\Gamma(s) = \int_0^\infty e^{-y}y^s \frac{dy}{y}.$$

Let

$$F(s) = \pi^{-s/2}\Gamma(s/2)\zeta(s).$$

Let $g(y) = \sum_{n=1}^{\infty} e^{-n^2\pi y}$, so that $2g(y) = \theta(y) - 1$. Then from the above integral for the gamma function, we obtain at once

$$\begin{aligned} F(s) &= \int_0^\infty x^{s/2}g(x)\frac{dx}{x} \\ &= \int_1^\infty x^{s/2}g(x)\frac{dx}{x} + \int_1^\infty x^{-s/2}g(1/x)\frac{dx}{x}. \end{aligned}$$

The functional equation of the theta function immediately implies that

$$F(s) = \frac{1}{s-1} - \frac{1}{s} + \int_1^\infty (x^{s/2} + x^{(1-s)/2})g(x)\frac{dx}{x}.$$

The integral on the right converges absolutely for all complex s, and uniformly for s in any strip $\sigma_1 \leqq \sigma \leqq \sigma_2$. The expression on the right then defines F for all values of $s \neq 0, 1$, and we see that

$$F(s) = F(1-s).$$

§2. *A special computation*

Example 1. Consider the function

$$h(x) = e^{-\pi x^2},$$

where $x^2 = x \cdot x$ as usual. *We contend that h is self dual, i.e.*

$$\hat{h} = h.$$

Proof. We differentiate the Fourier transform

$$\hat{h}(y) = \int h(x)e^{-2\pi ixy}\,dx$$

under the integral with respect to y (we may assume for this proof that we are in the one variable case, since the Fourier transform splits into a product of 1-variable transforms), and we integrate by parts. We then find that

$$\frac{dh(y)}{dy} = -2\pi y h(y).$$

Hence there exists a constant C such that

$$\hat{h}(y) = Ce^{-\pi y^2}.$$

Taking the value $\hat{h}(0)$ shows that $C = 1$, thus concluding the proof.

Example 2. Next, let f be an arbitrary function in the Schwartz space, and let B be a non-singular real matrix. Then the function f_B defined by

$$f_B(x) = f(Bx)$$

is also in the Schwartz space, and using the change of variables formula for the multiple integral, we find immediately that its Fourier transform is given by

$$\boxed{\hat{f}_B(y) = \frac{1}{\|B\|}\hat{f}({}^tB^{-1}y)}$$

where $\|B\|$ is the absolute value of the determinant of B, and ${}^tB^{-1}$ is the transpose of the inverse of B. This is clear since when we make the change of variables $z = Bx$, we have $dz = \|B\|\,dx$, and

$$\langle B^{-1}z, y\rangle = \langle z, {}^tB^{-1}y\rangle.$$

The Poisson formula will be applied to a special kind of function f in the Schwartz space. Let Q be a positive definite quadratic form over the reals, on $\mathbf{R}^N$. We can write

$$Q(x) = \langle Ax, x\rangle$$

where $\langle\ ,\ \rangle$ is the usual scalar product, $x \in \mathbf{R}^N$, and A is a symmetric matrix, such that for all $x \neq 0$ we have $Q(x) > 0$.

Let

$$g(x) = e^{-\pi Q(x)}.$$

We can write $A = B^2$ for some symmetric operator B, and thus

$$Q(x) = \langle Bx, Bx\rangle.$$

We are therefore in the situation arising from Examples 1 and 2, and we can apply the Poisson formula to $g(x)$. We find:

$$\sum_{l \in \mathbf{Z}^N} e^{-\pi\langle Al, l\rangle} = \frac{1}{\sqrt{\|A\|}} \sum_{l \in \mathbf{Z}^N} e^{-\pi\langle A^{-1}l, l\rangle}.$$

Or, if we let Q' be the quadratic form such that

$$Q'(x) = \langle A^{-1}x, x\rangle,$$

then we can rewrite this formula in the form

$$\sum_{l \in \mathbf{Z}^N} e^{-\pi Q(l)} = \frac{1}{\sqrt{\|A\|}} \sum_{l \in \mathbf{Z}^N} e^{-\pi Q'(l)}.$$

We shall apply this to a quadratic form obtained arithmetically. Let k be a number field, and $\mathfrak{a}$ a fractional ideal of k. Let

$$\alpha = \{\alpha_1, \ldots, \alpha_N\}$$

be a basis of $\mathfrak{a}$ over $\mathbf{Z}$. We let

$$\alpha' = \{\alpha_1', \ldots, \alpha_N'\}$$

be the dual basis with respect to the trace. Then α' is a basis for the fractional ideal

$$\mathfrak{a}' = (\mathfrak{d}\mathfrak{a})^{-1},$$

where $\mathfrak{d}$ is the different of K over $\mathbf{Q}$. (Proposition 4 of Chapter III, §1). We let $j = 1, \ldots, r_1 + 2r_2$ be indices for the conjugates of k in $\mathbf{C}$. We write symbolically

$$\xi = x_1\alpha_1 + \cdots + x_N\alpha_N,$$

and

$$\xi^{(j)} = x_1\alpha_1^{(j)} + \cdots + x_N\alpha_N^{(j)},$$

with real numbers $x_1, \ldots, x_N$.

Hecke's theta formula. *Let $c_1, \ldots, c_N$ be real numbers > 0, such that $c_{r_1+\nu} = c_{r_1+\nu+r_2}$ for $0 \leqq \nu \leqq r_2$. Let $d_{\mathfrak{a}}$ be the absolute value of the discriminant of $\mathfrak{a}$, so that*

$$(d_{\mathfrak{a}}) = \mathbf{N}\mathfrak{a}^2 d_k.$$

Let

$$g(x) = \exp\left(-\pi d_{\mathfrak{a}}^{-1/N} \sum_{j=1}^{N} c_j|\xi^{(j)}|^2\right)$$

and let

$$\Theta(c, \mathfrak{a}) = \sum_{x \in \mathbf{Z}^N} g(x).$$

Then we have the relation

$$\Theta(c, \mathfrak{a}) = \frac{1}{\sqrt{c_1 \cdots c_N}} \Theta(c^{-1}, \mathfrak{a}'),$$

where c^{-1} *stands symbolically for* $c_1^{-1}, \ldots, c_N^{-1}$.

Proof. Let us put

$$\begin{aligned} Q(c, \alpha, x) &= \sum_{j=1}^{N} c_j|\alpha_1^{(j)}x_1 + \cdots + \alpha_N^{(j)}x_N|^2 \\ &= \langle A_{c,\alpha}x, x\rangle. \end{aligned}$$

The $\nu\mu$-component of the matrix $A_{c,\alpha}$ is

$$\sum_{j=1}^{N} c_j\alpha_\nu^{(j)}\bar{\alpha}_\mu^{(j)}.$$

From Chapter III, §1, it is immediately verified that the inverse matrix of $A_{c,\alpha}$ is given by

$$\langle A_{c,\alpha}^{-1}x, x\rangle = Q(c^{-1}, \alpha', x).$$

Furthermore, the absolute value of the determinant is

$$\|A_{c,\alpha}\| = c_1 \cdots c_N|D(\alpha_1, \ldots, \alpha_N)|.$$

This yields all the data needed to apply the Poisson formula in the form given above for the exponential of a quadratic form, and concludes the proof.

§3. *Functional equation*

It is convenient to deal with the zeta function associated with an ideal class. We shall follow Hecke (cf. also Landau), which gives an N-dimensional version of one of the original proofs for the functional equation by Riemann.

Let $\mathfrak{K}$ be an ideal class of the ordinary ideal class group I/P. We define

$$\zeta(s, \mathfrak{K}) = \sum_{\mathfrak{b} \in \mathfrak{K}} \frac{1}{N\mathfrak{b}^s}$$

for Re$(s) > 1$. Let $\mathfrak{a}$ be an ideal in $\mathfrak{K}^{-1}$. The map

$$\mathfrak{b} \mapsto \mathfrak{a}\mathfrak{b} = (\xi)$$

establishes a bijection between the set of ideals in $\mathfrak{K}$ and equivalence classes of non-zero elements of $\mathfrak{a}$ (where two field elements are called equivalent if they differ by a unit). Let $R(\mathfrak{a})$ be a set of representatives for the non-zero equivalence classes. Then we may write

$$\mathbf{N}\mathfrak{a}^{-s}\zeta(s, \mathfrak{K}) = \sum_{\xi \in R(\mathfrak{a})} \frac{1}{\mathbf{N}\xi^s},$$

where the sum is taken over representatives ξ of equivalence classes of non-zero elements of $\mathfrak{a}$. Let $\alpha_1, \ldots, \alpha_N$ be a basis of $\mathfrak{a}$ over $\mathbf{Z}$. We write

$$\xi = x_1\alpha_1 + \cdots + x_N\alpha_N, \qquad x_i \in \mathbf{Z}.$$

Let S_∞ be the set of archimedean absolute values on k. For $v \in S_\infty$ we let σ_v be the embedding of k in k_v, identified with $\mathbf{R}$ or $\mathbf{C}$ (in the complex case, we fix one identification which otherwise is determined only up to conjugacy). We let

$$\xi_v = \sigma_v \xi,$$

and also use this same notation when we let x_i be real numbers.

Functional equation. *Let $\mathfrak{K}$ be an ideal class, $N = [k\colon \mathbf{Q}]$, d_k the absolute value of the discriminant of k,*

$$A = 2^{-r_2} d_k^{1/2} \pi^{-N/2}.$$

Let

$$F(s, \mathfrak{K}) = A^s \Gamma\left(\frac{s}{2}\right)^{r_1} \Gamma(s)^{r_2} \zeta(s, \mathfrak{K}).$$

Let $\mathfrak{K}'$ be the ideal class of $(\mathfrak{d}\mathfrak{a})^{-1}$, where $\mathfrak{d}$ is the different of $k/\mathbf{Q}$. Then $F(s, \mathfrak{K})$ is analytic except for simple poles at $s = 0$, $s = 1$, and

$$F(s, \mathfrak{K}) = F(1 - s, \mathfrak{K}').$$

Proof. We shall obtain an integral expression for the zeta function, and also see that it is entire except for a simple pole at $s = 1$, for which we shall determine the residue.

We recall that

$$\Gamma(s) = \int_0^\infty e^{-y} y^s \frac{dy}{y}, \qquad \text{for } \operatorname{Re}(s) > 0.$$

It will also be useful to note that if f is a function such that $f(y)/y$ is absolutely integrable from 0 to ∞, then

$$\int_0^\infty f(y)\,\frac{dy}{y} = \int_0^\infty f(ay)\,\frac{dy}{y}$$

for any number $a > 0$. In other words, the integral is an invariant integral on the multiplicative group of positive reals, for the measure dy/y. Note that the gamma function is expressed as such an integral. This is relevant to the zeta function, because for instance

$$\frac{\Gamma(s/2)}{a^s} = \int_0^\infty e^{-a^2 y} y^{s/2}\,\frac{dy}{y}.$$

(Here we made a multiplicative translation of f by a^2.)

Let

$$d_{\mathfrak{a}} = \mathbf{N}\mathfrak{a}^2 d_k$$

be the absolute value of the discriminant of $\mathfrak{a}$.

Let v be real. Let

$$a^2 = \pi\, d_{\mathfrak{a}}^{-1/N} |\xi_v|^2,$$

where ξ is one of our non-zero elements of $\mathfrak{a}$. Then we find

$$(\pi^{-1/2}\, d_k^{1/2N} \mathbf{N}\mathfrak{a}^{1/N})^s\, \frac{\Gamma(s/2)}{|\xi_v|^s} = \int_0^\infty \exp(-\pi\, d_{\mathfrak{a}}^{-1/N} |\xi_v|^2 y) y^{s/2}\,\frac{dy}{y}.$$

Let v be complex. By a similar argument, we find

$$(2^{-1}\pi^{-1}\, d_k^{1/N} \mathbf{N}\mathfrak{a}^{2/N})^s\, \frac{\Gamma(s)}{|\xi_v|^{2s}} = \int_0^\infty \exp(-\pi\, d_{\mathfrak{a}}^{-1/N} 2|\xi_v|^2 y) y^s\,\frac{dy}{y}.$$

Multiplying over all $v \in S_\infty$, and letting $y = \prod y_v$ be the variable in $(r_1 + r_2)$-space, with

$$\frac{dy}{y} = \prod_v \frac{dy_v}{y_v},$$

we obtain

$$A^s \Gamma(s/2)^{r_1} \Gamma(s)^{r_2}\, \frac{\mathbf{N}\mathfrak{a}^s}{\mathbf{N}\xi^s} = \int_0^\infty \cdots \int_0^\infty \exp(-\pi d_{\mathfrak{a}}^{-1/N} \textstyle\sum N_v |\xi_v|^2 y_v) \|y\|^{s/2}\,\frac{dy}{y},$$

where

$$\|y\| = \prod y_v^{N_v}.$$

For $\mathrm{Re}(s) \geqq 1 + \delta$, the sum over inequivalent $\xi \neq 0$ is absolutely and uniformly convergent. Hence for $\mathrm{Re}(s) > 1$ we find an expression for

$F(s, \mathfrak{K})$, namely

(1)
$$\boxed{\begin{aligned} F(s, \mathfrak{K}) &= A^s\Gamma(s/2)^{r_1}\Gamma(s)^{r_2}\zeta(s, \mathfrak{K}) \\ &= \int_0^\infty \cdots \int_0^\infty \sum_{\xi \in R(\mathfrak{a})} \exp(-\pi d_\mathfrak{a}^{-1/N} \sum N_v |\xi_v|^2 y_v) \|y\|^{s/2} \frac{dy}{y}. \end{aligned}}$$

We can abbreviate the notation to get a clearer picture of this expression. We let

$$G = \mathbf{R}^+ \times \cdots \times \mathbf{R}^+ = \prod \mathbf{R}_v^+$$

be the product of $r_1 + r_2$ copies of the positive reals. Then we can write

(2)
$$\boxed{F(s, \mathfrak{K}) = \int_G f(y)\|y\|^{s/2}\, d^*y,}$$

where $d^*y = dy/y$, and f is the big sum over all $\xi \neq 0$, $\xi \in R(\mathfrak{a})$.

Let V be the image of the group of units U in G. In other words, V is the image of the map

$$u \mapsto (|u_v|)_{v \in S_\infty}.$$

The kernel of this map is the group of roots of unity. Its image is contained in the subgroup G^0 consisting of all $y \in G$ such that $\|y\| = 1$, and is a discrete subgroup. Furthermore, G^0/V is compact. Also, we can write G as a product

$$G = \mathbf{R}^+ \times G^0,$$

because any $y \in G$ can be written uniquely as

$$y = t^{1/N}c$$

with $t \in \mathbf{R}^+$ and $c \in G^0$. Here $c = (c_v)$ and $t^{1/N}c = (t^{1/N}c_v)$. By changing variables, we could map G on Euclidean space $\mathbf{R}^{r+1}$. We prefer to carry out the proof formally using the present notation. We shall perform this change of variables at the end, to compute some needed constants. Observe that with the above product expression we have

$$\|y\| = t.$$

We may write

$$F(s, \mathfrak{K}) = \int_0^\infty \int_{G^0} f(t^{1/N}c)t^{s/2}\, d^*c\, \frac{dt}{t},$$

where d^*c is the appropriate measure on G^0, and $c = (c_v)$ is the variable in G^0. If we put indices $j = 1, \ldots, r_1 + r_2$ then

$$c = (c_1, \ldots, c_{r_1+r_2}).$$

Let E be a fundamental domain for V^2 in G^0. We have a disjoint decomposition

$$G^0 = \bigcup_{\eta \in V} \eta^2 E,$$

and hence if w is the number of roots of unity in k, we get

$$F(s, \mathfrak{K}) =$$

$$\int_0^\infty \int_E \frac{1}{w} \sum_{u \in U} \sum_{\xi \in R(\mathfrak{a})} \exp(-\pi d_\mathfrak{a}^{1/N} \sum N_v |\xi_v u_v|^2 t^{1/N} c_v) t^{s/2}\, d^*c \frac{dt}{t}$$

$$= \int_0^\infty \int_E \frac{1}{w} [\Theta(t^{1/N} c, \mathfrak{a}) - 1]\, d^*c\, t^{s/2} \frac{dt}{t}.$$

We split the integral from 0 to ∞ into two integrals, from 0 to 1 and from 1 to ∞. We let $\mu^*(E)$ be the integral of 1 over E, with respect to d^*c. We then find:

$$F(s, \mathfrak{K}) = \int_0^1 \int_E \frac{1}{w} \Theta(t^{1/N} c, \mathfrak{a}) t^{s/2}\, d^*c \frac{dt}{t} - \frac{\mu^*(E)}{ws}$$

$$+ \int_1^\infty \int_E \frac{1}{w} [\Theta(t^{1/N} c, \mathfrak{a}) - 1]\, d^*c\, t^{s/2} \frac{dt}{t}.$$

We now use the functional equation of the theta function. We see that

$$\Theta(t^{1/N} c, \mathfrak{a}) = \frac{1}{\sqrt{t}} \Theta(t^{-1/N} c^{-1}, \mathfrak{a}')$$

because $\|c\| = 1$ (c is in G^0!). We transform the first integral from 0 to 1, with a small change of variables, letting $t = 1/\tau$, $dt = -d\tau/\tau^2$. Note that the measure d^*c is invariant under the change $c \mapsto c^{-1}$ (think of the isomorphism with the additive Euclidean measure, invariant under taking negatives). We therefore find that

$$F(s, \mathfrak{K}) =$$

$$\int_1^\infty \int_E \frac{1}{w} [\Theta(t^{1/N} c, \mathfrak{a}) - 1]\, d^*c\, t^{\frac{s}{2}} \frac{dt}{t} - \frac{\mu^*(E)2}{ws}$$

$$+ \int_1^\infty \int_E \frac{1}{w} [\Theta(t^{1/N} c, \mathfrak{a}') - 1]\, d^*c\, t^{\frac{1-s}{2}} \frac{dt}{t} - \frac{\mu^*(E)2}{w(1-s)}. \tag{3}$$

This expression is invariant under the changes

$$s \mapsto 1 - s \qquad \text{and} \qquad \mathfrak{a} \mapsto \mathfrak{a}'.$$

This proves the functional equation.

Actually, our last expression yields more information on $F(s, \mathfrak{K})$. Indeed, the integrals are absolutely convergent for all complex s, thus giving us an analytic expression for $F(s, \mathfrak{K})$, disregarding the two simple polar terms at $s = 0$ and $s = 1$.

We shall now carry out explicitly the change of variables in the above proof, and compute $\mu^*(E)$. Let $u_1, \ldots, u_r$ be independent generators for the units modulo roots of unity, and let

$$\eta_i = (|u_i^{(1)}|, \ldots, |u_i^{(r+1)}|) = (\eta_{i1}, \ldots, \eta_{i,r+1})$$

be their images in G, so that $\eta_1, \ldots, \eta_r$ form a (multiplicative) **Z**-basis for V. Let

$$g \colon \mathbf{R}^+ \times \mathbf{R}^r \to G$$

be the map

$$(t, z_1, \ldots, z_r) \mapsto t^{1/N} \eta_1^{2z_1} \cdots \eta_r^{2z_r}.$$

Then our map is an isomorphism, and in terms of coordinates we have

$$y_j = t^{1/N} \eta_{1j}^{2z_1} \cdots \eta_{rj}^{2z_r}, \qquad j = 1, \ldots, r_1 + r_2.$$

The Jacobian determinant is then immediately computed to be

$$\Delta_g(t, z) = 2^{-r_2+r} \frac{y_1 \cdots y_{r+1}}{t} R,$$

where R is the regulator. Hence (2) can now be written

$$F(s, \mathfrak{K}) = \int_0^\infty \int_{\mathbf{R}^r} f(g(t, z)) t^{s/2} (2^{-r_2+r} R) \, dz \, \frac{dt}{t} \cdot$$

Thus the integral over G^0 corresponds to an integral over $\mathbf{R}^r$, and under our map, the fundamental domain E is the image of the unit cube (half closed) in this Euclidean space. The cosets of this unit cube with respect to the lattice of integral points $\mathbf{Z}^r$ in $\mathbf{R}^r$ correspond to the cosets of E with respect to elements of V^2 in G^0. This shows that

$$\mu^*(E) = 2^{-r_2+r} R = 2^{r_1-1} R.$$

This gives us the residue of $F(s, \mathfrak{K})$:

Theorem 1. *The polar part of $F(s, \mathfrak{K})$ at $s = 0$ and $s = 1$ is given by*

$$\frac{\mu^*(E)2}{w}\left(\frac{1}{s-1} - \frac{1}{s}\right) = \frac{2^{r_1}R}{w}\left(\frac{1}{s-1} - \frac{1}{s}\right).$$

The zeta function $\zeta(s, \mathfrak{K})$ has a simple pole at $s = 1$ with residue

$$\kappa = \frac{2^{r_1}(2\pi)^{r_2}R}{wd_k^{1/2}},$$

and no other singularity.

Proof. The first statement is obtained by plugging in our value for $\mu^*(E)$ in the expression (3). The second statement comes from evaluating

$$A^{-1}\Gamma(1/2)^{r_1}\Gamma(1)^{r_2}.$$

So Theorem 1 drops out.

We have obtained information on the zeta function of an ideal class. Taking the sum over the ideal classes immediately yields information on the zeta function itself, as follows.

Theorem 2. *Let*

$$F_k(s) = \sum_{\mathfrak{K}} F(s, \mathfrak{K}).$$

Also, let

$$\lambda = \frac{2^{r_1}hR}{w} \quad \text{and} \quad \kappa = \frac{2^{r_1}(2\pi)^{r_2}hR}{wd_k^{1/2}}.$$

Then

$$F_k(s) = F_k(1 - s),$$

and F_k has a simple pole at $s = 0$ and $s = 1$, with polar part

$$\lambda\left(\frac{1}{s-1} - \frac{1}{s}\right) = \frac{\lambda}{s(s-1)}.$$

The zeta function $\zeta_k(s)$ has only a simple pole at $s = 1$ with residue equal to κ.

We shall now keep our integrals for $t \geqq 1$, but put back the theta terms into the sums over ξ. In fact, we had

$$(\xi) = \mathfrak{a}\mathfrak{b} \quad \text{and} \quad \mathbf{N}\xi = \mathbf{N}\mathfrak{a}\mathbf{N}\mathfrak{b}.$$

We can make a similar construction for $\mathfrak{a}'$ and hence we find that

$$F(s, \mathfrak{K}) = \frac{\lambda}{s(s-1)} +$$

$$\int_{\|y\| \geqq 1} \sum_{\mathfrak{b} \in \mathfrak{K}} \exp\left(-\pi \mathbf{N}\mathfrak{b}^{2/N} d_k^{-1/N} \sum N_v \frac{|\xi_v|^2}{\mathbf{N}\xi^{2/N}} y_v\right) \|y\|^{\frac{s}{2}} \frac{dy}{y}$$

$$+ \int_{\|y\| \geqq 1} \sum_{\mathfrak{b} \in \mathfrak{K}'} \exp\left(-\pi \mathbf{N}\mathfrak{b}^{2/N} d_k^{-1/N} \sum N_v \frac{|\xi_v|^2}{\mathbf{N}\xi^{2/N}} y_v\right) \|y\|^{\frac{1-s}{2}} \frac{dy}{y}.$$

Each sum over $\mathfrak{b}$ is taken over the ideals in the given class.

We change variables, making the multiplicative translation

$$y'_v = \frac{|\xi_v|^2}{\mathbf{N}\xi^{2/N}} y_v.$$

Then $\|y'\| = \|y\|$, and we find:

Theorem 3. *Let* $\mathrm{Tr}(y) = \sum N_v y_v$. *Then*

$$F_k(s) = \frac{\lambda}{s(s-1)}$$

$$+ \sum_{\mathfrak{b}} \int_{\|y\| \geqq 1} \exp\left(-\pi\, d_k^{-1/N} \mathbf{N}\mathfrak{b}^{2/N}\, \mathrm{Tr}(y)\right)\left[\|y\|^{\frac{s}{2}} + \|y\|^{\frac{1-s}{2}}\right] \frac{dy}{y},$$

where the sum is taken over all ideals $\mathfrak{b} \neq 0$.

§4. *Application to the Brauer-Siegel theorem*

Following Siegel, we shall show how the formula of Theorem 3 implies an asymptotic relation between the class number, absolute value of the discriminant, and regulator of a number field k. We denote these numbers as usual by h_k, d_k, and R_k, respectively. We let $N_k = [k : \mathbf{Q}]$. We omit the subscript k if the reference to k is clear.

For the statement of the next theorem, we assume something about the zeros of the zeta function, in order to see clearly the simple logical structure of the argument. Siegel showed in a special case how one can supplement this argument by the technique of L-series to get a proof in a wider class of cases, and Brauer extended Siegel's argument more generally, using some of his theorems on characters. We shall do this in Chapter XVI.

Theorem 4. *Let k range over a sequence of number fields such that* $N_k/\log d_k \to 0$. *Assume that for some* $\delta > 0$, *the zeta functions* $\zeta_k(s)$

have no zeros on the interval $[1 - \delta, 1]$. *Then for this sequence of fields,*

$$\log(h_k R_k) \sim \log d_k^{1/2}.$$

Proof. We shall consider successively values of $s > 1$, and values of $s < 1$ to get inequalities for hR.

First take s real > 1, say

$$s = 1 + \frac{1}{\alpha}, \qquad \alpha \geqq 1.$$

For this case, we disregard the sum over $\mathfrak{b}$ in Theorem 3, except for the fact that it is $\geqq 0$. We then see that

$$\frac{\lambda}{s(s-1)} \leqq A^s \Gamma(s/2)^{r_1} \Gamma(s)^{r_2} \zeta_k(s).$$

For s near 1, the gamma factors $\Gamma(s/2)$ and $\Gamma(s)$ are bounded. Furthermore, using the series expression for $\zeta_{\mathbf{Q}}(s)$, comparing it with the integral, we have

$$\zeta_{\mathbf{Q}}\left(1 + \frac{1}{\alpha}\right) \leqq 1 + \alpha.$$

We also have the obvious bound

$$\zeta_k\left(1 + \frac{1}{\alpha}\right) \leqq \zeta_{\mathbf{Q}}\left(1 + \frac{1}{\alpha}\right)^N.$$

Using the value for λ we find

$$hR \leqq C^N d^{1/2} d^{1/2\alpha} (1 + \alpha)^N$$

for some universal constant C. Taking the log yields

$$\frac{\log hR}{\log d^{1/2}} \leqq \frac{N}{\log d^{1/2}} \log C + 1 + \frac{1}{\alpha} + \frac{N}{\log d^{1/2}} \log(1 + \alpha).$$

Given ϵ, we select α so large that $1/\alpha < \epsilon$. We then select k in the sequence so that $N_k/\log d_k^{1/2}$ is close to 0. This proves the right-hand side of the type of inequality we want to prove, and we note that the zeros of the zeta function have played no role in this inequality.

We now work on the other side, taking $s < 1$ and s close to 1. This time, we use only one term of the sum in Theorem 3, namely that term corresponding to the ideal $\mathfrak{b} = \mathfrak{o}$. Under our hypothesis on the zeros of $\zeta_k(s)$, we conclude that $F_k(s) < 0$ for $s < 1$ and s close to 1. We let $s = 1 - \epsilon/N$. We restrict the integral to the region defined by the inequalities

$$d^{1/N} \leqq y_j \leqq 2d^{1/N}.$$

We disregard the term with $\|y\|^{(1-s)/2}$, and give y_j its lower bound in this region. We then obtain at once an inequality

$$C(\epsilon)^{-N}d^{1/2}d^{-\epsilon/2} \leqq hR.$$

Taking the log and dividing by log $d^{1/2}$ yields

$$\frac{-N}{\log d^{1/2}}\log C(\epsilon) + 1 - \epsilon \leq \frac{\log hR}{\log d^{1/2}}.$$

Letting ϵ be small, we let k be so large that $N/\log d^{1/2}$ is very small. This yields the opposite inequality, and concludes the proof of Theorem 4.

The arguments we have just given will be repeated completely in Chapter XVI, so that the reader can compare the use of the adelic integral expressions of the zeta function with the use of Theorem 3.

§5. *Applications to the ideal function*

We shall see how the functional equation of the zeta function can be used to give growth estimate on vertical lines. For this we need some classical facts of complex variables, essentially of Phragmen-Lindelöf type. We shall then see how the behavior of zeros in the critical strip affects these growth estimates, and also affect the ideal function. The analytic techniques developed are standard and elementary, essentially at the level of Cauchy's Theorem and its immediate corollaries.

Phragmen-Lindelöf Theorem. *Let $f(s)$ be holomorphic in the upper part of a strip: $a \leqq \sigma \leqq b$, and $t \geqq t_1 > 0$. Assume that $f(s)$ is $O(e^{t^\alpha})$ with $1 \leqq \alpha$, and $t \to \infty$ in this strip, and that $f(s)$ is $O(t^M)$ for some real number $M \geqq 0$, on the sides of the strip, namely $\sigma = a$ and $\sigma = b$. Then $f(s)$ is $O(t^M)$ in the strip. In particular, if f is bounded on the sides, then f is bounded on the strip.*

Proof. The general statement reduces to the special case when f is bounded on the sides, by considering the function $f(s)/s^M$ instead of $f(s)$. We now prove this special case, and assume that f is bounded on the sides. Without loss of generality we can take t_1 large, so that $\theta = \arg s$ is close to $\pi/2$. We select an integer $m \equiv 2 \pmod 4$ such that $m > \alpha$. If $s = re^{i\theta}$, then

$$s^m = r^m(\cos m\theta + i\cdot\sin m\theta),$$

and $m\theta$ is close to π. Consider the function

$$g_\epsilon(s) = g(s) = f(s)e^{\epsilon s^m},$$

with $\epsilon > 0$. Then there is a constant B such that for large t we have

$$|g(s)| \leqq Be^{t^\alpha}e^{\epsilon r^m\cos m\theta}.$$

Consequently for large t_2, the function $g(s)$ is bounded by B on the horizontal segment $t = t_2$, between the vertical lines $\sigma = a$ and $\sigma = b$.

On the vertical sides of the rectangle shaded in Fig. 1, $g(s)$ is bounded since $f(s)$ is bounded, and $e^{\epsilon t^m \cos m\theta}$ is $\leqq 1$. Hence $g(s)$ is bounded on the boundary of the rectangle, consequently inside the rectangle, and in fact $|g(s)| \leqq B$ inside this rectangle. Hence we get

$$|f(s)| \leqq Be^{-\epsilon r^m \cos m\theta}$$

inside the rectangle. This is true for every $\epsilon > 0$, and hence

$$|f(s)| \leqq B$$

inside the rectangle. Our theorem is proved.

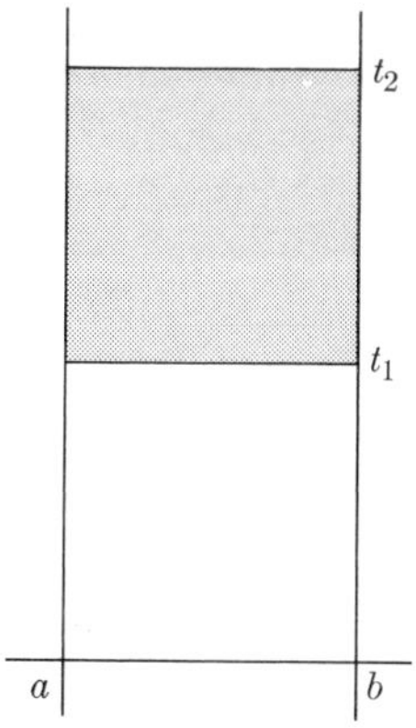

Figure 1

In the Phragmen-Lindelöf theorem we were interested in the crude asymptotic behavior for large t. In the next theorem, we want a more refined behavior, and so we must assume that the function is holomorphic in a whole strip.

First convexity theorem. *Let $s = \sigma + it$. Let f be holomorphic and bounded on the strip $a \leqq \sigma \leqq b$. For each σ let*

$$M_f(\sigma) = M(\sigma) = \sup_t |f(\sigma + it)|.$$

Then $\log M(\sigma)$ *is a convex function of* σ.

Proof. We must show that

$$M(\sigma)^{b-a} \leqq M(a)^{b-\sigma} M(b)^{\sigma-a}.$$

We first consider the case when $M(a) = M(b) = 1$. We must show that $M(\sigma) \leqq 1$. Suppose that $|f(s)| \leqq B$ in the strip. For $\epsilon > 0$, let

$$g_\epsilon(s) = \frac{1}{1 + \epsilon(s - a)}.$$

Then the real part of $1 + \epsilon(s - a)$ is $\geqq 1$, so that $|g_\epsilon(s)| \leqq 1$. Also, for $t \neq 0$,

$$|g_\epsilon(s)| \leqq \frac{1}{\epsilon|t|},$$

and therefore

$$|f(s)g_\epsilon(s)| \leqq \frac{B}{\epsilon|t|}.$$

Let ϵ be small, and select $t = \pm B/\epsilon$. On the boundary of the rectangle with sides at $\sigma = a$, $\sigma = b$, with top and bottom $\pm B/\epsilon$, we find that $|fg_\epsilon|$ is bounded by 1. Hence $|fg_\epsilon| \leqq 1$ on the whole rectangle. Letting ϵ tend to 0 we get what we want, namely, $|f| \leqq 1$ on the strip.

In general, let

$$h(s) = M(a)^{\frac{b-s}{b-a}} M(b)^{\frac{s-a}{b-a}}.$$

Then h is entire, has no zeros, and $1/h$ is bounded on the strip. We have

$$|h(a + it)| = M(a) \qquad \text{and} \qquad |h(b + it)| = M(b)$$

for all t. Consequently,

$$M_{f/h}(a) = M_{f/h}(b) = 1.$$

The first part of the proof implies that $|f/h| \leqq 1$, whence $|f| \leqq |h|$, thus proving our theorem.

Corollary. (Hadamard Three Circle Theorem.) *Let $f(z)$ be holomorphic on an annulus $\alpha \leqq |z| \leqq \beta$, centered at the origin. Let*

$$M(r) = \sup_{|z|=r} |f(z)|.$$

Then $\log M(r)$ *is a convex function of* $\log r$. *In other words,*

$$\log \beta/\alpha \log M(r) \leqq \log \beta/r \log M(\alpha) + \log r/\alpha \log M(\beta).$$

Proof. Let $f^*(s) = f(e^s)$. Then f^* is holomorphic and bounded on the strip $a \leqq \sigma \leqq b$, where $e^a = \alpha$ and $e^b = \beta$. We simply apply the theorem, to get the corollary.

In the next corollary, we analyze a growth exponent. Let f be holomorphic in the neighborhood of a vertical line $\sigma + it$, with fixed σ, and suppose that

$$f(\sigma + it) \ll |t|^\gamma$$

for some positive number γ. The inf of all such γ can be called the **growth exponent** of f, and will be denoted by $\psi(\sigma)$. Thus

$$f(\sigma + it) \ll |t|^{\psi(\sigma)+\epsilon}$$

for every $\epsilon > 0$, and $\psi(\sigma)$ is the least exponent which makes this inequality true.

Second convexity theorem. *Let f be holomorphic in the strip $a \leqq \sigma \leqq b$. For each σ assume that $f(\sigma + it)$ grows at most like a power of $|t|$, and let $\psi(\sigma)$ be the least number $\geqq 0$ for which*

$$f(\sigma + it) \ll |t|^{\psi(\sigma)+\epsilon}$$

for every $\epsilon > 0$. Assume for simplicity also that $f(\sigma + it) \ll e^{|t|^{\alpha}}$ in the strip, with some α, $1 \leqq \alpha$. Then $\psi(\sigma)$ is convex as a function of σ, and in particular is continuous on $[a, b]$.

Proof. The Phragmen-Lindelöf Theorem shows that there is a uniform M such that $f(\sigma + it) \ll |t|^M$ in the strip. Let $L_\epsilon(s)$ be the formula for the straight line segment between $\psi(a) + \epsilon$ and $\psi(b) + \epsilon$; in other words, let

$$L_\epsilon(s) = \frac{b-s}{b-a}[\psi(a) + \epsilon] + \frac{s-a}{b-a}[\psi(b) + \epsilon].$$

The function

$$f(s)(-is)^{-L_\epsilon(s)}$$

is then immediately seen to be bounded in the strip, and our theorem follows, since we get $\psi(\sigma) \leqq L_\epsilon(\sigma)$ for each σ in the strip, and every $\epsilon > 0$.

Remark. We wish to apply the second convexity theorem to the case of a function which satisfies the hypotheses of this corollary, except for the presence of a few poles, say the zeta function of a number field k, which has a pole of order 1 at $s = 1$. In that case, we consider

$$f(s) = (s-1)\zeta_k(s).$$

If for some σ we know that outside a neighborhood of the pole,

$$\zeta_k(\sigma + it) \ll |t|^{\psi(\sigma)+\epsilon},$$

then

$$f(\sigma + it) \ll |t|^{\psi(\sigma)+1+\epsilon}.$$

Furthermore $\psi(\sigma)$ is best possible for the zeta function, outside a neighborhood of the pole, if and only if $\psi(\sigma) + 1$ is best possible for the function f. The convexity of ψ follows from the convexity of $\psi + 1$, so that our result applies to the zeta function.

We shall deal with a fixed number field k, so that we sometimes write $\psi(\sigma)$ instead of $\psi_k(\sigma)$. I am indebted to Bombieri for the following formulas concerning $\psi_k(\sigma)$, and for pointing out Theorem 5. Bombieri tells me that the arguments go back to Hardy-Littlewood (1917). They are given in Titchmarsch's book on the zeta function (e.g. Chapter XIV) for the case $k = \mathbf{Q}$. They also apply to a wider class of zeta functions and Dirichlet series. Cf. L. Goldstein's paper, *Acta Arithmetica* (1969), pp. 205–215.

Since the zeta function is bounded for $\sigma \geqq 1 + \delta$, $\delta > 0$, it follows that

$$\boxed{\psi_k(\sigma) = 0 \qquad \text{if} \quad \sigma > 1.}$$

Let k be a number field of degree N over $\mathbf{Q}$. For any real σ, the gamma function satisfies the asymptotic relation

$$|\Gamma(\sigma + it)| \sim C(\sigma)e^{-\pi t/2}t^{\sigma}, \qquad t \to \infty,$$

this being obvious from the simplest form of Sterling's formula. Here, $C(\sigma)$ is a constant depending on σ. (We won't even require that it can be taken uniform in a strip.) From the functional equation, we see that for any s away from the poles, say away from the real axis, we have

$$\zeta_k(s) = A^{1-2s} \prod_{v \in S_\infty} \Gamma\left(\frac{N_v(1-s)}{2}\right) \Gamma\left(\frac{N_v s}{2}\right)^{-1} \zeta_k(1-s).$$

For a fixed σ, the term A^{1-2s} is bounded, as a function of t. If $\psi_k(\sigma)$ exists for some σ, then using the asymptotic formula for the gamma function, we conclude that $\psi_k(1 - \sigma)$ also exists, and we have the relation

$$\boxed{\psi_k(\sigma) = N(\tfrac{1}{2} - \sigma) + \psi_k(1 - \sigma).}$$

Since $\psi_k(\sigma) = 0$ when $\sigma > 1$, we conclude that $\psi_k(\sigma)$ exists when $\sigma < 0$. The Phragmen-Lindelöf theorem then implies that $\psi_k(\sigma)$ exists for all σ. We can therefore apply the convexity theorem, and we see that the graph of ψ_k looks at worst like this:

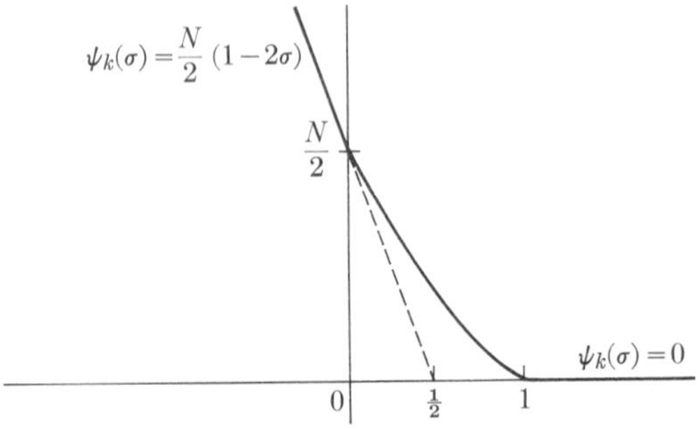

Figure 2

(Recall that a convex function on an open interval is necessarily continuous.)

The graph may in fact look better. We shall see that if we assume the Riemann Hypothesis, then in fact the graph follows the dotted line to $\frac{1}{2}$, and that $\psi_k(\sigma) = 0$ if $\sigma \geqq \frac{1}{2}$.

Theorem 5. *If ζ_k has no zero for $\sigma \geqq \beta > \frac{1}{2}$, then $\psi_k(\sigma) = 0$ for $\sigma \geqq \beta$.*

Proof. First observe that $\log \zeta_k(s)$ is analytic for $\sigma \geqq \beta$. We have

$$\operatorname{Re} \log \zeta_k(s) = \log |\zeta_k(s)| \ll \log |t|,$$

uniformly in a strip $a \leqq \sigma \leqq b$ and $\beta < a$, excluding a neighborhood of the poles, or say for $|t| \geqq t_1 > 0$.

The next lemma is the standard way of showing how to bound a holomorphic function by its real part. Recall that the real part of a holomorphic function f satisfies the maximum modulus principle (for instance, look at $e^{f(z)}$).

Lemma. *Let f be holomorphic on a closed disc of radius R, centered at the origin. Let $\|f\|_r = \max |f(z)|$ for $|z| = r$. Then*

$$\|f\|_r \leqq \frac{R+r}{R-r}\,[\|\operatorname{Re} f\|_R + |f(0)|].$$

Proof. Let $A = \|\operatorname{Re} f\|_R$. Assume first that $f(0) = 0$. Let

$$g(z) = \frac{f(z)}{z(2A - f(z))}.$$

Then g is holomorphic for $|z| \leqq R$. Furthermore, if $|z| = R$, then

$$|2A - f(z)| \geqq |f(z)|.$$

Hence $\|g\|_R \leqq 1/R$. By the maximum modulus principle, we have $\|g\|_r \leqq \|g\|_R$, and hence, if $|w| = r$, we get

$$\frac{|f(w)|}{r|2A - f(w)|} \leqq \frac{1}{R},$$

whence

$$|f(w)| \leqq \frac{r}{R}\,(2A + |f(w)|),$$

and therefore

$$\|f\|_r \leqq \frac{2r}{R-r}\,A,$$

which proves the lemma in this case.

In general, we apply the preceding estimate to the function

$$h(z) = f(z) - f(0).$$

Then

$$\|\mathrm{Re}\, h\|_R \leqq \|\mathrm{Re}\, f\|_R + |f(0)|,$$

and if $|w| = r$, we get

$$|f(w) - f(0)| \leqq \frac{2r}{R - r}[A + |f(0)|],$$

whence

$$|f(w)| \leqq \frac{2r}{R - r}[A + |f(0)|] + |f(0)| \leqq \frac{R + r}{R - r}[A + |f(0)|],$$

thereby proving the lemma.

We apply the lemma to the function $f(s) = \log \zeta_k(s)$, and to circles centered at the point $C + it$ for C large, passing through the points $a + it$ and $b + it$, with $\beta < a < b$. We then see that

$$|\log \zeta_k(b + it)| \ll \log |t|, \qquad t \to \infty.$$

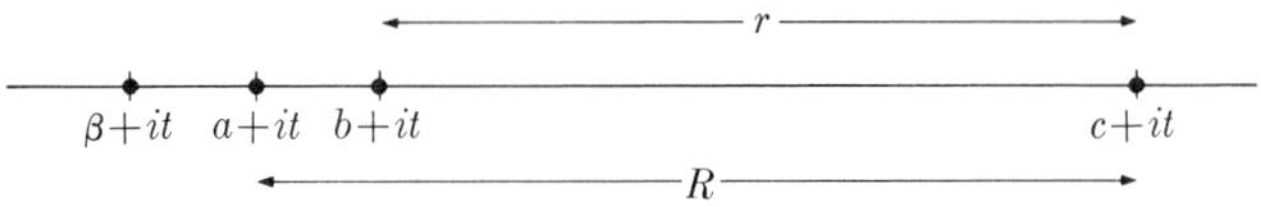

Figure 3

Indeed, for C large, $\zeta_k(s)$ is close to 1 in the half plane $\sigma \geqq C$.

Actually, we want $\log \zeta_k$ to behave like a power $(\log |t|)^\gamma$ with $\gamma < 1$. To see this, we use the three circles with center at $C + it$, passing through $a + it$, $b + it$, and $B + it$, with B large and close to C, as on the next figure.

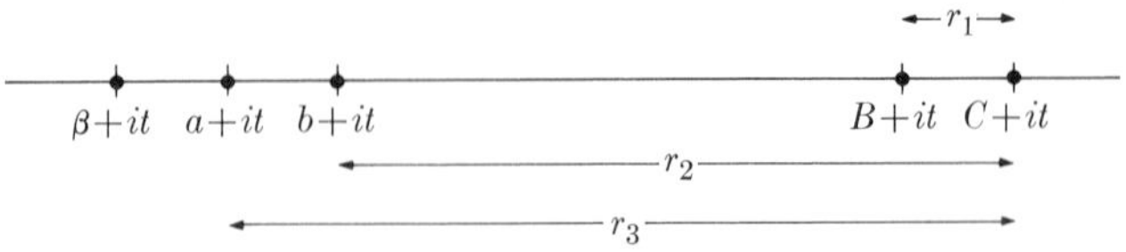

Figure 4

The Hadamard Three Circle Theorem then shows that

$$|\log \zeta_k(b + it)| \ll (\log |t|)^\gamma,$$

with

$$\gamma = \frac{\log \dfrac{C - b}{C - B}}{\log \dfrac{C - a}{C - B}} < 1.$$

This proves Theorem 5.

Remark. Of course, we have proved something stronger, namely that for $\sigma > \beta$, we have

$$\log \zeta_k(\sigma + it) \ll (\log |t|)^{\varphi(\sigma)+\epsilon},$$

and we can play the same game with $\varphi(\sigma)$ as we did with $\psi(\sigma)$, namely show that it is convex in σ, as in Titchmarsch, thus giving rise to a third convexity theorem. We use the technique of the Phragmen-Lindelöf Theorem, and the auxiliary function

$$(\log(-is))^{-L(s)}.$$

However, we won't need this here.

We apply Theorem 5 to the problem of estimating the number of ideals with norm $\leqq x$. We need another lemma from complex variables. First, we give an approximate formulation of the lemma. We have:

$$\frac{1}{2\pi i}\int_{2-i\infty}^{2+i\infty} \frac{y^s}{s}\,dx = \begin{cases} 1 & \text{if } y > 1 \\ \frac{1}{2} & \text{if } y = 1 \\ 0 & \text{if } 0 < y < 1. \end{cases}$$

This is a useful formulation to remember the formalism of what goes on, but we need a more precise value for the manner in which the integral converges, depending on y.

Lemma. *We have*

$$\frac{1}{2\pi i}\int_{2-iT}^{2+iT} \frac{y^s}{s}\,dx = \begin{cases} 1 + O\left(\dfrac{y^2}{T \cdot \log y}\right) & \text{if } y > 1 \\[2ex] 0 + O\left(\dfrac{y^2}{T \cdot \log y}\right) & \text{if } 0 < y < 1. \end{cases}$$

Proof. In the case $y > 1$, we take an integral over a rectangle as shown on Fig. 5.

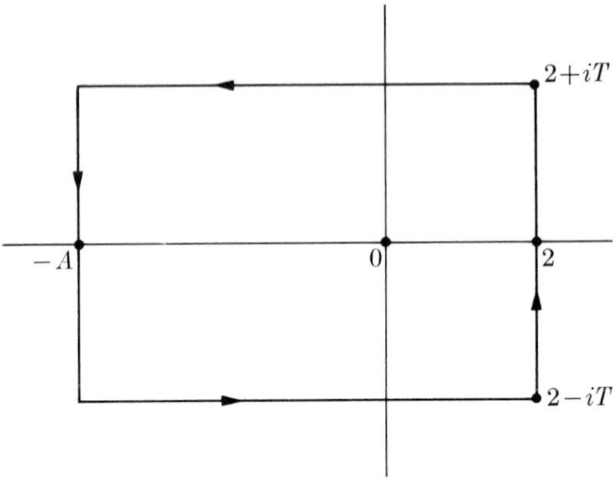

Figure 5

We shall let $A \to \infty$. The function y^s/s has residue 1 at $s = 0$, thus giving us the contribution of 1. We must then estimate the integral over the top, bottom, and left side of the rectangle.

As for the top, the integral is estimated by

$$\int_{-A}^{2} \frac{y^\sigma}{|\sigma + iT|}\, d\sigma \leqq \frac{1}{T} \int_{-A}^{2} y^\sigma\, d\sigma.$$

Letting A tend to infinity, we see that this integral is bounded by $y^2/T \log y$. The bottom is estimated similarly.

As for the left-hand side, the integral is estimated by

$$\int_{-T}^{T} \frac{y^{-A}}{|-A + it|}\, dt \leqq \frac{2T}{A},$$

which tends to 0 as A goes to infinity. This yields the estimate of the lemma when $y > 1$.

If $0 < y < 1$, we take a rectangle going to the right. Then there is no residue, so 1 is replaced by 0. The estimates on the bottom and side of the rectangle are carried out as before to yield the analogous estimate.

If $y = 1$, then one deals directly with the integral

$$\int_{2-iT}^{2+iT} \frac{1}{s}\, ds = i \int_{-T}^{T} \frac{1}{2 + it}\, dt = i \int_{-T}^{T} \frac{2 - it}{4 + t^2}\, dt.$$

Since t is an odd function, the term with $-it$ cancels. The integral of $1/(4+t^2)$ is an arctangent, which gives the desired result. We won't need this case in the applications, however.

Theorem 6. *Let $j_k(x)$ be the number of ideals of k with $\mathbf{N}\mathfrak{a} < x$. Assume that $\zeta_k(s)$ has no zero for $\sigma \geqq b$, where $\frac{1}{2} < b < 1$. Then for every ϵ, we have*

$$j_k(x) = \rho_k x + O(x^{b+\epsilon}),$$

where ρ_k is the residue of ζ_k at $s = 1$.

Proof. We consider the integral

$$(*) \qquad \frac{1}{2\pi i}\int_{2-iT}^{2+iT} \zeta_k(s)\,\frac{x^s}{s}\,ds.$$

There is no problem of convergence, which is absolute, and such that we can replace the zeta function by the sum $\sum 1/\mathbf{N}\mathfrak{a}^s$, as well as interchange the sum and the integral. In view of the lemma, we have to deal with the two sums

$$\sum_{\mathbf{N}\mathfrak{a}<x} \int_{2-iT}^{2+iT} \left(\frac{x}{\mathbf{N}\mathfrak{a}}\right)^s \frac{1}{s}\,ds$$

and

$$\sum_{\mathbf{N}\mathfrak{a}>x} \int_{2-iT}^{2+iT} \left(\frac{x}{\mathbf{N}\mathfrak{a}}\right)^s \frac{1}{s}\,ds.$$

We take x to lie exactly between two integers, and use the lemma with $y = x/\mathbf{N}\mathfrak{a}$. In the estimate, the term $\log y$ comes close to 0 when $\mathbf{N}\mathfrak{a}$ comes close to x, but even in the worst possible case when $\mathbf{N}\mathfrak{a}$ may differ from x by $\frac{1}{2}$, $\log(x/\mathbf{N}\mathfrak{a})$ behaves like x. Hence

$$\sum_{\mathbf{N}\mathfrak{a}<x} \frac{1}{2\pi i}\int_{2-iT}^{2+iT} \left(\frac{x}{\mathbf{N}\mathfrak{a}}\right)^s \frac{1}{s}\,ds = j_k(x) + O\left(\frac{x^3}{T}\right).$$

All we have to do is pick T large, say $T = x^3$, to make the error term negligible. (We used the fact that the order of magnitude of $j_k(x)$ is at most a constant times x, thus giving an upper bound for the number of terms in the above sum.)

For the sum with $\mathbf{N}\mathfrak{a} > x$, we estimate each term using the lemma, namely

$$\int_{2-iT}^{2+iT} \left(\frac{x}{\mathbf{N}\mathfrak{a}}\right)^s \frac{1}{s}\, ds \ll \left(\frac{x}{\mathbf{N}\mathfrak{a}}\right)^2 \frac{1}{T \cdot \log(x/\mathbf{N}\mathfrak{a})}$$

$$\ll \frac{1}{\mathbf{N}\mathfrak{a}^2} \frac{x^2}{T \cdot \log(x/\mathbf{N}\mathfrak{a})}.$$

Again, $\log(x/\mathbf{N}\mathfrak{a})$ behaves at worst like x. Selecting $T = x^3$ and summing over all $\mathfrak{a}$ yields an estimate $\ll \zeta_k(2)$, i.e., a bound for our sum. Thus our integral $(*)$ yields essentially $j_k(x)$, up to a bounded term.

Now we use Theorem 5, and move the integral to the left. If we had the Riemann Hypothesis, we would move the integral to the line $\sigma = \frac{1}{2} + \epsilon$. As it is, take any b with $\frac{1}{2} < b < 1$ so that ζ_k has no zero for $\sigma \geqq b$. Then

$$\zeta_k(b + it) \ll |t|^\epsilon$$

for every ϵ by Theorem 5. Consequently, shifting the integral $(*)$ to the line $\sigma = b$, we pick up a residue of $\rho_k x$ at $s = 1$. This gives us the main term for $j_k(x)$. The error introduced is given by the integral on the top, bottom, and left-hand side of the rectangle on Fig. 6.

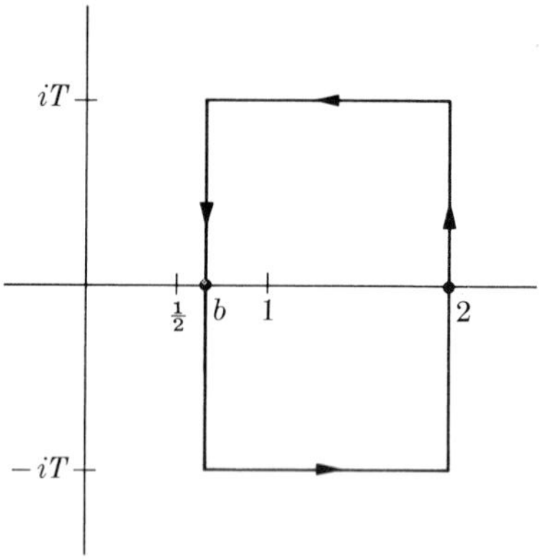

Figure 6

The integral on the left-hand side of the rectangle is bounded by

$$\int_{-T}^{T} |\zeta_k(b + it)| \frac{x^b}{|b + it|}\, dt \ll x^b T^\epsilon \int_{-T}^{T} \frac{1}{|b + it|}\, dt$$

$$\ll x^b T^\epsilon \log T.$$

With our choice of $T = x^3$, we find an error of $x^{b+\epsilon}$. For instance, on the Riemann Hypothesis, our error term is

$$x^{\frac{1}{2}+\epsilon}.$$

The integral over the top, say, is estimated by

$$\int_b^2 |\zeta_k(\sigma + iT)| \frac{x^\sigma}{|\sigma + iT|} \, d\sigma \ll \frac{T^\epsilon}{T} x^2,$$

which is small. This proves our theorem.

CHAPTER XIV

Functional Equation, Tate's Thesis

This chapter is essentially Tate's thesis, which has also appeared (finally) in the Brighton conference volume.

We first treat the local duality theory of local fields, i.e. completions of number fields under an absolute value. In §1 we give the additive theory and in §2 the multiplicative theory which are used later.

In §3 we give the local functional equation, and in §4 we perform certain local computations and tabulate special zeta functions, namely those used in practice. In §5 we discuss Haar measure and integration on restricted direct products, and in §6 we discuss the additive global duality theory. The main result here is that the adele group is self-dual, and that the additive discrete group of k embedded in it is its own orthogonal complement. Thus one may apply the Poisson summation formula to this situation (done in §7) and thereby get instantly the functional equation for the L-series, in an abstract form. We get actually more (as in the classical theory), since we express these as an everywhere convergent integral plus a simple term involving possible simple poles at $s = 1$ or $s = 0$.

Finally in §8, we make the results of §7 explicit, and tabulate various identities useful for reference in the subsequent applications.

One more word on notation. If G is a locally compact commutative group, we denote by **Inv(G)** the set of complex valued functions f on G which are continuous, in $L_1(G)$, and such that the Fourier transform $\hat{f}$ is also continuous and in $L_1(\hat{G})$. The Fourier inversion formula then holds for such functions for some choice (unique) of Haar measure on $\hat{G}$ depending on the choice of Haar measure on G. Such a pair of Haar measures is then called **self-dual**, and throughout our theory we shall always select the additive measures to be self-dual.

We shall use frequently the fact that if χ is a character on a compact group G, then

$$\int_G \chi(x)\,dx = \begin{cases} \text{measure of } G & \text{if } \chi = id. \\ 0 & \text{if } \chi \neq id. \end{cases}$$

Since this fact is trivial, we recall its proof. If $\chi \neq id.$, there exists an element y of G such that $\chi(y) \neq 1$. Making the translation by y does not change Haar measure, and hence

$$\int_G \chi(x)\,dx = \int_G \chi(x+y)\,dx = \chi(y)\int_G \chi(x)\,dx.$$

Subtracting and using $\chi(y) \neq 1$ gives what we want.

§1. *Local additive duality*

Let $k = k_v$ now denote the completion of a number field under the absolute value v. We call k a **local field.** Then k is either the real numbers, complex numbers, or a $\mathfrak{p}$-adic field, and v is described by the same terms. We denote by $|\ |_v$ the normalized absolute value, inducing the ordinary absolute value on the reals if v is archimedean, and the p-adic absolute value $|p|_v = 1/p$ if v is $\mathfrak{p}$-adic. If $N_v = [k_v : \mathbf{Q}_v]$ is the local degree, then we set

$$\|x\|_v = |x|_v^{N^v}.$$

If v is $\mathfrak{p}$-adic, and $\mathbf{N}\mathfrak{p}$ denotes the number of elements in the residue class field $\mathfrak{o}/\mathfrak{p}$ of k, then

$$\|x\|_{\mathfrak{p}} = \|x\|_v = (\mathbf{N}\mathfrak{p})^{-\nu},$$

where $\nu = \operatorname{ord}_{\mathfrak{p}} x$.

Suppose for the moment that $k = \mathbf{Q}_v$. We define a non-trivial character on the additive (locally compact) group of k as follows.

If v is real, we put

$$\lambda_0(x) \equiv -x \pmod 1.$$

If v is p-adic, and $\mathbf{Z}_p$, $\mathbf{Q}_p$ denote the p-adic integers and p-adic field respectively, then there is a canonical embedding of $\mathbf{Q}_p/\mathbf{Z}_p$ into $\mathbf{Q}/\mathbf{Z}$, namely onto that subgroup of $\mathbf{Q}/\mathbf{Z}$ having only powers of p in the denominator. Viewing $\mathbf{Q}/\mathbf{Z}$ as embedded in $\mathbf{R}/\mathbf{Z}$ = reals mod 1, we let λ_0 be the composition of these homomorphisms, sending $\mathbf{Q}_p$ into $\mathbf{R}/\mathbf{Z}$:

$$\lambda_0 : \mathbf{Q}_p \to \mathbf{Q}_p/\mathbf{Z}_p \to \mathbf{Q}/\mathbf{Z} \to \mathbf{R}/\mathbf{Z}.$$

If k is a finite extension of $\mathbf{Q}_v$ and $\mathrm{Tr} = \mathrm{Tr}^k_{\mathbf{Q}_v}$ is the trace, then the homomorphism

$$\lambda = \lambda_0 \circ \mathrm{Tr}$$

is a continuous, nontrivial homomorphism of k into the reals mod 1.

Theorem 1. *Let k be a local field. Then the bilinear map*

$$(x, y) \mapsto e^{2\pi i\lambda(xy)}$$

induces an identification of the additive group of k with its own character group.

Proof. It is easily verified that the pairing is continuous, and that the kernels on both sides are trivial, i.e. $= 0$. This induces a natural map of k into $\hat{k}$ which is injective, continuous, and dense. It is in fact bicontinuous, because if the character λ_x given by

$$\lambda_x(y) = e^{2\pi i \lambda(xy)}$$

is very close to 1, it must take on values close to 1 on a large compact subset of k. One sees at once that in that case, x must be close to 0. From this it follows that the image of k in the character group is complete, and hence closed. The map is therefore surjective and the theorem is proved.

In choosing a Haar measure on k, we choose one which is self-dual. We shall choose:

$dx =$ ordinary Lebesgue measure on the real line if k is real.

$dx =$ twice the ordinary Lebesgue measure if k is complex.

$dx =$ that measure for which the integers $\mathfrak{o}$ of k get measure $(\mathbf{N}\mathfrak{D})^{-1/2}$ if k is $\mathfrak{p}$-adic.

Here as usual, $\mathfrak{D} = \mathfrak{D}_{\mathfrak{p}}$ denotes the local different, i.e. the ideal such that $\mathfrak{D}^{-1}$ is the orthogonal complement of $\mathfrak{o}$ in the pairing of Theorem 1.

If μ denotes any Haar measure on k, and if $a \in k^*$ is a non-zero element of k, then

$$\mu(a\mathfrak{o}) = \|a\|\mu(\mathfrak{o}),$$

or symbolically, $d(ax) = \|a\|\, dx$.

Our assertion is clear if v is archimedean, and if v is $\mathfrak{p}$-adic, it suffices to verify it when $a = \pi$ is a prime element. In that case, $\pi\mathfrak{o}$ is of index $\mathbf{N}\mathfrak{p}$ in $\mathfrak{o}$, and is an open subgroup of $\mathfrak{o}$. Thus our assertion is obvious.

Theorem 2. *If we define the Fourier transform $\hat{f}$ of a function f in $L_1(k)$ by*

$$\hat{f}(y) = \int f(x) e^{-2\pi i \lambda(xy)}\, dx,$$

then with our choice of measure, the inversion formula

$$\hat{\hat{f}}(x) = f(-x),$$

holds for f in Inv(k).

Proof. We need only establish the inversion formula for one non-trivial function, since from abstract Fourier analysis we know it is true save possibly for a constant factor. For k real, we can take $f(x) = e^{-\pi x^2}$, for k complex, $f(x) = e^{-2\pi |x|^2}$, and for k $\mathfrak{p}$-adic, $f(x) =$ characteristic function of $\mathfrak{o}$. We leave the details of the computation to the reader (cf. §4).

§2. *Local multiplicative theory*

The **units** $U_v = U$ of our local field are the kernel of the homomorphism

$$a \mapsto \|a\|$$

for $a \in k^*$. If v is $\mathfrak{p}$-adic, then U is a compact open subgroup of k^*, and it is always a compact subgroup of k^*.

By a **quasi-character** of k^* we mean a continuous homomorphism c of k^* into the multiplicative group of complex numbers. A character is thus a quasi-character of absolute value 1. We say that c is **unramified** if it is trivial on U.

Proposition 1. *The unramified quasi-characters are the maps of the form*

$$c(a) = \|a\|^{s \log \|a\|},$$

where s is any complex number; s is determined by c if v is archimedean, and is determined only mod $2\pi i/\log \mathbf{N}\mathfrak{p}$ *if v is $\mathfrak{p}$-adic.*

Proof. An unramified quasi-character depends only on $\|a\|$. Use the fact that

$$k^* \approx U \times \mathbf{R}^+ \qquad \text{or} \qquad k^* \approx U \times \mathbf{Z}$$

according as v is archimedean or not. In the $\mathfrak{p}$-adic case, the decomposition is of course not canonical, and depends on the fact that once we have selected an element π of order 1, then any element $a \in k^*$ can be written

$$a = \pi^r u$$

for some integer r and a unit u.

Any quasi-character c restricted to the units U determines a character on U, since U is compact. Conversely, given a character χ of k^*, the function

$$c(a) = \chi(a)\|a\|^s$$

is a quasi-character.

If v is archimedean, and χ a character of k^*, we can write

$$\chi(a) = \left(\frac{a}{|a|}\right)^m \|a\|^{i\varphi},$$

where $m = m_v(\chi)$ is an integer, $m = 0$ or 1 if v is real, $\varphi = \varphi_v(\chi)$ is a real number, and m, φ are uniquely determined by χ.

If v is $\mathfrak{p}$-adic, then the subgroups $1 + \mathfrak{p}^\nu$ $(\nu \geqq 0)$ form a fundamental system of neighborhoods of 1 in U. Any quasi-character c must therefore vanish on one of these subgroups, and we call the ideal

$$\mathfrak{f}_\mathfrak{p} = \mathfrak{f}_{\mathfrak{p},\chi} = \mathfrak{p}^m$$

the **conductor** of c if m is the smallest integer for which $c(1 + \mathfrak{p}^m) = 1$. (If $m = 0$, then by definition, $\mathfrak{f} = \mathfrak{o}$.)

To use a unified notation for the archimedean and non-archimedean case, we shall refer to the integer $m_v(\chi)$ or $\mathrm{ord}_{\mathfrak{p}}\, \mathfrak{f}_\chi = m$ as the **ramification degree** of c, or χ.

Selecting a prime element π in case v is $\mathfrak{p}$-adic, and a decomposition

$$k^* \approx U \times \mathbf{R}^+ \qquad \text{or} \qquad k^* \approx U \times \mathbf{Z}$$

we let a' be the U-component of an element $a \in k^*$ (so $a' = a/|a|$ if v is archimedean). We let c' be the restriction of c to U. Using elementary results concerning $\mathbf{R}^+$ or $\mathbf{Z}$, we get:

Proposition 2. *The quasi-characters of k^* are the maps of the form*

$$a \mapsto c(a) = c'(a')\|a\|^s,$$

where c' is any character of U, uniquely determined by c. The complex number s is determined as in Proposition 1.

The real part of s in Proposition 2 is uniquely determined by the quasi-character, and will be called its **real part** or also $\mathrm{Re}(c)$.

Now for Haar measure. If $g(a)$ is in $C_c(k^*)$ (continuous functions with compact support), then $g(x)\|x\|^{-1}$ is in $C_c(k^+ - 0) = C_c(k - 0)$. Hence we may define on $C_c(k^*)$ a non-trivial functional

$$g \mapsto \int_{k-0} g(x)\|x\|^{-1}\, dx,$$

which is obviously invariant under multiplicative translation, is positive, and thus comes from a Haar measure. Passing to the limit, we have:

Proposition 3. *A function $g(a)$ is in $L_1(k^*)$ if and only if $g(x)\|x\|^{-1}$ is in $L_1(k - 0)$, and for such functions, we have*

$$\int_{k^*} g(a)\, d_1^*a = \int_{k-0} g(x)\|x\|^{-1}\, dx,$$

where d_1^*a is the measure on k^* just mentioned, and dx is the measure on (the additive group of) k.

In fact it will be convenient to take a Haar measure on k^* which differs from the above by a constant in the $\mathfrak{p}$-adic case, and gives the units measure 1 in general. Thus we take:

$$d^*a = \frac{da}{\|a\|} \qquad \text{if } v \text{ is archimedean.}$$

$$d^*a = \frac{\mathbf{N}\mathfrak{p}}{\mathbf{N}\mathfrak{p} - 1}\,\frac{da}{\|a\|} \qquad \text{if } v \text{ is } \mathfrak{p}\text{-adic.}$$

Proposition 4. *If v is $\mathfrak{p}$-adic, then* $\int_U d^*a = (\mathbf{N}\mathfrak{D})^{-1/2}$.

Proof. This is seen immediately, taking into account that $\|a\| = 1$ if $a \in U$, that the units are the complement of $\mathfrak{p}$ in $\mathfrak{o}$, together with the definition of the additive Haar measure in §1.

§3. *Local functional equation*

In this section, $f(x)$ denotes a complex valued function on k^+, and $f(a)$ its restriction to k^*. We consider functions satisfying the following conditions:

Z1$_v$. *$f(x)$ and $\hat{f}(x)$ are continuous and in $L_1(k^+)$.*

Z2$_v$. *$f(a)\|a\|^\sigma$ and $\hat{f}(a)\|a\|^\sigma$ are in $L_1(k^*)$ for $\sigma > 0$.*

For such functions, and a quasi-character c, we define a zeta function:

$$\zeta(f, c) = \int f(a)c(a)\, d^*a.$$

If $c(a) = \chi(a)\|a\|^s$, where χ is a character of k^*, then we also write

$$\zeta(f, \chi, s) = \int f(a)\chi(a)\|a\|^s\, d^*a.$$

Once χ is fixed, our zeta function can be viewed as a function of a complex variable, which in view of our hypotheses on f, is holomorphic for $\mathrm{Re}(s)$ (or $\mathrm{Re}(c)) > 0$. In this domain, one sees immediately that one can differentiate under the integral sign. Two quasi-characters are called **equivalent** if we have $c_1(a) = c_2(a)\|a\|^{s_1}$ for some complex number s_1. We can view a zeta function as a complex valued function on equivalence classes of quasi-characters, and it is clear what is meant by analytic continuation on these.

If c is a quasi-character, we define $\hat{c}(a) = \|a\|c^{-1}(a)$. The functional equation will come from the following fundamental Lemma.

Lemma. *For any quasi-character in the domain $0 < \mathrm{Re}(c) < 1$, and two functions f, g satisfying* **Z1**$_v$ *and* **Z2**$_v$, *we have*

$$\zeta(f, c)\zeta(\hat{g}, \hat{c}) = \zeta(\hat{f}, \hat{c})\zeta(g, c).$$

Proof. We can write $\zeta(f, c)\zeta(\hat{g}, \hat{c})$ as an absolutely convergent double integral over $k^* \times k^*$, namely:

$$\iint f(a)\hat{g}(b)c(ab^{-1})\|b\|\, d^*a\, d^*b.$$

The measure is invariant under shearing automorphism $(a, b) \to (a, ab)$, and our integral is thus equal to

$$\iint f(a)\hat{g}(ab)c(b^{-1})\|ab\|\, d^*a\, d^*b.$$

Writing down the definition of $\hat{g}$ and the multiplicative measures $d^*a\, d^*b$ we get (up to an obvious constant factor)

$$\iiint f(a)g(x)c(b^{-1})e^{-2\pi i\lambda(axb)}\, dx\, da\, db,$$

which is symmetric in f and g. This proves our Lemma.

If we can show that there exists one function f for which $\zeta(\hat{f}, \hat{c})$ is not 0, then the quotient $\zeta(f, c)/\zeta(\hat{f}, \hat{c})$ is defined and does not depend on the function f. We shall denote it by $\rho(c)$. In the next section we shall exhibit for each equivalence class of quasi-characters on a local field a function f for which $\rho(c)$ is defined. We thus get:

Theorem 3. *A zeta function has an analytic continuation to the domain of all quasi-characters given by a functional equation of the type*

$$\zeta(f, c) = \rho(c)\zeta(\hat{f}, \hat{c}).$$

The factor $\rho(c)$, which is independent of the function f, is a meromorphic function defined in the domain $0 < \mathrm{Re}(c) < 1$ by the functional equation, and for all quasi-characters by analytic continuation.

From the functional equation, we get the following properties:

1. $\rho(c)\rho(\hat{c}) = c(-1)$.
2. $\rho(\bar{c}) = c(-1)\overline{\rho(c)}$
3. If $\mathrm{Re}(c) = \frac{1}{2}$, then $|\rho(c)| = 1$.

Proofs. For the first, we have

$$\zeta(f, c) = \rho(c)\zeta(\hat{f}, \hat{c}) = \rho(c)\rho(\hat{c})\zeta(\hat{\hat{f}}, \hat{\hat{c}}),$$

and

$$\zeta(f, c) = c(-1)\zeta(\hat{\hat{f}}, \hat{\hat{c}}),$$

using the fact that $\hat{\hat{f}} = f^-$ and $\hat{\hat{c}} = c$. The first property follows. For the second, we have

$$\begin{aligned}\overline{\zeta(f, c)} &= \zeta(\bar{f}, \bar{c}) = \rho(\bar{c})\zeta(\hat{\bar{f}}, \hat{\bar{c}})\\ &= \rho(\bar{c})c(-1)\zeta(\bar{\hat{f}}, \bar{\hat{c}}) = \rho(\bar{c})c(-1)\overline{\zeta(\hat{f}, \hat{c})},\end{aligned}$$

and

$$\overline{\zeta(f, c)} = \overline{\rho(c)\zeta(\hat{f}, \hat{c})},$$

so that the second property follows. As to the third, if the exponent of c is equal to $\frac{1}{2}$, then

$$c(a)\bar{c}(a) = |c(a)|^2 = c(a)\hat{c}(a).$$

Hence $\bar{c}(a) = \hat{c}(a)$. Using the first two properties yields

$$\rho(c)\overline{\rho(c)} = 1,$$

which proves the third property.

In the next section, we give explicitly, for each class of quasi-characters, a weight function f_c which makes the zeta function have the usual shape, and in particular, defines $\rho(c)$

§4. *Local computations*

v archimedean. We use the following notation:

$$x = k_v^+\text{-variable} \qquad a = k_v^*\text{-variable}$$
$$dx = N_v \text{ times Lebesgue measure} \qquad d^*a = da/\|a\|.$$

Given any character χ of k_v^*, we have

$$\chi(a) = \left(\frac{a}{|a|}\right)^m |a|^{iN_v\varphi},$$

where $m = m_v(\chi)$ and $\varphi = \varphi_v(\chi)$. If v is real, $m = 0$ or 1.

We put

$$s_v = s_v(\chi) = N_v(s + i\varphi) + |m|,$$
$$\hat{s}_v = N_v(1 - s - i\varphi) + |m|.$$

If v is real,

$$f_{\chi,v}(x) = x^m e^{-\pi x^2}.$$

If v is complex,

$$f_{\chi,v}(x) = \begin{cases} \dfrac{1}{2\pi}\,\bar{x}^{|m|}e^{-2\pi|x|^2} & \text{if } m \geqq 0 \\[2mm] \dfrac{1}{2\pi}\,x^{|m|}e^{-2\pi|x|^2} & \text{if } m \leqq 0. \end{cases}$$

Observe that our functions $f_{\chi,v}$ depend only on m, and thus may be denoted by $f_m = f_{m_v}$. If c is a quasi-character, and χ the associated character on the units, then we write $f_c = f_\chi$.

Theorem 4. *With the above notation, we have in all cases, putting* $c(a) = \chi(a)\|a\|^s$:

$$\hat{f}_m(x) = i^{|m|}f_{-m}(x) \qquad (\text{if } v \text{ real}, f_{-m} = f_m)$$
$$\zeta(f_c, c) = \zeta(f_{\chi,v}, \chi, s) = (N_v\pi)^{-s_v/2}\Gamma(s_v/2)$$
$$\zeta(\hat{f}_c, \hat{c}) = \zeta(\hat{f}_{\chi,v}, \chi, 1-s) = i^{|m|}(N_v\pi)^{-\hat{s}_v/2}\Gamma(\hat{s}_v/2).$$

Proof. If v is real, our first assertion concerning $\hat{f}$ is easy and is left to the reader.

For the zeta functions, we use repeatedly the definition of the Gamma function:

$$\Gamma(s) = \int_0^\infty e^{-u}u^{s-1}\,du.$$

The computations are also quite simple and are again left to the reader.

For v complex, things are slightly harder. We establish the formula for $\hat{f}_m$ first for $m \geqq 0$ by induction. To fit classical notation, let us use z as a complex variable,

$$z = x + iy = re^{i\theta}.$$

For $m = 0$, we break up the Fourier integral into two real integrals and use the classical formula

$$\int_{-\infty}^{\infty} e^{-\pi u^2 + 2\pi i x u}\,du = e^{-\pi x^2}.$$

Assume we have proved our formula for some $m \geqq 0$, so we have

$$\int f_m(w)e^{-2\pi i\lambda(zw)}\,dw = i^m f_{-m}(z).$$

Writing this out, we get

$$\int_{-\infty}^{\infty}\int_{-\infty}^{\infty} (u - iv)^m e^{-2\pi(u^2+v^2)+4\pi i(xu-yv)}2\,du\,dv = i^m(x+iy)^m e^{-2\pi(x^2+y^2)}.$$

Applying the operator $D = (4\pi i)^{-1}[\partial/\partial x + i(\partial/\partial y)]$ to both sides (a simple task in view of the fact that since z^m is analytic, $D(x+iy)^m = 0$) we obtain our contention for $m+1$. The induction step is carried out.

To handle the case $m < 0$, we put a roof on the formula

$$\hat{f}_{-m}(z) = i^{|m|}f_m(z),$$

which we have already proved, and remember that $\hat{\hat{f}}(z) = f(-z)$.

For the assertions concerning the zeta functions, we may assume without loss of generality that $\varphi = 0$, and that our character χ is of type

$c_m(a) = e^{im\theta}$. Then

$$\zeta(f_m, c_m, s) = \int f_m(a)c_m(a)\|a\|^s \, d^*a$$

$$= \int_0^\infty \int_0^{2\pi} \frac{1}{2\pi} r^{2(s-1)+|m|} e^{-2\pi r^2} 2r \, dr \, d\theta$$

$$= \int_0^\infty (r^2)^{(s-1)+|m|/2} e^{-2\pi r^2} \, d(r^2),$$

from which our assertion follows immediately after a change of variables. The function $\zeta(\hat{f}, \hat{c})$ is now computed using the first part of our theorem and the definitions.

***v* $\mathfrak{p}$-adic.** We use the following notation:

$x = k_v^+$-variable $\qquad\qquad a = k_v^*$-variable

dx gives $\mathfrak{o}$ measure $(\mathbf{N}\mathfrak{D})^{-1/2}$ $\qquad d^*a = \dfrac{\mathbf{N}\mathfrak{p}}{\mathbf{N}\mathfrak{p} - 1} \dfrac{da}{\|a\|}$.

We denote by $m_{\chi,v} = m$ the order of the conductor of a character χ, so $m \geqq 0$. As in the archimedean case, our function $f_{\chi,v}$ depends only on this integer, and in fact, we put

$$f_m(x) = \begin{cases} e^{2\pi i\lambda(x)} & x \in \mathfrak{D}^{-1}\mathfrak{f}_\chi^{-1} \\ 0 & x \notin \mathfrak{D}^{-1}\mathfrak{f}_\chi^{-1} \end{cases}$$

($\mathfrak{D}$ and $\mathfrak{f}_\chi$ should of course carry the index $\mathfrak{p}$).

For convenience of notation, we write $\mathfrak{D}_\chi = \mathfrak{D}\mathfrak{f}_\chi$.

Proposition 5. *We have*

$$\hat{f}_m(x) = \begin{cases} (\mathbf{N}\mathfrak{D})^{1/2}(\mathbf{N}\mathfrak{f}_\chi) & x \equiv 1 \pmod{\mathfrak{f}_\chi} \\ 0 & x \not\equiv 1 \pmod{\mathfrak{f}_\chi}. \end{cases}$$

Proof. This comes immediately from the fact that the integral of a character over a compact group is $\mu(G)$ or 0 according as the character is trivial or not. (The compact group here is $(\mathfrak{D}_\chi)^{-1}$.)

We observe that f_0 is the characteristic function of $\mathfrak{D}^{-1}$ while $\hat{f}_0$ is $(\mathbf{N}\mathfrak{D})^{1/2}$ times the characteristic function of $\mathfrak{o}$.

We now give explicitly a zeta function for unramified characters. If χ is unramified, the value $\chi(\pi)$ does not depend on the particular choice of prime element π, and is denoted $\chi(\mathfrak{p})$.

Theorem 5. *Let χ be an unramified character of k^*, and let f be the characteristic function of an ideal $\mathfrak{p}^n$. Then*

$$\zeta(f, \chi, s) = \frac{(\mathbf{N}\mathfrak{D})^{-1/2}\chi(\mathfrak{p})^n(\mathbf{N}\mathfrak{p})^{-ns}}{1 - \dfrac{\chi(\mathfrak{p})}{\mathbf{N}\mathfrak{p}^s}}.$$

Proof. This is an easy computation, using the definition of multiplicative Haar measure in terms of the additive one, and taking the integral as a sum over integrals over the annuli $\mathfrak{p}^\nu - \mathfrak{p}^{\nu+1}$ for ν ranging from n to ∞. On each such annulus, $\|a\|^s$ is constant, and $\chi(a) = \chi(\pi^\nu)$, since χ is assumed unramified. We leave the details to the reader.

Corollary 1. *We have*

$$\zeta(f_0, \chi_0, s) = \frac{(\mathbf{N}\mathfrak{D})^{s-1/2}}{1 - \dfrac{1}{\mathbf{N}\mathfrak{p}^s}}$$

and

$$\zeta(\hat{f}_0, \chi_0, 1 - s) = \frac{1}{1 - \mathbf{N}\mathfrak{p}^{s-1}}.$$

Proof. Put $n = -\text{ord}\,\mathfrak{D}$ in the first case, and $n = 0$ in the second.

Corollary 2. *Let χ be an unramified character of k^*, and let $f_0 = f_\chi$ be the characteristic function of $\mathfrak{D}^{-1}$. Then*

$$\zeta(f_0, \chi, s) = \frac{(\mathbf{N}\mathfrak{D})^{s-1/2}\chi(\mathfrak{D}^{-1})}{1 - \dfrac{\chi(\mathfrak{p})}{\mathbf{N}\mathfrak{p}^s}}$$

and

$$\zeta(\hat{f}_0, \bar{\chi}, 1 - s) = \frac{1}{1 - \dfrac{\chi^{-1}(\mathfrak{p})}{\mathbf{N}\mathfrak{p}^{1-s}}}.$$

We observe that for unramified χ, the zeta function has the usual term $1 - (\mathbf{N}\mathfrak{p})^{-s}$ in the denominator. For ramified characters, it does not.

Theorem 6. *Let π be a prime element, χ a character of k^*, $m > 0$ the order of its conductor, and $\{\epsilon\}$ a set of unit representatives for $U/(1 + \mathfrak{f}_\chi)$. Let $o(\chi) = \text{ord}\,(\mathfrak{D}_\chi)$, and put*

$$\eta(x) = e^{2\pi i\lambda(x)}.$$

Let $c(a) = \chi(a)\|a\|^s$. Then

$$\zeta(f_m, c) = \zeta(f_m, \chi, s) = (\mathbf{N}\mathfrak{D}_\chi)^s\mu(1 + \mathfrak{f}_\chi)\tau(\chi),$$

where

$$\tau(\chi) = \sum_{\epsilon} (\chi\eta)(\epsilon\pi^{-o(\chi)}).$$

Furthermore,

$$\zeta(\hat{f}_m, \hat{c}) = \zeta(\hat{f}_m, \bar{\chi}, 1 - s) = (\mathbf{N}\mathfrak{D})^{1/2}(\mathbf{N}\mathfrak{f}_\chi)\mu(1 + \mathfrak{f}_\chi).$$

(Note: The measure μ is of course that of d^*a, and π in $2\pi i$ is 3.1416 . . . .)

Proof. By definition,

$$\zeta(f_m, c) = \int_{\mathfrak{D}_\chi^{-1}} \eta(a)\chi(a)\|a\|^s \, d^*a$$

$$= \sum_{-o(\chi)}^{\infty} (\mathbf{N}\mathfrak{p})^{-\nu s} \int_{A_\nu} \eta(a)\chi(a) \, d^*a,$$

where A_ν is the usual annulus $\mathfrak{p}^\nu - \mathfrak{p}^{\nu+1}$. We contend that all the terms in this sum after the first are 0.

Case 1. $\nu \geqq -\text{ord}\,\mathfrak{D}$. Then $\eta(a) = 1$ on A_ν and the integral is

$$\int_{A_\nu} \chi(a) \, d^*a = \int_U \chi(a\pi^\nu) \, d^*a = \chi(\pi^\nu)\int_U \chi(a) \, d^*a,$$

which is 0, since χ is non-trivial on U.

Case 2. $-\text{ord}\,\mathfrak{D} > \nu > -\text{ord}\,\mathfrak{D} - \text{ord}\,\mathfrak{f}_\chi$. (This occurs only if $m > 1$.) To handle this case, we break up A_ν into disjoint sets of type $a_0 + \mathfrak{D}^{-1} = a_0(1 + \mathfrak{D}^{-1}\mathfrak{p}^{-\nu})$. On such a set, λ is constant, $= \lambda(a_0)$, and our integral is equal to

$$\eta(a_0)\int_{a_0+\mathfrak{D}^{-1}} \chi(a) \, d^*a.$$

This is equal to 0 because we can move this integral by multiplicative translation to an integral over $1 + \mathfrak{D}^{-1}\mathfrak{p}^{-\nu}$ on which our character is non-trivial.

Thus we get

$$\zeta(f_m, \chi, s) = (\mathbf{N}\mathfrak{D}_\chi)^s \int_{A_{-o(\chi)}} \eta(a)\chi(a) \, d^*a.$$

Using our representatives of cosets of $U/(1 + \mathfrak{f}_\chi)$, it is a trivial matter to transform this expression into the one given in the theorem.

For $\zeta(\hat{f}_m, \bar{\chi}, 1 - s)$ we take into account the fact that $\hat{f}_m$ is $(\mathbf{N}\mathfrak{D})^{1/2}(\mathbf{N}\mathfrak{f}_\chi)$ times the characteristic function of $1 + \mathfrak{f}_\chi$, a set on which

$$\chi^{-1}(a)\|a\|^{1-s} = 1.$$

Our result is then immediate.

Corollary. *If* $c(a) = \chi(a)\|a\|^s$, *where* χ *is a character with conductor* $\mathfrak{f}$, *of order* $m > 0$, *then*

$$\rho(c) = (\mathbf{N}\mathfrak{D}_\chi)^{s-1/2}(\mathbf{N}\mathfrak{f})^{-1/2}\tau(\chi)$$

and $(\mathbf{N}\mathfrak{f})^{-1/2}\tau(\chi)$ *has absolute value* 1.

Proof. The first statement comes by taking quotients of the zeta functions. The second comes from the general fact that for $\mathrm{Re}(c) = \frac{1}{2}$, we have $|\rho(c)| = 1$. We then merely set $s = \frac{1}{2}$ above.

§5. Restricted direct products

Earlier, in Chapter VII, we studied the topology of restricted direct products, and the special cases of adeles and ideles. Here we consider the Haar measure and Pontrjagin duality.

We let $\{v\}$ be any set of indices, and G_v a locally compact commutative group, with a given compact open subgroup H_v for all but a finite number of v.

A **quasi-character** of G is then a continuous homomorphism into $\mathbf{C}^*$.

If c is a quasi-character of G, then its restriction to G_v is denoted by c_v, and c_v is trivial on H_v for all but a finite number of v by continuity and the fact that the multiplicative group of complex numbers contains no small subgroup other than 1. Furthermore, we have the formula:

$$c(a) = \prod_v c_v(a_v),$$

all but a finite number of the terms on the right being equal to 1.

Conversely, given a quasi-character c_v of G_v which is trivial on H_v for all but a finite number of v, we can define a quasi-character c on G by this formula.

We note that c is a character if and only if c_v is a character for all v.

If $\hat{G}$ is the character group of G, and $H^\perp$ is the orthogonal complement of a closed subgroup of G, i.e. the subgroup of characters which are trivial on H, then we have in a natural way

$$\hat{G}/H^\perp \approx H, \qquad \text{and} \qquad (G/H)^\wedge \approx H^\perp.$$

It is an easy matter to verify the following theorem in our special case of restricted direct products.

Theorem 7. *The restricted direct product of the groups* $\hat{G}_v$ *relative to the subgroups* $H_v^\perp$ *(which are compact by compact-discrete duality) is naturally isomorphic, topologically and algebraically, to the character group* $\hat{G}$ *of* G.

The isomorphism is of course given by the correspondence

$$\chi = \prod \chi_v.$$

Haar measure. Assume that we have chosen a Haar measure da_v on each G_v which gives H_v measure 1 for almost all v. We wish to define a Haar measure on G for which, in some sense, $da = \prod da_v$. To do this, we use once more our open subgroups G_S which are products of locally compact groups, almost all of which are compact, and hence such that we can take the product measure on G_S. There exists a unique Haar measure on G inducing this product measure on each G_S (trivial verification), which we denote by $\prod da_v$.

Lemma. *If $f(a)$ is a function on G, then*

$$\int_G f(a)\, da = \lim_S \int_{G_S} f(a)\, da$$

if either (1) *$f(a)$ is measurable, $f(a) \geqq 0$, in which case $+\infty$ is allowed as value of the integrals; or* (2) *$f(a)$ is in $L_1(G)$, in which case the values of the integrals are complex numbers.*

Proof. In either case, $\int f(a)\, da$ is the limit of the integral taken for larger and larger compact subsets of G, and any compact is contained in some G_S.

Theorem 8. *Assume that for each v we are given a continuous function $f_v \in L_1(G_v)$ such that $f_v = 1$ on H_v for almost all v. We define*

$$f(a) = \prod f_v(a_v)$$

on G (actually a finite product). Then f is continuous. If, furthermore,

$$\prod_v \int |f_v(a_v)|\, da_v = \lim_S \prod_{v \in S} \int |f_v(a_v)|\, da_v$$

is $< \infty$, then $f(a)$ is in $L_1(G)$, and

$$\int_G f(a)\, da = \prod_v \int_{G_v} f_v(a_v)\, da_v.$$

Proof. Immediate.

Fourier transform. We keep the notation as above, and let ξ denote a variable element of $\hat{G}$. Let $d\xi_v$ be the measure of $\hat{G}_v$ dual to da_v in G_v. If $f_v(a_v)$ is the characteristic function of H_v, then its Fourier transform

$$\hat{f}_v(\xi_v) = \int f_v(a_v)\overline{\xi_v(a_v)}\, da_v$$

is the measure of H_v times the characteristic function of $H_v^\perp$. Consequently, from the inversion formula, we get

$$\left(\int_{H_v} da_v\right)\left(\int_{H_v^\perp} d\xi_v\right) = 1$$

and the measure of $H_v^\perp$ is 1 for almost all v. We may thus put

$$d\xi = \prod d\xi_v.$$

Theorem 9. *Let $f_v(a_v)$ be in $L_1(G_v)$, continuous, and assume $\hat{f}_v$ is in $L_1(\hat{G}_v)$,* i.e. *assume that $f_v \in \mathrm{Inv}(G_v)$. Assume also that f_v is the characteristic function of H_v for almost all v. Then the function*

$$f(a) = \prod f_v(a_v)$$

is in $\mathrm{Inv}(G)$, *and*

$$\hat{f}(\xi) = \prod \hat{f}_v(\xi_v).$$

Proof. By Theorem 8, applied to the function $f(a)\overline{c(a)} = \prod f_v(a_v)\overline{c_v(a_v)}$ we see that the Fourier transform of the product is the product of the Fourier transforms. Since f_v is in $\mathrm{Inv}(G_v)$, it follows that $\hat{f}_v$ is in $\mathrm{Inv}(\hat{G}_v)$ for all v. For almost all v, $\hat{f}_v$ is the characteristic function of $H_v^\perp$. Hence $\hat{f}$ is in $L_1(\hat{G})$ and thus f is in $\mathrm{Inv}(G)$.

Corollary. *The measure $d\xi = \prod d\xi_v$ is dual to $\prod da_v$.*

§6. Global additive duality and Riemann-Roch theorem

Let k be a number field (finite extension of the rationals $\mathbf{Q}$). Its completion at the absolute value v is k_v, and all objects discussed in the local case in §1–§4 should have the index v or $\mathfrak{p}$ in the $\mathfrak{p}$-adic case, e.g. $\mathfrak{o}_v$, λ_v, $\mathfrak{D}_\mathfrak{p}$, $\| \|_v$, c_v, etc.

As mentioned above, the **adele** group of k is the locally compact group equal to the restricted direct product of the k_v^+ with respect to the compact subgroups $\mathfrak{o}_\mathfrak{p}$, given at the non-archimedean absolute values. We let

$$x = (\ldots, x_v, \ldots,)$$

denote a variable element of the adele group $A_k = A$. We define a continuous homomorphism

$$\lambda(x) = \sum \lambda_v(x_v)$$

of A into the reals mod $\mathbf{Z}$, and the duality of Theorem 7 applied to our present case, combined with the self-duality of the local theory, gives:

Theorem 10. *The adele group is self-dual, under the pairing*

$$\langle x, y\rangle = \prod_v e^{2\pi i\lambda_v(x_v y_v)} = e^{2\pi i\lambda(xy)}.$$

Our next goal is to prove that the additive group of k, embedded in A on the diagonal:

$$\alpha \mapsto (\alpha, \alpha, \alpha, \ldots)$$

is its own orthogonal complement. We frequently write k instead of k^+.

Theorem 11. *The additive group k is its own orthogonal complement in the self-duality of A.*

Proof. We first prove that k is orthogonal to itself. This amounts to proving that if $x \in k$, then $\sum \lambda_v(x) = 0$. We can verify this at once if $k = \mathbf{Q}$ is the field of rational numbers (using a partial fraction decomposition of a rational number in terms of rational numbers having only prime powers in their denominators). If k is finite over $\mathbf{Q}$, and Tr_v resp. Tr denote the local trace resp. the global trace, then

$$\sum_v \lambda_v(x) = \sum_w \sum_{v|w} \lambda_w(\mathrm{Tr}_v(x)) = \sum_w \lambda_w(y),$$

where $y = \sum_{v|w} \mathrm{Tr}_v(x) = \mathrm{Tr}(x)$, and w ranges over the absolute values of $\mathbf{Q}$. This reduces the statement to $\mathbf{Q}$.

We have proved $k^\perp \supset k$. But A/k compact implies $k^\perp$ discrete. Hence $k^\perp/k$ is both discrete and compact, hence finite. Since $k^\perp$ is obviously a vector space over k, we must have $k^\perp = k$ thereby concluding the proof of the theorem.

Proposition 6. *Let F_∞ be as in Theorem 3 of Chapter VII, §2. Then with our choice of measure, F_∞ has volume $d_k^{1/2}$.*

Proof. This is an easy determinant computation. Remember that at complex v, our measure is twice Lebesgue measure.

Proposition 7. *Let F be the subset of A_k equal to*

$$\prod_{v \notin S_\infty} \mathfrak{o}_v \times F_\infty.$$

Then F has measure 1.

Proof. This follows from our choice of measures dx_v, which insure that $\mathfrak{o}_v$ has measure $(\mathbf{N}\mathfrak{D}_\mathfrak{p})^{-1/2}$ for $v = v_\mathfrak{p}$.

We are now ready to apply the duality of Theorem 11 to integration theory.

The arguments which follow could be applied to any locally compact commutative group and closed subgroup. To preserve the notation of the applications, we give the proof in the context of a self-dual commutative group A with a discrete closed subgroup k equal to its own orthogonal complement. Then the integral over k is equal to the sum over k. Of course, convergence in that case means absolute convergence. We also assume that the measure on A is self-dual.

Poisson formula. *Let f be continuous and in $L_1(A)$. Assume that*

$$\sum_{\alpha \in k} |f(x + \alpha)|$$

is uniformly convergent for x in a compact subset of A, and that

$$\sum_{\alpha \in k} \hat{f}(\alpha)$$

is convergent. Then

$$\sum_{\alpha \in k} \hat{f}(\alpha) = \sum_{\alpha \in k} f(\alpha).$$

Proof. We give a measure db on the factor group A/k which is such that the formula

$$\int_{A/k} \int_k f(\alpha + b)\, d\alpha\, db = \int_A f(a)\, da$$

holds, if $d\alpha$ corresponds to summation over k, and da is the given measure on A.

Let $g(x) = \int_k f(x + \alpha)\, d\alpha$. We contend that $\hat{g}(\alpha) = \hat{f}(\alpha)$ for $\alpha \in k$. Indeed, denoting by $\langle\ ,\ \rangle$ the pairing of an element of a group and a character, and taking into account that

$$(A/k)^{\wedge} = k^{\perp} = k$$

we have:

$$\begin{aligned}\hat{g}(\beta) &= \int_{A/k} g(b)\overline{\langle b, \beta \rangle}\, db \\ &= \int_{A/k} \int_k f(b + \alpha)\overline{\langle b, \beta \rangle}\, d\alpha\, db \\ &= \int_{A/k} \int_k f(b + \alpha)\overline{\langle b + \alpha, \beta \rangle}\, d\alpha\, db\end{aligned}$$

(because $\langle \alpha, \beta \rangle = 1$ by assumption)

$$\begin{aligned}&= \int_A f(a)\overline{\langle a, \beta \rangle}\, da \\ &= \hat{f}(\beta).\end{aligned}$$

Now the measure on A is self-dual. Hence the Fourier inversion can be applied to $\hat{\hat{g}}$ evaluated at 0. The assertion of the theorem follows at once from the definition of $\hat{\hat{g}}(0)$.

Classically, as in Chapter XIII, the Poisson formula is applied to the case of the reals, and the discrete subgroup $\mathbf{Z}$. We shall apply it to the adeles.

In fact, we shall need to apply it in the adele case, to a multiplicative translation of f.

Riemann-Roch theorem. *If $f(x)$ satisfies the conditions*

(1) *$f(x)$ is continuous and in $L_1(A)$.*

(2) *$\sum_{\alpha \in k} f(a(x + \alpha))$ is convergent for ideles a and adeles x uniformly for these variables ranging over compact subsets of the idele and adele groups respectively.*

(3) *$\sum_{\alpha \in k} \hat{f}(a\alpha)$ is convergent for all ideles a.*

Then

$$\frac{1}{\|a\|} \sum_{\alpha \in k} \hat{f}\left(\frac{\alpha}{a}\right) = \sum_{\alpha \in k} f(a\alpha).$$

Proof. The function $g(x) = f(ax)$ satisfies the conditions of the Poisson formula, as we see using the relation

$$\hat{g}(x) = \frac{1}{\|a\|} \hat{f}\left(\frac{x}{a}\right).$$

Our assertion is therefore immediate.

§7. *Global functional equation*

In the multiplicative theory, we take the ideles $J = J_k$ as our restricted direct product of the local multiplicative groups k_v^* with respect to the units U_v and apply §5. The quasi-characters will be trivial for almost all U_v, i.e. are unramified for almost all v.

It will be convenient to write J as a direct product (topologically and algebraically) by embedding the positive reals $\mathbf{R}^+$ in it, namely, we map an element t of $\mathbf{R}^+$ on the idele

$$(t^{1/N}, \ldots, t^{1/N}, 1, 1, \ldots)$$

having $t^{1/N}$ as component at every archimedean v, and 1 at all others. This is a norm preserving embedding, since

$$\sum_{v \in S_\infty} N_v = N \quad (= [k : \mathbf{Q}]).$$

It is then clear that

$$J \approx \mathbf{R}^+ \times J^0,$$

i.e. every idele a can be written uniquely as a product

$$a = tb$$

with $t \in \mathbf{R}^+$ and $b \in J^0$, and this product decomposition is also topological. There is a unique measure on J^0 (denoted by d^*b) such that we have formally

$$d^*a = d^*b \times \frac{dt}{t}\cdot$$

We make one restriction on the quasi-characters to be considered in the sequel. We *assume* that they are trivial on k^*. Then they can be considered as quasi-characters on the **idele classes** $C_k = J_k/k^*$. Such characters will also be called **Hecke characters.** Since we know that $J_k^0/k^* = C_k^0$ is compact, it follows that the restriction of a quasi-character to C_k^0 is a character, and thus that we have a situation similar to the one in the local archimedean theory. If c is a quasi-character trivial on C_k^0, then we must have

$$c(a) = \|a\|^s$$

for some complex number s uniquely determined by c. If c is any quasi-character, then there is a unique real number σ such that $|c(a)| = \|a\|^\sigma$, and we call σ the **real part** of c, $\mathrm{Re}(c)$. Given a character χ on C_k, then $\chi(a)\|a\|^s$ is a quasi-character, and conversely every quasi-character can be so written (although χ is not determined uniquely, only up to some $\|a\|^{it}$).

It will sometimes be convenient to normalize characters on C_k by prescribing that they should take the value 1 on our embedded $\mathbf{R}^+$ (the embedding was canonical). This is clearly equivalent to stating that

$$\sum_{v \in S_\infty} N_v \varphi_v(\chi) = 0.$$

A quasi-character c determines uniquely such a character χ, so that the formula $c(a) = \chi(a)\|a\|^s$ holds.

As in the local theory, we let $\hat{c}(a) = \|a\|c(a)^{-1}$ so that with the above convention,

$$\hat{c}(a) = \chi^{-1}(a)\|a\|^{1-s} = \bar{\chi}(a)\|a\|^{1-s}.$$

We shall now supplement the construction preceding Theorem 6 of Chapter VII, §3, by a measure computation.

As before, we let v_0 be a fixed archimedean absolute value, and

$$S'_\infty = S_\infty - v_0.$$

As before, $r = r_1 + r_2 - 1$.

Let $\epsilon_1, \ldots, \epsilon_r$ be units such that $l(\epsilon_i)$ generate the lattice of units. These are called **fundamental units.** They are generators of the group of units modulo the group of roots of unity.

The absolute value of the determinant

$$\det(\log \|\epsilon_i\|_v)$$

taken with $i = 1, \ldots, r$ and v in S'_∞ is the volume of a fundamental parallelotope P in Euclidean r-space, up to a sign. Its absolute value is called the **regulator** of k and is denoted by $R = R_k$. We denote by $d = d_k$ the absolute value of the discriminant.

Proposition 8. *Let the notation be as above, and l as in Theorem 6, Chapter VII, §3. Then the measure of $l^{-1}(P)$ is*

$$\frac{2^{r_1}(2\pi)^{r_2}}{d_k^{1/2}} R.$$

Proof. Let Q be the unit cube in r-space. Since l is a homomorphism, we have

$$\frac{\text{measure of } l^{-1}(P)}{\text{measure of } l^{-1}(Q)} = \frac{\text{volume of } P}{\text{volume of } Q} = R.$$

Thus it suffices to compute the measure of $l^{-1}(Q)$, and we leave it as an exercise (easy, using the definitions of our multiplicative measure).

Proposition 9. *If E is a fundamental domain for J^0/k^*, then its measure is*

$$\kappa = \frac{2^{r_1}(2\pi)^{r_2} hR}{w d_k^{1/2}}$$

(notation as in Theorem 6 of Chapter VII, §3).

Proof. Trivial from Proposition 8.

We approach the end of our journey. To get global zeta functions, we consider functions f on the adeles satisfying the following conditions:

Z1. *$f(x)$ and $\hat{f}(x)$ are continuous and in $L_1(A)$,* i.e. *f is in* $\mathrm{Inv}(A)$.

Z2. *The sums* $\sum_{\alpha \in k} f(a(x+\alpha))$ *and* $\sum_{\alpha \in k} \hat{f}(a(x+\alpha))$ *are both convergent, absolutely and uniformly for ideles a and adeles x ranging over compact subsets of the idele and adele groups respectively.*

Z3. *The functions* $f(a)\|a\|^\sigma$ *and* $\hat{f}(a)\|a\|^\sigma$ *are in* $L_1(J)$ *for* $\sigma > 1$.

Note that in view of **Z1** and **Z2**, the Riemann-Roch theorem is valid for functions of the above type. The purpose of **Z3** is to enable us to define zeta functions. With each such f we define, for quasi-characters c with $\mathrm{Re}(c) > 1$ a zeta function

$$\zeta(f, c) = \int f(a)c(a)\, d^*a,$$

the integral being over the idele group. If $c(a) = \chi(a)\|a\|^s$, then

$$\zeta(f, \chi, s) = \int f(a)\chi(a)\|a\|^s\, d^*a.$$

(We always assume quasi-characters and characters are trivial on k^*.) Once the character χ is fixed, our zeta function becomes a function of the parameter s, and from our assumption **Z3** it follows that it is holomorphic in the domain $\mathrm{Re}(s) > 1$. We can say invariantly that it is holomorphic in the domain of quasi-characters with $\mathrm{Re}(c) > 1$.

Theorem 12. *By analytic continuation we may extend the definition of any zeta function* $\zeta(f, c)$ *to the domain of all quasi-characters of* J/k^*. *The extended function is single valued and holomorphic, except at* $c(a) = 1$ *and* $c(a) = \|a\|$, *where it has simple poles with residues* $-\kappa f(0)$ *and* $+\kappa\hat{f}(0)$ *respectively, where* κ = *volume of multiplicative fundamental domain of* $J_k^0 \bmod k^*$. *We have the functional equation*

$$\zeta(f, c) = \zeta(\hat{f}, \hat{c}),$$

where $\hat{c}(a) = \|a\|c^{-1}(a)$.

Proof. We have

$$\zeta(f, c) = \int_{\|a\| \leqq 1} f(a)c(a)\, d^*a + \int_{\|a\| \geqq 1} f(a)c(a)\, d^*a.$$

The second integral obviously converges for $\mathrm{Re}(c)$ equal to any real number, because it converges for $\mathrm{Re}(c) > \sigma_0$ for some σ_0, and hence converges all the better for $\mathrm{Re}(c) \leqq \sigma_0$. We shall now transform the first integral and in fact we shall prove:

Theorem 13. *We have*

$$\zeta(f, c) =$$

$$\int_{\|a\| \geqq 1} f(a)c(a)\, d^*a + \int_{\|a\| \geqq 1} \hat{f}(a)\hat{c}(a)\, d^*a + \delta_\chi \left[\frac{\kappa \hat{f}(0)}{s-1} - \frac{\kappa f(0)}{s} \right],$$

where δ_χ is 1 or 0 according as the character χ induced by c on J^0 is trivial or not in which case s is the unique complex number such that

$$c(a) = \|a\|^s.$$

The two integrals are convergent for all c, uniformly in every strip

$$\sigma_0 \leqq \mathrm{Re}(c) \leqq \sigma_1.$$

The uniformity of convergence of the integrals in a given strip is clear from the above remarks. Furthermore, let us replace (f, c) by $(\hat{f}, \hat{c})$ in the expression on the right. We take into account that

$$\hat{\hat{f}}(0) = f(-0) = f(0),$$

and that $\hat{\hat{f}}(a) = f(-a)$. Then changing variables in the second integral, we see that $c(-1)$ will come out as a factor in front of the integral. But we have assumed that c is trivial on k^*. Hence the expression on the right is invariant under the substitution sending (f, c) into $(\hat{f}, \hat{c})$, and thus the functional equation follows.

Let us now complete our proofs by transforming the integral taken over $\|a\| \leqq 1$. We can write the ideles as a product:

$$J = J^0 \times \mathbf{R}^+.$$

For any fixed t, we have

$$\int_{J^0} f(tb)c(tb)\, d^*b + f(0)\int_E c(tb)\, d^*b$$
$$= \sum_{\alpha \in k^*} \int_{\alpha E} f(tb)c(tb)\, d^*b + f(0) \int_E c(tb)\, d^*b.$$

Using the invariance of measure under multiplicative translations, and the fact that $c(\alpha) = 1$ for $\alpha \in k^*$, we see that this expression is equal to

$$\sum_{\alpha \in k^*} \int_E f(\alpha tb)c(tb)\, d^*b + f(0) \int_E c(tb)\, d^*b.$$

By Property **Z2**, which allows us to interchange sum and integral, this is equal to

$$\int_E \sum_{\alpha\in k} f(\alpha tb)c(tb)\, d^*b = \int_E \sum_{\alpha\in k} \hat{f}\left(\frac{\alpha}{tb}\right) \frac{1}{\|tb\|}\, c(tb)\, d^*b \qquad \text{(Riemann Roch).}$$

If we had started with the expression

$$\int_{J^0} \hat{f}(t^{-1}b)\hat{c}(t^{-1}b)\, d^*b + \hat{f}(0)\int_E \hat{c}(t^{-1}b)\, d^*b,$$

made the transformation sending b to b^{-1} which preserves the measure, and then applied the same arguments as above, we would end up with the same expression that we found above; in other words, we find the equality

$$\int_{J^0} f(tb)c(tb)\, d^*b + f(0)\int_E c(tb)\, d^*b = \int_{J^0} \hat{f}(t^{-1}b)\hat{c}(t^{-1}b)\, d^*b + \hat{f}(0)\int_E \hat{c}(t^{-1}b)\, d^*b.$$

Now we observe that $c(tb) = c(t)c(b) = t^s c(b)$, whence

$$\int_E c(tb)\, d^*b = \begin{cases} \kappa t^s & \text{if } c(a) = \|a\|^s \\ 0 & \text{if } c \text{ is non-trivial on } J^0, \end{cases}$$

always using the fact that the integral over a compact group of a non-trivial character is 0, and that the integral of the trivial character is the measure of the group.

If we integrate our expressions from $t = 0$ to $t = 1$, then on the right-hand side of our equality we can replace t^{-1} by t and the limits of integration from 1 to ∞. Theorem 13 is now clear, and this concludes the proof.

§8. *Global computations*

The purpose of this section is to derive explicitly certain convenient global formulas used in the applications, using a particular weight function g_χ closely related to f_χ. These will be products of local functions, and the proof that the product converges for $\sigma > 1$ will be given in the next chapter. Although it is simple (and classical), we must emphasize that this proof is the final step in showing that Theorem 12 is not empty, and applies to the classical zeta functions or L-functions.

Proposition 10. *If g is a translation of f,* i.e. $g(x) = f(bx)$, *then*

$$\hat{g}(y) = \|b\|^{-1}\hat{f}(y/b) \qquad \textit{and} \qquad \zeta(g, c) = c(b)^{-1}\zeta(f, c).$$

Proof. Directly from the definitions. The assertion is valid locally or globally, i.e. on k_v^* or J_k. In the local case, $\| \| = \| \|_v$ of course, and b is either in k_v^* or an idele.

To fix some notation, we put for every character χ,

$$\mathfrak{D}_\chi = \mathfrak{D}\mathfrak{f}_\chi \qquad d_\chi = \mathbf{N}\mathfrak{D}_\chi.$$

If $\chi = \chi_0$, then $d_0 = d_k$ is simply the absolute value of the discriminant of the number field k. We use similar conventions for the local case, putting an index $\mathfrak{p}$ on our symbols.

If v is archimedean, $N = [k : \mathbf{Q}]$, we let

$$g_{\chi,v}(x) = f_{\chi,v}(d_\chi^{1/2N}x)(N_v\pi)^{|m_v(\chi)|/2},$$

where $f_{\chi,v}$ is the function of §4.

If v is $\mathfrak{p}$-adic, we let

$$g_{\chi,v}(x) = \frac{1}{\mu_v(1 + \mathfrak{f}_{\chi,v})} f_{\chi,v}(x),$$

it being understood as usual, that if χ is unramified, then $\mathfrak{f}_{\chi,v} = \mathfrak{o}_v$ and $1 + \mathfrak{f}_{\chi,v} = \mathfrak{o}_v$ also, so that its measure is $d_\mathfrak{p}^{-1/2}$. We let

$$g_\chi(x) = \prod g_{\chi,v}(x_v).$$

In particular, if $\chi = \chi_0$, then for v archimedean,

$$g_{0,v}(x) = f_{0,v}(d_k^{1/2N}x)$$

and for v $\mathfrak{p}$-adic,

$$g_{0,v}(x) = d_\mathfrak{p}^{1/2} f_{0,v}(x),$$

where $d_\mathfrak{p} = \mathbf{N}\mathfrak{D}_\mathfrak{p}$.

We observe that g_χ has been obtained from f_χ by a translation at the archimedean v, and multiplication by constant factors, designed to cancel certain local extraneous terms, occurring both in the zeta function of f_χ and $\hat{f}_\chi$.

To begin with, we observe a symmetry at the origin.

Proposition 11. *Let $\chi = \chi_0$ be the trivial character. Then g_0 and $\hat{g}_0$ are $\geqq 0$, and*

$$g_0(0) = \hat{g}_0(0) = d_k^{1/2}(2\pi)^{-r_2}.$$

Proof. Immediate from the definitions.

Proposition 12. *Let b be the idele having components $b_v = d_k^{1/N}$ at archimedean v, and $b_\mathfrak{p} = \pi^{-\nu_\mathfrak{p}}$, where $\nu_\mathfrak{p} = \operatorname{ord}_\mathfrak{p} \mathfrak{D}$. Then $\|b\| = 1$, and*

$$\hat{g}_0(x) = g_0(b^{-1}x).$$

Proof. This is an easy consequence of Proposition 10, together with the explicit determination of g_0 in terms of f_0.

If χ is a character of C_k, and $\mathfrak{p}$ is unramified for χ, then the value of χ on the idele having a prime π at the $\mathfrak{p}$-component and 1 for all other components is independent of the choice of such prime element π, and will be denoted by $\chi(\mathfrak{p})$. We then define

$$L(s, \chi) = \prod_{\mathfrak{p} \notin S_\chi} \frac{1}{1 - \dfrac{\chi(\mathfrak{p})}{\mathbf{N}\mathfrak{p}^s}}$$

the product being taken over all $\mathfrak{p}$ which are unramified for χ, letting S_χ be the set of $\mathfrak{p}$ which are ramified for χ.

We put

$$\Lambda(s, \chi) = (2^{-r_2}\pi^{-N/2}d_\chi^{1/2})^s \prod_{v \in S_\infty} \Gamma(s_v/2)L(s, \chi),$$

where we recall that

$$s_v = s_v(\chi) = N_v(s + i\varphi_v(\chi)) + |m_v(\chi)|.$$

Theorem 14. *Assume that χ is normalized so that*

$$\sum_{v \in S_\infty} N_v\varphi_v(\chi) = 0.$$

Then:

$$\zeta(g_\chi, \chi, s) = \Lambda(s, \chi) \prod_{\mathfrak{p} \in S_\chi} \tau_\mathfrak{p}(\chi) \prod_{\mathfrak{p} \notin S_\chi} \chi(\mathfrak{D}_\mathfrak{p}^{-1})2^{-i\Phi},$$

where Φ is the sum of $\varphi_v(\chi)$ over the complex v. We also have

$$\zeta(\hat{g}_\chi, \bar{\chi}, 1 - s) = \Lambda(1 - s, \bar{\chi})(\mathbf{N}\mathfrak{f}_\chi)^{1/2}\, i^M\, 2^{i\Phi},$$

where $M = \sum_{v \in S_\infty} |m_v(\chi)|$, and these two expressions are equal.

Proof. Just put together the local results of the computations of §4, together with Proposition 10, and be careful about all the possible cancellations which take place.

If we had divided g_χ by $(\mathbf{N}\mathfrak{f}_\chi)^{1/2}$, we see that $\Lambda(s, \chi)$ and the resulting zeta function would have differed by a constant of absolute value 1, and similarly for $\Lambda(1 - s, \bar{\chi})$.

Corollary 1. *We have the functional equation*

$$W(\chi)\Lambda(s, \chi) = \Lambda(1 - s, \bar{\chi}),$$

where $W(\chi)$ is a constant of absolute value 1, given by

$$W(\chi) = 4^{-i\Phi} i^{-M} (\mathbf{N}\mathfrak{f}_\chi)^{-1/2} \prod_{\mathfrak{p} \in S_\chi} \tau_\mathfrak{p}(\chi) \prod_{\mathfrak{p} \notin S_\chi} \chi(\mathfrak{D}_\mathfrak{p}^{-1}).$$

Proof. From the local computations of §4, we know that each expression $\tau_\mathfrak{p}(\chi)$ has absolute value $(\mathbf{N}\mathfrak{f}_{\chi,\mathfrak{p}})^{1/2}$ which is just enough to cancel out in the equality

$$\zeta(g_\chi, \chi, s) = \zeta(\hat{g}_\chi, \bar{\chi}, 1 - s).$$

Corollary 2. *For a fixed character χ, put $\Lambda(s) = \Lambda(s, \bar{\chi})$. Then*

$$\Lambda(\bar{s}) = \overline{\Lambda(1 - s)} u(\chi),$$

where $u(\chi)$ has absolute value 1.

Proof. A trivial computation, using the relation

$$\Lambda(\bar{s}, \chi) = \overline{\Lambda(s, \bar{\chi})}.$$

Corollary 3. *Let $\Lambda_0(s) = \Lambda(s, \chi_0)$. Then*

$$\Lambda_0(s) = \zeta(g_0, \chi_0, s) = (2^{-2r_2} \pi^{-N} d_k)^{s/2} \Gamma^{r_1}(s/2) \Gamma^{r_2}(s) \zeta_k(s)$$

and

$$\Lambda_0(s) = \Lambda_0(1 - s).$$

Proposition 13. *Let*

$$\kappa = \frac{2^{r_1} (2\pi)^{r_2} h R}{w d_k^{1/2}}$$

be the volume of the fundamental domain for J_k^0 mod k^*. Then the residue of $\zeta(g_0, s) = \zeta(g_0, \chi_0, s)$ at $s = 1$ is

$$\lambda = \frac{2^{r_1} h R}{w}$$

and the residue of $\zeta_k(s)$ at 1 is κ itself.

Proof. The residue for $\zeta(g_0, \chi_0, s)$ comes from the general Theorem 12 and that for the zeta function comes from $s = 1$ in Corollary 3 above together with the values $\Gamma(\frac{1}{2}) = \pi^{1/2}$, and $\Gamma(1) = 1$.

Theorem 15. *We have an integral expression*

$$\zeta(g_0, s) = \int_{\|a\| \geqq 1} \hat{g}_0(a)(\|a\|^s + \|a\|^{1-s})\, d^*a + \frac{\lambda}{s(s-1)}\cdot$$

Proof. If we write down the integral expression of Theorem 13, §7 and use Proposition 10 together with the fact that $\|b\| = 1$ and that the multiplicative measure is invariant under multiplicative translation, we get what we want.

This formula is the analogue of the formula proved in Chapter XIII, §3. Note that the integral terms are $\geqq 0$.

CHAPTER XV

Density of Primes and Tauberian Theorem

We shall give a proof of Ikehara's Tauberian theorem (cf. also Widder's book on Laplace Transforms), and prove the density theorem of primes in generalized arithmetic progressions determined by Hecke characters. In addition to giving a density for primes in given ideal classes, it also gives densities for primes distributed suitably in Euclidean N-space.

The reader will note that the Tauberian theorem has as a corollary the asymptotic behavior of the coefficients of a Dirichlet series having a simple pole at, say, an integer $d > 1$ and holomorphic otherwise for $\mathrm{Re}(\sigma) \geqq d$. If the residue is, say 1, then by translation we are brought to evaluating sums of type

$$\sum_{n<x} n^d a_n,$$

and summing or integrating by parts shows that if $\sum_{n<x} a_n \sim x$, then $\sum n^d a_n \sim x^{d+1}/(d+1)$. This can then be applied to the zeta function of a variety defined over the ring of algebraic integers of a number field. Reducing mod $\mathfrak{p}$ for almost all $\mathfrak{p}$, and applying the estimates of Lang-Weil, "Number of points of varieties in finite fields," *Am. J. of Math.* (1954) pp. 819–827, one sees that the zeta function has an analytic behavior on $\mathrm{Re}(\sigma) \geqq d$ such that we can apply the Tauberian theorem if d is the dimension of the variety under consideration.

§1. *The Dirichlet integral*

Let $\varphi(x)$ be a real valued function of bounded variation in any finite subinterval of $0 \leqq x < \infty$. The function

$$(1) \qquad f(s) = \int_0^\infty e^{-sx}\, d\varphi(x) \qquad (s = \sigma + it \text{ complex})$$

contains as special case the Dirichlet series if $\varphi(x)$ is taken to be a step function. We shall look into this later. For now, we deal with the integral.

Suppose that for a special value s_0 the function

$$g(y) = \int_0^y e^{-s_0 x}\, d\varphi(x)$$

is bounded in $0 \leqq y < \infty$. If $0 \leqq y_1 < y_2$, we have

$$\begin{aligned}\int_{y_1}^{y_2} e^{-sx}\, d\varphi(x) &= \int_{y_1}^{y_2} e^{-(s-s_0)x} e^{-s_0 x}\, d\varphi(x)\\ &= e^{-(s-s_0)x} g(x)\Big|_{y_1}^{y_2} + (s - s_0)\int_{y_1}^{y_2} e^{-(s-s_0)x} g(x)\, dx.\end{aligned}$$

We see that for $\operatorname{Re}(s - s_0) \geqq \epsilon > 0$ and bounded values of $\dfrac{|s - s_0|}{\sigma - \sigma_0}$ the left side is uniformly small for large y_1. Therefore (1) will converge for these s-values.

Since the assumption about $g(y)$ is satisfied if s_0 is taken to be a point where (1) converges, it follows that (1) has a certain right half-plane as plane of convergence and that this convergence is uniform in any compact subset of the interior of the half-plane of convergence. Since each $\int_0^y e^{-sx}\, d\varphi(x)$ is analytic, it follows that (1) is analytic in the interior of our half-plane.

Assume now that $\varphi(x) \geqq 0$, that (1) converges for some real $s_0 > 0$. Integrating $d(e^{-sx}\varphi(x))$, we get

$$\begin{aligned}(2)\qquad \int_0^\xi e^{-sx}\, d\varphi(x) &= -\varphi(0) + e^{-s\xi}\varphi(\xi) + s\int_0^\xi e^{-sx}\varphi(x)\, dx\\ &= -\varphi(0) + e^{-(s-s_0)\xi} e^{-s_0\xi}\varphi(\xi)\\ &\quad + s\int_0^\xi e^{-(s-s_0)x} e^{-s_0 x}\varphi(x)\, dx.\end{aligned}$$

If we put $s = s_0$ in the first line of (2), we see that the left-hand side is bounded, and the last two terms on the right are $\geqq 0$. Hence $e^{-s_0\xi}\varphi(\xi)$ is bounded in ξ. It follows that for $\operatorname{Re}(s) > s_0$ we have

$$(3)\qquad f(s) = -\varphi(0) + s\int_0^\infty e^{-sx}\varphi(x)\, dx$$

(including of course the existence of the integral on the right side).

§2. *Ikehara's Tauberian theorem*

Throughout this section, we suppose that $\varphi(x)$ is a monotone increasing function, with $\varphi(x) = 0$ for $x \leqq 0$. We let

$$H(x) = e^{-x}\varphi(x),$$

and the monotonicity of φ means for $H(x)$ that

$$H(x_2) \geqq H(x_1)e^{x_1 - x_2}, \qquad \text{for } x_2 \geqq x_1.$$

For a given $\lambda > 0$, consider the class of all monotonically increasing functions $\varphi(x)$ with $\varphi(x) = 0$ for $x \leqq 0$ that have the following properties:

(1) The integral for $f(s)$ converges for $\text{Re}(s) > 1$.

(2) For $\epsilon > 0$, $s = 1 + \epsilon + it$, put

$$h_\epsilon(t) = f(s) - \frac{1}{s-1}.$$

Our property states that $h(t) = \lim_{\epsilon \to 0} h_\epsilon(t)$ exists uniformly in t for $|t| \leqq 2\lambda$. (Whence $h(t)$ is continuous for $|t| \leqq 2\lambda$.)

Tauberian theorem. *There are two functions $P_1(\lambda)$ and $P_2(\lambda)$ of λ alone such that for any φ in our class, we have*

$$P_1(\lambda) \geqq \overline{\lim_{y \to \infty}}\, H(y) \geqq \underline{\lim_{y \to \infty}}\, H(y) \geqq P_2(\lambda) > 0$$

and such that

$$\lim_{\lambda \to \infty} P_1(\lambda) = \lim_{\lambda \to \infty} P_2(\lambda) = 1.$$

Should one know therefore that $\varphi(x)$ belongs to our class for all λ then

$$\lim_{x \to \infty} e^{-x}\varphi(x) = 1.$$

This is the formula used in our applications.

We shall now prove the Tauberian theorem. We define π to be the integral

$$\pi = \int_{-\infty}^{+\infty} \frac{\sin^2 v}{v^2}\, dv > 0$$

(which gives the customary value).

Lemma. *Under the previous hypotheses, we have*

$$\lim_{y \to \infty} \int_{-\infty}^{\lambda y} H\left(y - \frac{v}{\lambda}\right) \frac{\sin^2 v}{v^2}\, dv = \pi.$$

Proof. With $s = 1 + \epsilon + it$, we have using (3):

$$\frac{h_\epsilon(t) - 1}{s} = \frac{1}{s}\left(f(s) - \frac{1}{s-1} - 1\right)$$

$$= \int_0^\infty e^{-(s-1)x} H(x)\,dx - \frac{1}{s-1}$$

$$= \int_0^\infty (H(x) - 1)e^{-\epsilon x - itx}\,dx,$$

taking into account the integral $\displaystyle\int_0^\infty e^{-(s-1)x}\,dx = \frac{1}{s-1}\cdot$ Thus

$$\frac{h_\epsilon(t) - 1}{s} = \lim_{\xi\to\infty} \int_0^\xi (H(x) - 1)e^{-\epsilon x - itx}\,dx$$

uniformly in $|t| \leqq 2\lambda$ so long as ϵ is fixed.

Our next goal is to get formula (6) below. We multiply our last expression by the function $e^{ity}(1 - |t|/2\lambda)$ and integrate over t from -2λ to 2λ. On the right we can interchange the integral and the limit. Putting

$$F_\epsilon(t) = \left(1 - \frac{|t|}{2\lambda}\right)\frac{h_\epsilon(t) - 1}{s}$$

we get:

$$\int_{-2\lambda}^{2\lambda} e^{ity} F_\epsilon(t)\,dt$$

$$= \lim_{\xi\to\infty} \int_{-2\lambda}^{2\lambda} e^{ity}\left(1 - \frac{|t|}{2\lambda}\right)\left[\int_0^\xi (H(x) - 1)e^{-\epsilon x - itx}\,dx\right]dt.$$

The two integrations (which are over finite intervals) can be interchanged, and one obtains:

(4) $$\int_{-2\lambda}^{2\lambda} e^{ity} F_\epsilon(t)\,dt$$

$$= \int_0^{2\lambda} (H(x) - 1)e^{-\epsilon x}\left[\int_{-2\lambda}^{2\lambda}\left(1 - \frac{|t|}{2\lambda}\right)e^{i(y-x)t}\,dt\right]dx.$$

The inner integral on the right is elementary. We have

$$\int_{-2\lambda}^{2\lambda}\left(1 - \frac{|t|}{2\lambda}\right)e^{i(y-x)t}\,dt = 2\int_0^{2\lambda}\left(1 - \frac{|t|}{2\lambda}\right)\cos((y - x)t)\,dt,$$

which after a change of variables and integration by parts is equal to

$$\frac{2\sin^2(\lambda(y-x))}{\lambda(y-x)^2}.$$

Thus (4) becomes

$$(5)\qquad \int_{-2\lambda}^{2\lambda} e^{ity}F_\epsilon(t)\,dt = 2\int_0^\infty (H(x)-1)e^{-\epsilon x}\frac{\sin^2(\lambda(y-x))}{\lambda(y-x)^2}\,dx.$$

The integral $\int_0^\infty e^{-\epsilon x}\frac{\sin^2(\lambda(y-x))}{\lambda(y-x)^2}\,dx$ exists since the similar integral obtained by putting $\epsilon = 0$ exists. Adding it to both sides of (5), we get:

$$(6)\qquad \int_{-2\lambda}^{2\lambda} e^{ity}F_\epsilon(t)\,dt + 2\int_0^\infty e^{-\epsilon x}\frac{\sin^2(\lambda(y-x))}{\lambda(y-x)^2}\,dx$$
$$= 2\int_0^\infty H(x)e^{-\epsilon x}\frac{\sin^2(\lambda(y-x))}{\lambda(y-x)^2}\,dx.$$

We now take the limit as $\epsilon \to 0$. What happens to the left side as $\epsilon \to 0$? The first part converges to

$$\int_{-2\lambda}^{2\lambda} e^{ity}F(t)\,dt,$$

where $F(t)$ is the continuous function $\left(1-\frac{|t|}{2\lambda}\right)\frac{h(t)-1}{s}$ because of the uniformity of $h_\epsilon(t) \to h(t)$.

The second integral has a tail end

$$\int_\xi^\infty e^{-\epsilon x}\frac{\sin^2\lambda(y-x)}{\lambda(y-x)^2}\,dx \leqq \int_\xi^\infty \frac{\sin^2\lambda(y-x)}{\lambda(y-x)^2}\,dx$$

which is small for large ξ, uniformly in ϵ. But as $\epsilon \to 0$,

$$\int_0^\xi e^{-\epsilon x}\frac{\sin^2\lambda(y-x)}{\lambda(y-x)^2}\,dx \to \int_0^\xi \frac{\sin^2\lambda(y-x)}{\lambda(y-x)^2}\,dx.$$

Hence the second integral has the limit

$$\int_0^\infty \frac{\sin^2\lambda(y-x)}{\lambda(y-x)^2}\,dx = \int_{-\infty}^{\lambda y}\frac{\sin^2 v}{v^2}\,dv.$$

What about the right side of (6)? We have just proved that it has a limit as $\epsilon \to 0$. The integrand is positive and increasing as $\epsilon \to 0$. Therefore

$$\int_0^{\xi} H(x)e^{-\epsilon x} \frac{\sin^2 \lambda(y-x)}{\lambda(y-x)^2}\, dx$$

remains below this limit for all $\epsilon > 0$. Hence

$$\int_0^{\xi} H(x) \frac{\sin^2 \lambda(y-x)}{\lambda(y-x)^2}\, dx$$

is also below this limit. We see that

$$\int_0^{\infty} H(x) \frac{\sin^2 \lambda(y-x)}{\lambda(y-x)^2}\, dx$$

exists. Its tail end is small and greater than the tail end of the right side of (6). It follows that the right side has the limit

$$\int_0^{\infty} H(x) \frac{\sin^2 \lambda(y-x)}{\lambda(y-x)^2}\, dx = \int_{-\infty}^{\lambda y} H\left(y - \frac{v}{\lambda}\right) \frac{\sin^2 v}{v^2}\, dv.$$

Hence finally:

$$(7) \qquad \int_{-2\lambda}^{2\lambda} e^{ity} F(t)\, dt + 2\int_{-\infty}^{\lambda y} \frac{\sin^2 v}{v^2}\, dv = 2\int_{-\infty}^{\lambda y} H\left(y - \frac{v}{\lambda}\right) \frac{\sin^2 v}{v^2}\, dv.$$

What happens to (7) as $y \to \infty$? The first integral on the left is the Fourier constant of the continuous function $F(t)$ and goes to 0 by the Riemann-Lebesgue Lemma. The second integral on the left goes to π, and this proves our Lemma.

We shall now apply our Lemma. Observe that if $v > \lambda y$, then $H\left(y - \frac{v}{\lambda}\right) = 0$ so that we can also write

$$\lim_{y \to \infty} \int_{-\infty}^{+\infty} H\left(y - \frac{v}{\lambda}\right) \frac{\sin^2 v}{v^2}\, dv = \pi.$$

The proof from now on is formal. For both inequalities, the idea is to consider the integral between finite limits, depending on λ.

Note that the integrand is $\geqq 0$. Cutting down the domain of integration we get

$$\overline{\lim_{y\to\infty}} \int_{-\sqrt{\lambda}}^{\sqrt{\lambda}} H\left(y - \frac{v}{\lambda}\right) \frac{\sin^2 v}{v^2}\, dv \leqq \pi.$$

Using the monotonicity of φ and the corresponding property of H, we get in the interval $[-\sqrt{\lambda}, \sqrt{\lambda}]$

$$H\left(y - \frac{v}{\lambda}\right) \geqq H\left(y - \frac{1}{\sqrt{\lambda}}\right) e^{-2/\sqrt{\lambda}}.$$

Hence

$$\overline{\lim_{y\to\infty}}\, H\left(y - \frac{1}{\sqrt{\lambda}}\right) e^{-2/\sqrt{\lambda}} \int_{-\sqrt{\lambda}}^{\sqrt{\lambda}} \frac{\sin^2 v}{v^2}\, dv \leqq \pi.$$

Since λ is fixed, y can be replaced by $y + 1/\sqrt{\lambda}$. Hence

$$\overline{\lim_{y\to\infty}}\, H(y) \leqq \frac{\pi e^{2/\sqrt{\lambda}}}{\displaystyle\int_{-\sqrt{\lambda}}^{\sqrt{\lambda}} \frac{\sin^2 v}{v^2}\, dv} = P_1(\lambda),$$

and we see that $\lim_{\lambda\to\infty} P_1(\lambda) = 1$, thereby proving the first half of the Tauberian theorem.

From this half, it follows that $H(y)$ is bounded. Therefore,

$$\int_{\sqrt{y}}^{\infty} H\left(y - \frac{v}{\lambda}\right) \frac{\sin^2 v}{v^2}\, dv \leqq C \int_{\sqrt{y}}^{\infty} \frac{\sin^2 v}{v^2}\, dv$$

goes to 0 as $y \to \infty$. Hence we may write also

$$\lim_{y\to\infty} \int_{-\infty}^{\sqrt{y}} H\left(y - \frac{v}{\lambda}\right) \frac{\sin^2 v}{v^2}\, dv = \pi. \tag{8}$$

(We take $\sqrt{y}$ as a limit of integration so that $y - \sqrt{y} \to \infty$ with y.) If y is large enough, then $H(y) < 2P_1(\lambda)$. Thus $H\left(y - \frac{v}{\lambda}\right)$ in (8) will be $< 2P_1(\lambda)$ if y is large enough.

We now put

$$b = \frac{4}{\pi} P_1(\lambda) + \sqrt{\lambda}$$

and cut down the integration domain in (8) for large y from $-b$ to b. This neglects

$$\int_{-\infty}^{-b} H\left(y - \frac{v}{\lambda}\right) \frac{\sin^2 v}{v^2}\, dv \leqq 2P_1(\lambda) \int_{-\infty}^{-b} \frac{1}{v^2}\, dv = 2P_1(\lambda)/b$$

and

$$\int_{b}^{\sqrt{y}} H\left(y - \frac{v}{\lambda}\right) \frac{\sin^2 v}{v^2}\, dv \leqq 2P_1(\lambda) \int_{b}^{\sqrt{y}} \frac{1}{v^2}\, dv \leqq 2P_1(\lambda)/b.$$

Therefore

$$\frac{4P_1(\lambda)}{b} + \lim_{y\to\infty} \int_{-b}^{b} H\left(y - \frac{v}{\lambda}\right) \frac{\sin^2 v}{v^2}\, dv \geqq \pi.$$

Again by monotonicity, in this interval,

$$H\left(y + \frac{b}{\lambda}\right) e^{2b/\lambda} \geqq H\left(y - \frac{v}{\lambda}\right).$$

We get

$$\frac{4P_1(\lambda)}{b} + \lim_{y\to\infty} H\left(y + \frac{b}{\lambda}\right) e^{2b/\lambda} \int_{-b}^{b} \frac{\sin^2 v}{v^2}\, dv \geqq \pi.$$

Replacing y by $y - \dfrac{b}{\lambda}$ and the integral by π we get

$$\lim_{y\to\infty} H(y) \geqq e^{-2b/\lambda}\left(1 - \frac{4P_1(\lambda)}{\pi b}\right) = P_2(\lambda).$$

It is clear that $\lim_{\lambda\to\infty} P_2(\lambda) = 1$, and this proves the Tauberian theorem.

§3. *Tauberian theorem for Dirichlet series*

Let

$$f(s) = \sum_{n=1}^{\infty} a_n/n^s = \sum a_n e^{-s \log n}$$

be a function defined by a Dirichlet series, which converges for $\operatorname{Re}(s) > 1$, has real $a_n \geqq 0$, and such that f is regular on the line $\operatorname{Re}(s) = 1$ with exception of a pole of first order at $s = 1$ with residue 1.

Let $\varphi(x)$ be the step function which jumps at the places $x = \log n$ by the amount a_n and is 0 at 0. Then

$$\varphi(x) = \sum_{\log n < x} a_n.$$

Denoting by $\Phi(x)$ the function

$$\Phi(x) = \sum_{n<x} a_n,$$

we have $\varphi(x) = \Phi(e^x)$ or $\Phi(x) = \varphi(\log x)$. Our function $f(s)$ satisfies the condition of the Tauberian theorem for all λ, and hence

$$\lim_{x\to\infty} \Phi(x)/x = 1 \qquad \text{or} \qquad \Phi(x) \sim x.$$

We shall now see formally how to extend this to a wider class of Dirichlet series.

Theorem 1. *Let $f(s)$ be as above. Let $g(s) = \sum b_n/n^s$ be a Dirichlet series with complex coefficients b_n, and assume that there is a number C such that $|b_n| < Ca_n$. Assume that the series for $g(s)$ converges for $\mathrm{Re}(s) > 1$, and that g is regular on $\mathrm{Re}(s) = 1$ with the possible exception of a pole of first order and residue α at $s = 1$. Let $\Psi(x) = \sum_{n<x} b_n$. Then $\Psi(x) \sim \alpha x$.*

Proof. We naturally set $\alpha = 0$ if there is no pole at $s = 0$.

Suppose the b_n are real. Then the function $(Cf + g)/(C + \alpha)$ for large enough constant C satisfies the same conditions as $f(s)$. From this our assertion is immediate.

In case the b_n are complex, we write

$$g^*(s) = \sum \overline{b_n}/n^s$$

so that $g^*(\bar{s}) = \overline{g(s)}$, and

$$g = \tfrac{1}{2}(g + g^*) + \tfrac{1}{2}\,\frac{(g - g^*)}{i}.$$

Then one sees immediately that our theorem follows for $g(s)$.

For the prime number theorem, we need another asymptotic behavior, which we formulate in a proposition.

Proposition 1. *Let b_n $(n = 2, 3, \ldots)$ be complex numbers such that*

$$\Psi(N) = \sum_{n=2}^{N} b_n = \alpha N + o(N)$$

for some complex α. Then:

$$\pi(N) = \sum_{n=2}^{N} \frac{b_n}{\log n} = \alpha \frac{N}{\log N} + o\left(\frac{N}{\log N}\right).$$

Proof. We have $b_n = \Psi(n) - \Psi(n-1)$ for $n \geqq 2$, putting $\Psi(1) = 0$. Hence

$$\pi(N) = \sum_{n=2}^{N} \frac{\Psi(n) - \Psi(n-1)}{\log n} = \sum_{2}^{N} \frac{\Psi(n)}{\log n} - \sum_{1}^{N-1} \frac{\Psi(n)}{\log(n+1)}$$

$$= \frac{\Psi(N)}{\log N} + \sum_{n=2}^{N-1} \Psi(n)\left(\frac{1}{\log n} - \frac{1}{\log(n+1)}\right).$$

It will therefore suffice to show that the sum is $o\left(\frac{N}{\log N}\right)\cdot$ To estimate this sum, we can replace $\Psi(n)$ by Cn for some constant C. Furthermore,

$$\frac{1}{\log n} - \frac{1}{\log(n+1)} = \frac{\log\left(1 + \frac{1}{n}\right)}{\log(n)\log(n+1)} < \frac{1/n}{(\log n)^2}.$$

Thus it suffices to show

$$\sum_{2}^{N-1} \frac{1}{(\log n)^2} = o\left(\frac{N}{\log N}\right).$$

As for this, the sum can be split into two sums, with $2 \leqq n < N^{1/2}$ and $N^{1/2} \leqq n < N$. Thus our sum is bounded by

$$\frac{N^{1/2}}{(\log 2)^2} + \frac{N}{(\log N^{1/2})_2}$$

which is obviously $o\left(\frac{N}{\log N}\right)$. Our proposition is proved.

§4. *Non-vanishing of the L-series*

We let χ be a Hecke character. If $\mathfrak{p}$ is unramified for χ, then we recall that $\chi(\mathfrak{p})$ is the value $\chi(\pi)$ for any prime element π (viewed as idele with $\mathfrak{p}$-component equal to π and other components equal to 1). If $\mathfrak{p}$ is ramified for χ, then we let $\chi(\mathfrak{p}) = 0$. This is the same thing we have already encountered for instance in Chapter XII, §1, for characters of finite period.

We extend χ to ideals $\mathfrak{a}$ by multiplicativity, so that if

$$\mathfrak{a} = \prod_{\mathfrak{p}} \mathfrak{p}^{\nu_{\mathfrak{p}}},$$

then

$$\chi(\mathfrak{a}) = \prod \chi(\mathfrak{p})^{\nu_{\mathfrak{p}}}.$$

With every Hecke character χ, we associate its L-series

$$L(s, \chi) = \sum_{\mathfrak{a}} \frac{\chi(\mathfrak{a})}{\mathbf{N}\mathfrak{a}^s} = \prod_{\mathfrak{p}} \frac{1}{1 - \dfrac{\chi(\mathfrak{p})}{\mathbf{N}\mathfrak{p}^s}}.$$

The character taking the value 1 will be called the **trivial character** χ_0. Its L-series is then the zeta function $\zeta_k(s)$ of the field k. We have the usual logarithmic derivative

$$\frac{d}{ds} \log L(s, \chi) = \sum_{\mathfrak{p}, m} (\log \mathbf{N}\mathfrak{p})\chi(\mathfrak{p}^m)\mathbf{N}\mathfrak{p}^{-ms}$$

with the sum taken over all primes $\mathfrak{p}$ and $m \geqq 1$. The sum converges absolutely and uniformly for $\mathrm{Re}(s) \geqq 1 + \delta$. As with characters of finite period, we see that the contribution to a pole at 1 (if it exists at all) is all due to the sum taken only for $m = 1$.

Theorem 2. *Let χ be a Hecke character, $\chi \neq \chi_0$. Then*

$$L(1, \chi) \neq 0.$$

Proof. Assume that $L(1, \chi) = 0$. We have for s real > 1:

$$L(s, \chi) = \exp\left(\sum_{\mathfrak{p}, m} \frac{\chi(\mathfrak{p}^m)}{m\mathbf{N}\mathfrak{p}^{ms}}\right),$$

where $\exp(x) = e^x$. Consider the function

$$f(s) = L^3(s, \chi_0)L^4(s, \chi)L(s, \chi^2) = \exp\left(\sum_{\mathfrak{p}, m} \frac{3 + 4\chi(\mathfrak{p}^m) + \chi^2(\mathfrak{p}^m)}{m\mathbf{N}\mathfrak{p}^{ms}}\right).$$

Then

$$|f(s)| = \exp\left[\sum_{\mathfrak{p}, m} \frac{3 + 4\cos\theta + \cos 2\theta}{m\mathbf{N}\mathfrak{p}^{m\sigma}}\right],$$

where $\theta = \arg \chi(\mathfrak{p}^m)$. Since $3 + 4\cos\theta + \cos 2\theta \geqq 0$, we see that $|f(s)| \geqq 1$ for $\mathrm{Re}(s) > 1$. Assume that $\chi^2 \neq \chi_0$. Then if $L(1, \chi) = 0$, our function $f(s)$ must have a zero at $s = 1$. Its series represents the function for $\mathrm{Re}(s) > 1$, and since f is in particular continuous at $s = 1$, it follows that $f(s)$ must tend to 0 as s tends to 1. Contradiction.

If $\chi^2 = \chi_0$, consider

$$L(s, \chi_0)L(s, \chi) = \exp\left(\sum_{\mathfrak{p},m} \frac{1 + \chi(\mathfrak{p}^m)}{m\mathbf{N}\mathfrak{p}^{ms}}\right).$$

The term inside exp is a Dirichlet series with coefficients $\geqq 0$, which dominates the series

$$\sum_{\mathfrak{p},m} \frac{2}{2m\mathbf{N}\mathfrak{p}^{2ms}}$$

which diverges for $s = \frac{1}{2}$ (being the log of the zeta function). This contradicts the following Lemma on Dirichlet series with coefficients $\geqq 0$.

Lemma 1. *Let $f(s) = \sum a_n n^{-s}$ be a function defined by a Dirichlet series with a_n real $\geqq 0$, such that the series converges for* $\mathrm{Re}(s) > \sigma_0$. *Suppose that $f(s)$ is holomorphic at σ_0. Then the series converges for* $\mathrm{Re}(s) > \sigma_0 - \delta$ *for some $\delta > 0$ (and hence represents $f(s)$ in this bigger half-plane).*

Proof. Let δ be small > 0. We may assume $\sigma_0 = 0$ (after a translation). We have for $0 < \sigma < \delta$,

$$f(\sigma) = \sum_n a_n e^{-(\sigma-\delta)\log(n)} e^{-\delta\log(n)}.$$

We replace the exponents e^z by the series $\sum_\nu z^\nu/\nu!$. Since all coefficients are positive we can interchange $\sum_n \sum_\nu$ and we get the power series expansion for f in a neighborhood of δ, which converges for $\sigma = -2\delta$ if we took δ small enough. We can then unwind the power series back into the Dirichlet series, in the interval $-2\delta \leqq \sigma < \delta$, and this shows that the Dirichlet series converges for $\mathrm{Re}(s) \geqq -\delta$.

Theorem 3. *Let χ be a Hecke character which is non-trivial on J^0. Then $L(s, \chi)$ has no zero on the line $s = 1 + it$.*

Proof. This is essentially a corollary of Theorem 2, if we replace s by $s + it$, and χ by the character

$$a \mapsto \chi(a)\|a\|^{-it}.$$

§5. *Densities*

For each number $x > 0$ we denote by P_x the set of primes such that $\mathbf{N}\mathfrak{p} \leqq x$, and by A_x the set of integral ideals $\mathfrak{a}$ such that $\mathbf{N}\mathfrak{a} \leqq x$. If S is a finite set of primes, we denote by A_x^S those integral ideals $\mathfrak{a}$ which are prime to S and such that $\mathbf{N}\mathfrak{a} \leqq x$, and similarly for P_x^S.

As a special case of the Tauberian theorem, we get:

Theorem 4. *Let κ be the residue of the zeta function $\zeta_k(s)$ at 1. Let $n(A_x^S)$ and $n(P_x)$ be the number of elements in A_x^S and P_x respectively. Then these two numbers are asymptotic to*

$$n(A_x^S) \sim \kappa\beta x$$
$$n(P_x) \sim x/\log x,$$

where $\beta = \prod_{\mathfrak{p}\in S} (1 - 1/\mathbf{N}\mathfrak{p})$.

Indeed, the residue at 1 of the function obtained from the zeta function $\zeta_k(s)$ by omitting the factors involving the primes in S has residue $\alpha\beta$, whence the first assertion. As for the second, we apply the Tauberian theorem to the logarithmic derivative of the zeta function, of type

$$\sum_{\mathfrak{p},m} \frac{\log \mathbf{N}\mathfrak{p}}{\mathbf{N}\mathfrak{p}^{ms}}.$$

We split this sum as usual into two sums, one over all $\mathfrak{p}$, and $m = 1$, and the other sum with $m > 1$. This second sum gives no contribution to the residue at 1, and the first sum is

$$\sum_{\mathfrak{p}} \frac{\log \mathbf{N}\mathfrak{p}}{\mathbf{N}\mathfrak{p}^{s}}.$$

This is a Dirichlet series $\sum b_n/n^s$, where $b_n = 0$ if n is not a prime power. For each integer $n \geqq 2$, let $\mu(n)$ be the number of $\mathfrak{p}$ such that $\mathbf{N}\mathfrak{p} = n$. Then $b_n = \mu(n) \log n$. The residue of the logarithmic derivative of $\zeta_k(s)$ at $s = 1$ is equal to 1. By Theorem 1, we get

$$\sum_{n<x} b_n \sim x.$$

We now apply Proposition 1 to conclude the proof.

We now study the question of equidistribution of primes.

Let G be a compact commutative group. Let $F = \bigcup F_r$ be a set which is the union of finite subsets F_r, with $r = 1, 2, \ldots$ and $F_r \subset F_{r+1}$. Let

$\lambda: F \to G$ be a map. We shall say that F is **λ-equidistributed in** G if for every character χ of G we have

$$\lim_{r\to\infty} \frac{1}{n(F_r)} \sum_{\xi \in F_r} \chi \circ \lambda(\xi) = \int_G \chi.$$

Recall the trivial fact that $\int_G \chi = 1$ if $\chi = \chi_0$ and 0 if $\chi \neq \chi_0$.

We take for granted the fact that any continuous function on a compact group can be uniformly approximated by linear combinations of characters with complex coefficients.

Let us call a real function f on G Riemann integrable if there exist sequences of continuous real functions $\{g_n\}$, $\{h_n\}$ such that

$$g_n \leqq f \leqq h_n$$

and g_n, h_n converge to f monotonically increasing and decreasing respectively, and such that

$$\int_G (g_n - h_n)$$

tends to 0 as $n \to \infty$.

A complex function is called integrable if both its real and imaginary parts are Riemann integrable.

If F is λ-equidistributed on G and if f is any integrable function on G, then

$$\lim_{r\to\infty} \frac{1}{n(F_r)} \sum_{\xi \in F_r} f \circ \lambda(\xi) = \int_G f.$$

This follows at once by approximating f by continuous functions as above, and then approximating each continuous function uniformly by linear combinations of characters (use three epsilons). In practice, f is taken to be the characteristic function of suitable subsets of G. For instance, if G is finite, we take f to be the characteristic function of an element of G, so that $\int_G f = 1/n(G)$.

All desired theorems of equidistribution now follow from the following result.

Theorem 5. *Let χ be a Hecke character which is non-trivial on J^0, and S a finite set containing those primes where χ ramifies. Then*

$$\lim_{r\to\infty} \frac{1}{n(A_r^S)} \sum_{\mathfrak{a} \in A_r^S} \chi(\mathfrak{a}) = 0$$

$$\lim_{r\to\infty} \frac{1}{n(P_r^S)} \sum_{\mathfrak{p} \in P_r^S} \chi(\mathfrak{p}) = 0.$$

Proof. This is immediate, since we know that the L-series is holomorphic at 1, and does not vanish on the line $1 + it$. Thus the residue of both the L-series and its logarithmic derivative is 0, whence our results follow from Theorem 1, Proposition 1, Theorem 3, and the Tauberian theorem.

Let $J = J_k$ be the ideles of k. Let S be a finite set of primes containing the archimedean primes, and denote by J^S the subgroup of J consisting of those ideles having components which are units at the primes outside S, and 1 for the primes in S.

Thus

$$J^S = 1 \times \cdots \times 1 \times \prod_{\mathfrak{p} \notin S} U_{\mathfrak{p}}.$$

Care should be exercised to avoid confusing this with J_S, which consists of the ideles having arbitrary components in S, and units outside S. By continuity, any character of the idele classes will vanish on some J^S and on the multiplicative group k^* of k embedded in J. If G is a compact group, and $\lambda\colon J/k^*J^S \to G$ a continuous homomorphism, then for any character χ of G, the composite function $\chi \circ \lambda$ is a character of the idele classes, i.e. a Hecke character. The set of primes P^S not in S can be viewed as embedded in J/k^*J^S, as follows. Let π be an element of order 1 at a prime $\mathfrak{p} \notin S$. Then π is viewed as the idele having π as $\mathfrak{p}$-component, and 1 as component for all other primes. Modulo k^*J^S the coset of π does not depend on the choice of such element, and thus the map sending $\mathfrak{p}$ into this coset gives our embedding of P^S into J/k^*J^S. (We could also embed $\mathfrak{p}$ on the idele π^{-1}. This is in fact what we shall do in the subsequent examples, to fit the classical description relative to the archimedean primes.)

Let $\sigma\colon J_k \to G$ be a continuous homomorphism such that

$$\sigma(J_k^0) = G,$$

and whose kernel contains k^*. If ψ is a non-trivial character of G, then $\chi = \psi \circ \sigma$ is non-trivial on J_k^0, and hence we can apply our previous results, especially Theorem 3, and the Tauberian theorem, combined with the preceding discussion. Thus we obtain:

Theorem 6. *Let P be the set of primes. Let $\tau\colon P \to J_k$ be the following map. For each $\mathfrak{p}$, select a prime element $\pi_{\mathfrak{p}}$ in $k_{v_{\mathfrak{p}}}^*$ and let $\tau(\mathfrak{p})$ be the idele having component 1 at all v except $v_{\mathfrak{p}}$, at which it has component $\pi_{\mathfrak{p}}$. We view P as filtered by the sets P_r consisting of those $\mathfrak{p}$ such that $\mathbf{N}\mathfrak{p} \leqq r$. Let G be a compact commutative group, and let $\sigma\colon J_k \to G$ be a continuous homomorphism such that $\sigma(J_k^0) = G$, and whose kernel contains k^*. Let $\lambda = \sigma \circ \tau$. Then P is λ-equidistributed in G.*

Example 1. Let H be an open subgroup of J containing k^*, i.e. one of those subgroups which are class groups to class fields, and let

$$\lambda : J \to J/H$$

be the canonical isomorphism. Then we get the equidistribution of primes in our generalized ideal classes, which according to the Artin map of class field theory, is the same as the equidistribution of primes having elements of the Galois group as Artin symbols in the corresponding class field.

Example 2. Take $k = \mathbf{Q}(i)$, the Gaussian field. Let S consist of the archimedean absolute value. We have

$$J/k^*J^S \approx k_\infty^*/(\pm 1, \pm i),$$

where k_∞^* is the multiplicative group of complex numbers. We may then consider the ideals as points in the Gauss plane, in the first quadrant, and get equidistribution of ideals and primes in sectors, taking for λ the radial projection on the unit circle.

Example 3. (Suggested by Serre.) Let k be a number field of class number 1, so that

$$J = k^*J_S,$$

where S is the set of archimedean absolute values. Let U be the group of units of $\mathfrak{o}_k$, viewed as a subgroup of

$$k_\infty^* = \prod_{v \in S} k_v^*$$

(i.e. embedded on the diagonal). We have an injection

$$k_\infty^* \to J = k^*J_S$$

if we associate with each element of k_∞^* the idele having the same components in S, and component 1 outside S. We then obtain a canonical isomorphism

$$k_\infty^*/U \approx J/k^*J^S.$$

Let $\sigma : k_\infty^*/U \to$ circle be a continuous homomorphism whose restriction to the subgroup of k_∞^* consisting of all elements of norm 1 is surjective. Then Theorem 6 applies to this case, and one gets the equidistribution of $\sigma(\mathfrak{p})$, where $\sigma(\mathfrak{p}) = \sigma(\pi)$ for any generator π of $\mathfrak{p}$.

In particular, if k is a real quadratic field of class number 1, we may take an embedding $k \to \mathbf{R}$ of k into one of its (real) completions, giving rise to an absolute value denoted by $|\ |$, and $k_\infty^* = \mathbf{R}^* \times \mathbf{R}^*$. We let

$$\sigma(a, b) = |a|^{2\pi i/\log \epsilon},$$

where ϵ is a fundamental unit, and we obtain the equidistribution of the $\log \pi \pmod{\log \epsilon}$.

CHAPTER XVI

The Brauer-Siegel Theorem

Using the integrals expressing the zeta function, one can give certain estimates concerning its residue in order to derive asymptotic results relating the class number, regulator, and discriminant of a number field, and notably the following.

If k ranges over a sequence of number fields Galois over $\mathbf{Q}$, of degree N and absolute value of the discriminant d, such that $N/\log d$ tends to 0, then we have

$$\log(hR) \sim \log d^{1/2}.$$

One may of course ask whether it is possible to lift the restriction of normality, and the condition that $N/\log d$ tends to 0. With the present approach, these questions involve Artin's conjecture on the non-abelian L-series and the Riemann hypothesis (as will be clear in the proof). The existence of infinite unramified extensions proved by Golod-Shafarevic shows that the assumption $N/\log d \to 0$ is necessary. Indeed, if k is a number field admitting an infinite tower of unramified extensions K, then $N_K/\log d_K$ is constant.

We observe that the discriminant of the field $k = \mathbf{Q}(\zeta)$, where ζ is a p-th root of unity (p a prime), is $d_k = p^{p-2}$ and so our statement applies to such fields. Similarly for towers of p^r-th roots of unity.

The study of the behavior of $N/\log d$ is thus of considerable interest. We shall use the essentially elementary fact that for all number fields with

$$N > 1 \quad (\text{i.e. } k \neq \mathbf{Q})$$

the number $N/\log d$ is bounded. This follows at once from Minkowski's theorem that in every ideal class there exists an integral ideal $\mathfrak{a}$ such that

$$\mathbf{N}\mathfrak{a} \leqq C_N d^{1/2},$$

where C_N is the Minkowski constant. Taking the N-th root, a simple computation, using the fact that $1 \leqq \mathbf{N}\mathfrak{a}$, shows that there is an absolute constant C such that $N/\log d \leqq C$.

§1. *An upper estimate for the residue*

Lemma 1. *There exists an absolute constant* c_1 *such that the inequality*

$$\kappa(k) \leqq c_1^N (1+\alpha)^N d_k^{1/2\alpha} \qquad (N = [k : \mathbf{Q}])$$

holds for all number fields k *and all* $\alpha \geqq 1$.

Proof. According to Chapter XIV, Theorem 14, Corollary 3 and Theorem 15 together with the fact that the integrals expressing the zeta function are $\geqq 0$ for real s, we get for $s > 1$:

$$(2^{-2r_2}\pi^{-N}d_k)^{s/2}\Gamma^{r_1}\left(\frac{s}{2}\right)\Gamma^{r_2}(s)\zeta_k(s) \geqq \kappa\,\frac{d_k^{1/2}(2\pi)^{-r_2}}{s(s-1)}\,.$$

If we put $s = 1 + \alpha^{-1}$, then the gamma factors are uniformly bounded. We have obvious contributions of type c_1^N and $d_k^{1/2\alpha}$. From the product expansion for the zeta function we have the inequalities

$$\zeta_k\left(1+\frac{1}{\alpha}\right) \leqq \zeta_{\mathbf{Q}}\left(1+\frac{1}{\alpha}\right)^N \leqq (1+\alpha)^N.$$

The lemma follows at once.

Lemma 2. *There exists a constant* c_2 *such that for* $k \neq \mathbf{Q}$,

$$\log(hR)/\log(d^{1/2}) \leqq c_2.$$

If k *ranges over a sequence of fields such that* $N/\log d$ *tends to* 0, *then for this sequence*

$$\limsup\left[\left(\frac{\log hR}{\log d^{1/2}} - 1\right)\frac{1}{N}\right] \leqq 0.$$

Proof. We use the elementary estimate that the number of roots of unity w in a number field k is $\leqq c_3N^2$ for some absolute constant c_3. (Use the fact that the field of n-th roots of unity over $\mathbf{Q}$ has degree $\varphi(n)$, together with an obvious estimate of $\varphi(n)$, using $\varphi(p^r) = (p-1)p^{r-1}$ and the multiplicativity.)

From Lemma 1, and the value for κ, we get

$$\frac{\log hR}{\log d^{1/2}} - 1 \leqq \frac{N}{\log d^{1/2}}\log(c_1(1+\alpha)) + \frac{1}{\alpha} + \frac{N}{\log d^{1/2}}\log c_2.$$

Putting $\alpha = 1$ proves the first assertion. Fixing α, and taking our sequence of fields shows that for each α large, and all but a finite number of fields in our sequence, the difference on the left is $\leqq \alpha^{-1} + \epsilon$ with arbitrarily small ϵ. This proves our assertion.

§2. *A lower bound for the residue*

Lemma 3. *Let s_0 be real, $0 < s_0 < 1$, and assume that $\zeta(g_0, s_0) \leqq 0$ (or what is the same thing, that $\zeta_k(s_0) \leqq 0$). Then*

$$\kappa(k) \geqq s_0(1 - s_0)2^{-N}e^{-4\pi N}d_k^{(s_0-1)/2}.$$

Proof. By Theorem 15 of Chapter XIV, §8, we have

$$\frac{\kappa g_0(0)}{s_0(1 - s_0)} \geqq \int_{\|a\| \geqq 1} \hat{g}_0(a)\|a\|^{s_0}\, d^*a.$$

We shrink the domain of integration to a domain $P = \prod P_v$, where P_v is the set of units U_v for v non-archimedean, and for v archimedean, P_v is the domain

$$1 \leqq \|a_v d^{-1/2N}\|_v \leqq 2.$$

This lowers the value of the integral, and the integral over P is the product of the local integrals, which we now compute.

For v $\mathfrak{p}$-adic, we know that $g_{0,v} = d_{\mathfrak{p}}^{1/2}f_{0,v}$ and hence $\hat{g}_{0,v} = d_{\mathfrak{p}}^{1/2}\hat{f}_{0,v} = d_{\mathfrak{p}}$ times the characteristic function of $\mathfrak{o}_v$. Hence in this case, our local integral becomes

$$\int_{P_v} \hat{g}_{0,v}(a)\, d^*a = d_{\mathfrak{p}}^{1/2}.$$

For v archimedean, we use Proposition 9 of Chapter XIV, §8, to get $\hat{g}$ in terms of $\hat{f}$. Changing variables, setting $z = a_v d^{-1/2N}$, our integral over P_v becomes

$$\|d^{1/2N}\|_v^{(s_0-1)} \int \hat{f}_{0,v}(z)\, d^*z,$$

the range of integration being $1 \leqq \|z\|_v \leqq 2$. In this range, we replace $\hat{f}_{0,v}(z)$ by its lower bound, namely $e^{-4\pi}$ if v is real and $\dfrac{1}{2\pi}\,e^{-4\pi}$ if v is complex. The measure of the annulus between 1 and 2 is easily computed to be log 2 or 2π log 2 respectively, and thus finally we get the lower bound

$$\|d^{1/2N}\|_v^{(s_0-1)}e^{-4\pi}\log 2$$

for v archimedean. Taking the product yields

$$\kappa d^{1/2}(2\pi)^{-r_2} \geqq s_0(1 - s_0)\, d^{1/2}d^{(s_0-1)/2}e^{-4\pi N}\,(\log 2)^N$$

using N instead of $r_1 + r_2$. The estimate of the lemma is a weakening of the estimate we have just obtained.

Our goal is to prove the following theorem.

Theorem 1. *Let* $\epsilon > 0$. *There exists a number* $c_4(\epsilon)$ *such that for all fields* k *normal over* $\mathbf{Q}$, *the inequality holds:*

$$\kappa(k) \geqq c_4(\epsilon)^{-N} d_k^{-\epsilon}.$$

Proof. If we had the Riemann hypothesis, we could dispense with our hypothesis that k is normal over $\mathbf{Q}$. Indeed, our arguments are split into two cases.

Case 1. For all normal fields k the function $\zeta_k(s)$ does not vanish for real s with $1 - \epsilon/N < s < 1$.

Then from the integral representation, we know that the zeta function takes on negative values for s close to 1 and to the left of 1. Consequently, under our present case, $\zeta_k(1 - \epsilon/N) \leqq 0$ and putting $s_0 = 1 - \epsilon/N$ in Lemma 3 gives us what we want. The argument works if k is not normal.

Case 2. There exists a field k_0 normal over $\mathbf{Q}$ of degree N_0, such that $\zeta_{k_0}(s_0) = 0$ for some real s_0 with $1 - \epsilon/N_0 < s_0 < 1$.

In order to treat this case, it will be necessary to take a detour through L-series, and we shall prove in the next section:

Theorem 2. *There exists a constant* c_5 *such that for all number fields* k *and normal extensions* K *of* k, *the following inequality holds:*

$$\kappa(K)/\kappa(k) \leqq c_5^{N_K - N_k}(1 + \alpha)^{N_K - N_k}(d_K/d_k)^{1/2\alpha}$$

for all $\alpha \geqq 1$.

Let us assume this theorem for the time being. We use the following fundamental lemma of Brauer's which will be proved in an appendix.

Lemma. *Let* G *be a finite group, and* χ_{reg} *the character of the regular representation. Then there exist cyclic subgroups* $H_j \neq 1$, *positive rational numbers* λ_j, *and one-dimensional characters* $\psi_j \neq 1$ *of* H_j *such that*

$$\chi_{\text{reg}} = \chi_0 + \sum \lambda_j \psi_j^*$$

(*where the* * *means induced character*).

We shall use the lemma several times, and to begin with, we use it to note that if K is normal over k, and $\zeta_k(s_0) = 0$ for some s_0, then $\zeta_K(s_0) = 0$ also. (This is an open question in the non-normal case. Its answer would of course be implied by Artin's conjectures.) We use Artin's formalism:

$$\zeta_K(s) = \zeta_k(s) \prod L(s, \psi_j^*, K/k)^{\lambda_j}$$

and the fact that the L-series are abelian L-series of the type discussed in Chapters XII and XIV.

We treat Case 2 as follows. We may consider s_0, the special value of s between $1 - \epsilon/N_0$ and 1, and the discriminant of k_0 as depending only on ϵ. Given a field k normal over $\mathbf{Q}$, let $K = kk_0$. Then K is normal over k_0 and we can use the preceding remark: $\zeta_K(s_0) = 0$.

By Lemma 3, we get

$$\kappa(K) \geqq s_0(1 - s_0)2^{-N_K}e^{2\pi N_K}d_K^{-(1-s_0)/2}.$$

An elementary estimate gives

$$N_K \leqq N_0 N_k \quad \text{and} \quad d_K \leqq d_k^{N_0} d_0^{N_k},$$

whence

$$d_K^{-(1-s_0)/2} \geqq d_K^{-\epsilon/2N_0} \geqq d_k^{-\epsilon/2} d_0^{-\epsilon N_k/2N_0},$$

and we get

$$\kappa(K) \geqq c_5(\epsilon)^{-N_k} d_k^{-\epsilon/2}.$$

By Theorem 2 which compares residues in k and K, choosing $\alpha = N_0/\epsilon$ we obtain an inequality

$$\kappa(k) \geqq \kappa(K) c_8(\epsilon)^{-N_k} d_k^{-\epsilon/2},$$

so that Theorem 1 follows from our last two inequalities.

§3. *Comparison of residues in normal extensions*

Our purpose is now to prove Theorem 2. For this, we use again Brauer's lemma on group representations, and the decomposition of the zeta function:

$$\zeta_K(s) = \zeta_k(s) \prod L(s, \psi_j^*, K_j/k)^{\lambda_j}.$$

Each L-series is equal to $L(s, \psi_j)$, where ψ_j is a character $\neq 1$ of the idele class group of K_j. We have

$$\kappa(K)/\kappa(k) = \prod L(1, \psi_j)^{\lambda_j},$$

the factors on the right being finite, since each ψ_j is different from the trivial character.

We need an upper estimate for each factor $|L(1, \psi_j)|$. We note that the ψ_j are characters of finite period.

We have:

Lemma 4. *Let k be a number field, $\psi \neq 1$ a character of finite period of C_k, and $\alpha \geqq 1$. Then*

$$|L(1, \psi)| \leqq c_6^N (1 + \alpha)^N d_\psi^{1/2\alpha}.$$

Proof. We have, with the same notation as Chapter XIV, §8,

$$\zeta(g_\psi, \psi, 1) = \int_{\|a\| \geqq 1} g_\psi(a)\psi(a)\|a\| \, d^*a + \int_{\|a\| \geqq 1} \hat{g}_\psi(a)\bar{\psi}(a) \, d^*a.$$

A direct computation shows that $|\hat{g}_\psi| \leqq |g_\psi|$. Hence we get the upper bound:

$$|\zeta(g_\psi, \psi, 1)| \leqq 2\int_{\|a\| \geqq 1} |g_\psi(a)| \, \|a\|^s \, d^*a \qquad (s > 1)$$

$$\leqq 2\zeta(|g_\psi|, \chi_0, s) \qquad (s > 1).$$

Our character is unramified at complex v. Let ν be the number of ramified real v, and $\mu = r_1 - \nu$. We let

$$\Gamma(s, \psi) = \Gamma\left(\frac{s+1}{2}\right)^\nu \Gamma\left(\frac{s}{2}\right)^\mu \Gamma(s)^{r_2}.$$

Then evaluating local integrals in an easy way, we get from the expression of the zeta function in terms of local factors the inequality:

$$d_\psi^{1/2} 2^{-r_2} \pi^{-N/2} \Gamma(1, \psi)|L(1, \psi)| \leqq 2(d_\psi^{1/2} 2^{-r_2} \pi^{-N/2})^s \Gamma(s, \psi)\zeta_k(s)$$

for $s > 1$. If we put $s = 1 + \alpha^{-1}$ and use the same trivial estimate as in §1 for the zeta function we get our lemma.

Let us put

$$N_j = [K_j : \mathbf{Q}].$$

We apply Lemma 4 to the field K_j and characters ψ_j. We get:

$$\kappa(K)/\kappa(k) \leqq \prod c_6^{N_j\lambda_j}(1 + \alpha)^{N_j\lambda_j} d_{\psi_j}^{\lambda_j/2\alpha}.$$

We use the relation

$$N_K = N_k + \sum N_j\lambda_j$$

obtained by evaluating the character of the regular representation of $G(K/k)$ at 1 and multiplying by $[k : \mathbf{Q}]$. From it and Artin's conductor-discriminant formula (cf. [3]) one gets at once:

$$d_K = d_k \prod d_{\psi_j}^{\lambda_j}.$$

(Compute with the different instead of the discriminant, because the different is multiplicative in towers.) In view of these decompositions of the degree and the discriminant, our estimate for the quotient of the residues follows trivially.

For the convenience of the reader, let us give the proof of the decomposition of the discriminant. According to Artin's formula, we have

$$D_{K/k} = N_{K/k}(\mathfrak{D}_{K/k}) = \prod N_{K_j/k}(\mathfrak{D}_{K_j/k}\mathfrak{f}_{\psi_j})^{\lambda_j}.$$

We multiply both sides by

$$N_{K/k}(\mathfrak{D}_{k/\mathbf{Q}}) = \mathfrak{D}_{k/\mathbf{Q}}^{[K:k]}$$

and use our relation for the degrees. This yields

$$N_{K/k}(\mathfrak{D}_{K/\mathbf{Q}}) = \mathfrak{D}_{k/\mathbf{Q}}\prod N_{K_j/k}(\mathfrak{D}_{K_j/\mathbf{Q}}\mathfrak{f}_{\psi_j})^{\lambda_j}.$$

If we now take $N_{k/\mathbf{Q}}$ of both sides, we get what we want.

§4. *End of the proofs*

From the lower bound of the residue obtained in §2, we get an inequality of type

$$\log (hR) - \log d_k^{1/2} \geqq -Nc_7(\epsilon) - 2\epsilon \log d_k^{1/2}.$$

We had noted that $N/\log d$ is bounded for all number fields $\neq \mathbf{Q}$. This allows us to complement our first assertion in Lemma 2:

Theorem 3. *There exists a constant c_8 such that for all fields k normal over $\mathbf{Q}$, we have*

$$|\log(hR)| \geqq c_8 \log d^{1/2}.$$

Furthermore, if k ranges over a sequence of fields normal over $\mathbf{Q}$ for which $N/\log d$ tends to 0, then the above inequality implies that

$$\liminf\,[\log(hR)/\log d^{1/2}] \geqq 1 - 2\epsilon.$$

Combined with our preceding results (Lemma 2) we get:

Theorem 4. *If k ranges over a sequence of fields normal over $\mathbf{Q}$ for which $N/\log d$ tends to 0, then*

$$\log(Rh) \sim \log d^{1/2}.$$

It is a simple exercise to estimate the discriminant of the smallest normal extension k' containing a given number field k over $\mathbf{Q}$. One finds that

$$d_{k'} \leqq d_k^{N'/2},$$

where $N' = [k' : \mathbf{Q}]$. If we apply Theorem 2 to k' and k, and take $\alpha = \frac{1}{2}\epsilon$

with $\epsilon < \frac{1}{2}$, we find the inequality

$$\kappa(k) \geqq \kappa(k')c_9(\epsilon)^{-N'}d_{k'}^{-\epsilon}.$$

On the other hand, if we apply Theorem 1 to k', we get

$$\kappa(k') \geqq c_4(\epsilon)^{-N'}d_{k'}^{-\epsilon}$$

so that finally,

$$Rh/d^{1/2} \geqq c_{10}(\epsilon)^{-N'}d_{k'}^{-2\epsilon},$$

and

$$\log(Rh) - \log d^{1/2} \geqq -N'c_{10}(\epsilon) - 2\epsilon \log d_{k'}.$$

Using the estimate of d_k in terms of d_k stated above, we get finally:

$$\left[\frac{\log(Rh)}{\log d^{1/2}} - 1\right]\frac{1}{N'} \geqq -\frac{c_{10}(\epsilon)}{\log d^{1/2}} - 2\epsilon.$$

There is only a finite number of number fields with bounded discriminant. The left-hand side of our inequality is bounded below and does not possess any negative limit point, if we let k range over all number fields $\neq \mathbf{Q}$. From Lemma 2, we get our main result:

Theorem 5. *If k ranges over all number fields $\neq \mathbf{Q}$ and N' is the degree over $\mathbf{Q}$ of the smallest normal field k' over $\mathbf{Q}$ containing k, then the set of values*

$$\left[\frac{\log(Rh)}{\log d^{1/2}} - 1\right]\frac{1}{N'}$$

is bounded, and possesses 0 as its only limit point.

Corollary. *If k ranges over number fields of fixed degree N over $\mathbf{Q}$, then we have the asymptotic relation*

$$\log(hR) \sim \log d^{1/2}$$

for $d \to \infty$.

Proof. Immediate, taking into account that $N' \leqq N!$.

Appendix: Brauer's lemma

In this appendix, we prove the lemma on group characters which has been used several times in the chapter. I am indebted to Serre for the exposition (derived from Brauer's).

Let G be a finite group. We denote by 1_G the trivial character, by r_G the character of the regular representation, and we let $u_G = r_G - 1_G$. If H is a subgroup of G and ψ a character of H, we let ψ^* be the induced character.

If A is a cyclic group of order a, we define the function θ_A on A by the conditions:

$$\theta_A(\sigma) = \begin{cases} a & \text{if } \sigma \text{ is a generator of } A \\ 0 & \text{otherwise.} \end{cases}$$

We let $\lambda_A = \varphi(a)r_A - \theta_A$ (where φ is the Euler function), and $\lambda_A = 0$ if $a = 1$.

The desired result is contained in the following two propositions.

Proposition 1. *Let G be a finite group of order g. Then*

$$u_G = \frac{1}{g} \sum \lambda_A^*,$$

the sum being taken over all cyclic subgroups of G.

Proof. Given two functions χ, ψ on G, we have the usual scalar product:

$$\langle \psi, \chi \rangle_G = \frac{1}{g} \sum_{\sigma \in G} \psi(\sigma)\overline{\chi(\sigma)}.$$

Let ψ be any function on G. Then:

$$\begin{aligned} \langle \psi, gu_G \rangle &= \langle \psi, gr_G \rangle - \langle \psi, g1_G \rangle \\ &= g\psi(1) - \sum_{\sigma \in G} \psi(\sigma). \end{aligned}$$

On the other hand, using the standard fact that the induced character is the transpose of the restriction, we obtain

$$\begin{aligned} \sum_A \langle \psi, \lambda_A^* \rangle &= \sum_A \langle \psi \mid A, \lambda_A \rangle \\ &= \sum_A \langle \psi \mid A, \varphi(a)r_A - \theta_A \rangle \\ &= \sum_A \varphi(a)\psi(1) - \sum_A \frac{1}{a} \sum_{\sigma \text{ gen } A} a\psi(\sigma) \\ &= g\psi(1) - \sum_{\sigma \in G} \psi(\sigma). \end{aligned}$$

Since the functions on the right and left of the equality sign in the statement of our proposition have the same scalar product with an arbitrary function, they are equal. This proves our proposition.

Proposition 2. *If $A \neq \{1\}$, the function λ_A is a linear combination of irreducible non-trivial characters of A with positive integral coefficients.*

Proof. If A is cyclic of prime order, then by Proposition 1, we know that $\lambda_A = gu_A$, and our assertion follows from the standard structure of the regular representation.

In order to prove the assertion in general, it suffices to prove that the Fourier coefficients of λ_A with respect to a character of degree 1 are integers $\geqq 0$. Let ψ be a character of degree 1. We take the scalar product with respect to A, and obtain:

$$\begin{aligned}\langle \psi, \lambda_A \rangle &= \varphi(a)\psi(1) - \sum_{\sigma \text{ gen}} \psi(\sigma) \\ &= \varphi(a) - \sum_{\sigma \text{ gen}} \psi(\sigma) \\ &= \sum_{\sigma \text{ gen}} (1 - \psi(\sigma)).\end{aligned}$$

The sum $\sum \psi(\sigma)$ taken over generators of A is an algebraic integer, and is in fact a rational number (for any number of elementary reasons), hence a rational integer. Furthermore, if ψ is non-trivial, all real parts of

$$1 - \psi(\sigma)$$

are > 0 if $\sigma \neq id$ and are 0 if $\sigma = id$. From the last two inequalities, we conclude that the sums must be equal to a positive integer. If ψ is the trivial character, then the sum is clearly 0. Our proposition is proved.

CHAPTER XVII

Explicit Formulas

We shall follow the paper of Weil [14]. One should note that the logical structure of the proofs is extremely simple. We use only the following facts, whose proofs come from arithmetic:

$|L(s)|$ is bounded in every half-plane $\mathrm{Re}(s) \geqq 1 + a$, $a > 0$.

The functional equation of $\Lambda(s)$.

The fact that $\Lambda(s)$ is bounded in every strip $\sigma_0 \leqq \sigma \leqq \sigma_1$ (excluding a neighborhood of its poles). This comes from the usual integral expressions.

The rest of the arguments are analytical. In particular, we use repeatedly Stirling's formula giving the asymptotic behavior of the gamma function. It should be noted that the analysis involves the evaluation of a few Fourier transforms, and definite integrals. The main result consists in showing that the sum of a certain function extended to the prime powers is essentially equal to a sum of its Mellin transform extended to the zeros of the zeta function. The precise statement is given in §3. One part of the proof depends in a rather technical manner on the Fourier transform of a distribution, and I am much indebted to Schwartz for the arguments involved in the proof of Proposition 4, §5. (Weil's paper at this point becomes much too sketchy to be followed.)

The reader who wishes some exercises can extend the theorems of A. E. Ingham, *The distribution of prime numbers*, Cambridge Tract No. 30, 1932, to the L-series associated with an arbitrary Hecke character.

§1. *Weierstrass factorization of the L-series*

Throughout this chapter we use the results of Chapter XIV, §8. If k is a number field, χ a character of the idele classes, and $d_\chi = \mathbf{N}(\mathfrak{D}\mathfrak{f}_\chi)$, we put $A = 2^{-r_2}\pi^{-(N/2)}d_\chi^{1/2}$ and

$$G_0(s, \chi) = A^s = G_0(s, \bar{\chi})$$
$$G_v(s, \chi) = \Gamma(s_v/2) \qquad (v \text{ archimedean}),$$

where $s_v = s_v(\chi) = \frac{1}{2}(\mathrm{N}_v(s + i\varphi_v) + |m_v|)$, and

$$L(s, \chi) = \text{usual product over } \mathfrak{p} \text{ unramified for } \chi.$$

Then we set

$$\Lambda(s, \chi) = G_0(s, \chi)\prod G_v(s, \chi)L(s, \chi) = \Lambda(s)$$

and we have the functional equation

$$W(\chi)\Lambda(s, \chi) = \Lambda(1 - s, \bar{\chi}),$$

or also

$$\Lambda(\bar{s}) = \overline{\Lambda(1 - s)}u(\chi),$$

where $W(\chi)$ and $u(\chi)$ have absolute value 1.

As usual, δ_χ is 1 if $\chi = \chi_0$ and 0 otherwise.

We wish to prove that

$$[s(s - 1)]^{\delta_\chi}\Lambda(s)$$

is an entire function of order 1, and hence by a general and standard theorem in complex variables that we have

$$\Lambda(s) = ae^{bs}[s(s - 1)]^{-\delta_\chi} \prod_\omega \left(1 - \frac{s}{\omega}\right) e^{s/\omega},$$

where ω ranges over the zeros of $\Lambda(s)$, with their multiplicities, and a, b are constants.

We shall need to estimate Gamma factors, and for this use the Stirling formula

$$\log \Gamma(s) = (s - \tfrac{1}{2}) \log s - s + \tfrac{1}{2} \log 2\pi + \int_0^\infty \frac{P_1(x)}{s + x}\, dx,$$

where

$$P_1(x) = [x] - x + \tfrac{1}{2}$$

is the saw-tooth function. The remainder term is therefore $O(1/|s|)$ uniformly in each region

$$-\pi + \delta \leqq \arg s \leqq \pi - \delta, \qquad \delta > 0.$$

For a fixed complex number a, we obtain

$$\log \Gamma(s + a) = (s + a - \tfrac{1}{2}) \log s - s + \tfrac{1}{2} \log 2\pi + O(1/|s|)$$

uniformly in the above region.

In particular, if a is real, and if we set $r = |s|$ and $\theta = \arg s$, then

$$|\Gamma(s + a)| = r^{\sigma+a-1/2}e^{-t\theta}e^{-\sigma}(2\pi)^{1/2}e^{O(1/r)}$$

uniformly in the above-mentioned region, and if a, φ are real then

$$|\Gamma(s + a + i\varphi)| = r^{\sigma+a-1/2}e^{-t\theta-\varphi\theta}e^{-\sigma}(2\pi)^{1/2}e^{O(1/r)}.$$

Letting $G(s)$ be the product of the G_v, G_0, i.e. essentially a product of Gamma factors, we see immediately that $|G(s)|$ is $O(e^{|s|^{1+\epsilon}})$ for every $\epsilon > 0$ in the half-plane $\sigma \geqq 1$. Furthermore, for every real $a > 0$, we know from the product expansion that $L(s)$ is bounded in the half-plane $\sigma \geqq 1 + a$. Hence $\Lambda(s)$ is $O(e^{|s|^{1+\epsilon}})$ in this half-plane.

By the functional equation, we get the same estimate in the half-plane $\sigma \leqq -a$.

On the other hand, the expression of $\Lambda(s)$ as a sum of two integrals converging for all s plus a term involving $s(s - 1)$ shows that $\Lambda(s)$ is bounded in every strip $\sigma_0 \leqq \sigma \leqq \sigma_1$, excluding a neighborhood of the poles $s = 0, 1$ if these occur, i.e. if $\chi = \chi_0$. We have therefore shown that our estimate in fact holds for all s, excluding such a neighborhood, and have thus proved that our function is of order 1.

§2. *An estimate for* Λ'/Λ

We recall two lemmas from complex variables.

Lemma 1. *Let $f(s)$ be holomorphic in the upper part of a strip: $\sigma_0 \leqq \sigma \leqq \sigma_1$, and $t \geqq t_1 > 0$. Assume that $f(s)$ is $O(e^{t^c})$ for some constant $c > 0$, and $t \to \infty$ in this strip, and that $|f(s)|$ is $O(t^M)$ for some positve integer M, on the sides of the strip $\sigma = \sigma_0$ and $\sigma = \sigma_1$. Then $f(s)$ is $O(t^M)$ in the strip.*

This is nothing but the Phragmen-Lindelöf Theorem, proved in Chapter XIII, §5.

Lemma 2. *Suppose $f(z)$ is holomorphic in a circle $|z - z_0| \leqq R$, and has at least n zeros in the circle $|z - z_0| \leqq r < R$ (counting multiplicities). Assume $f(z_0) \neq 0$. Then*

$$[(R - r)/r]^n \leqq B/|f(z_0)|,$$

where B is the maximum of $|f(z)|$ on the larger circle.

Proof. We may assume $z_0 = 0$. Let

$$f(z) = \prod_{i=1}^{n} (z - a_i)\varphi(z),$$

where a_i are the zeros of f in the small circle. Then obviously on the large circle, we have

$$|\varphi(z)| \leqq |f(z)|/(R - r)^n \leqq B/(R - r)^n.$$

Since $|a_i| \leqq r$ for each i, we get our inequality by looking at $\varphi(0)$.

We return to our L-series. Put

$$L_1(s) = s(s - 1)L(s).$$

Consider a strip $\sigma_0 < 0 < 1 < \sigma_1$. *We contend that there exists an integer M such that $L_1(s)$ is $O(|t|^M)$ in this strip.*

To prove this, note that

$$|L_1(s)| = |s(s - 1)L(s)| = |s(s - 1)G(s)^{-1}G(1 - \bar{s})L(1 - \bar{s})|$$

by the functional equation. Inside our strip, the function $\Lambda(s)$ is bounded because of its expression as an integral. Hence by the asymptotic formula for gamma functions, we see that $L_1(s)$ is $O(e^{c|t|})$ for some constant c, inside our strip. On $\sigma = \sigma_1$, we know that $L(s)$ is bounded by its expression as a product, and thus $L(1 - \bar{s})$ is bounded on $\sigma = \sigma_0$. On the other hand for two complex numbers a, b we see from §1 that $|\Gamma(s + a)/\Gamma(b - \bar{s})|$ is $O(|t|^M)$ (for some M depending on a, b) inside our strip. (The point is that the terms $e^{-t\theta}$ cancel.) Hence $L_1(s)$ is $O(|t|^M)$ on the lines $\sigma = \sigma_0$ and $\sigma = \sigma_1$ for sufficiently large M. We now get our contention from Lemma 1.

Applying Lemma 2 to a pair of circles centered at $1 + a + it$ with fixed $a > 0$ and constant radius, we get:

Proposition 1. *The number of zeros of $\Lambda(s)$ (equal to the number of zeros of $L(s)$) in a box $0 \leqq \sigma \leqq 1$ and $T \leqq |t| \leqq T + 1$ is O ($\log T$).*

Corollary. *There is a number α, and for each integer m with $|m| \geqq 2$ there is a number T_m in the interval*

$$m < T_m < m + 1$$

such that $\Lambda(s)$ has no zero in the (horizontal) strip

$$|t - T_m| \leqq \frac{\alpha}{\log |m|}.$$

Returning to our Weierstrass product, we take its log derivative. For any s, s_0, we have

$$\Lambda'/\Lambda(s) - \Lambda'/\Lambda(s_0)$$
$$= \sum_{\omega} \left(\frac{1}{s-\omega} - \frac{1}{s_0 - \omega} \right) - \delta_\chi \left(\frac{1}{s} + \frac{1}{s-1} - \frac{1}{s_0} - \frac{1}{s_0 - 1} \right).$$

Proposition 2. *Let $0 < a \leqq 1$, and m an integer with $|m| \geqq 2$. Let $s = \sigma + iT_m$ with $-a \leqq \sigma \leqq 1 + a$ and T_m as above. Then*

$$|\Lambda'/\Lambda(s)| \leqq B(\log |m|)^2,$$

where B is a number depending on a but not on m and σ.

Proof. Let us take $s_0 = 1 + a + iT_m$ and write

$$\omega = \beta + i\gamma.$$

We have

$$|\Lambda'/\Lambda(s) - \Lambda'/\Lambda(s_0)| \leqq \sum_{\omega} \left| \frac{s_0 - s}{(s-\omega)(s_0 - \omega)} \right| + B_1,$$

where B_1 is a uniform bound clearly valid for the terms to the right of δ_χ.
For the sum, we get the inequality

$$\sum_{\omega} \left| \frac{s_0 - s}{(s-\omega)(s_0-\omega)} \right| \leqq (a + 1 - \sigma) \sum_{\omega} \frac{1}{|(s-\omega)(s_0-\omega)|}.$$

Under our hypotheses, we have

$$|s_0 - \omega|^2 = (1 + a - \beta)^2 + (T_m - \gamma)^2 \geqq a^2 + (T_m - \gamma)^2.$$

On the other hand, putting $b = a/\log |m|$ (which we may assume $\leqq 1$),

$$\begin{aligned} |s - \omega|^2 \geqq (T_m - \gamma)^2 &\geqq \tfrac{1}{2}(T_m - \gamma)^2 + \tfrac{1}{2}b^2 \\ &\geqq \tfrac{1}{2}b^2[a^2 + (T_m - \gamma)^2], \end{aligned}$$

since $0 < a \leqq 1$. From this we get

$$|\Lambda'/\Lambda(s) - \Lambda'/\Lambda(s_0)| \leqq B_1 + \frac{2(a + 1 - \sigma)}{b} \sum_{\omega} \frac{1}{a^2 + (T_m - \gamma)^2}.$$

We also have

$$\sum_{\omega} \frac{1}{a^2 + (T_m - \gamma)^2} \leqq \frac{(a+1)^2}{a^2} \sum_{\omega} \frac{1}{(a+1)^2 + (T_m - \gamma)^2}.$$

We shall compare this expression with $\mathrm{Re}(\Lambda'/\Lambda(s_0))$ which is itself $\leqq |\Lambda'/\Lambda(s_0)|$.

We have

$$\Lambda'/\Lambda(s_0) = b + \sum_{\omega}\left[\frac{1}{s_0 - \omega} + \frac{1}{\omega}\right] - \delta_\chi\left(\frac{1}{s_0} + \frac{1}{s_0 - 1}\right).$$

The real part of the middle sum over ω is equal to

$$\sum_{\omega}\left[\frac{1 + a - \beta}{(1 + a - \beta)^2 + (T_m - \gamma)^2} + \frac{\beta}{\beta^2 + \gamma^2}\right]$$

which is itself

$$\geqq \sum_{\omega} \frac{a}{(1 + a)^2 + (T_m - \gamma)^2}.$$

From this our proposition is now immediate, taking into account the following proposition.

Proposition 3. *Let a be a number > 0. Then $L'/L(s)$ is bounded for* $\mathrm{Re}(s) = 1 + a$, *and*

$$\Gamma'/\Gamma(s) = \log s + O(1/|s|^2)$$

for $\mathrm{Re}(s) = 1 + a$ *and* $|s| \to \infty$.

Proof. The first assertion follows at once from the product expansion of L, and the second follows from Stirling's formula (differentiating inside the integral giving the error term).

§3. *The basic sum*

Let $F(x)$ be a complex valued function on the real line, and assume that there exists $a' > 0$ such that

$$F(x)e^{(1/2+a')|x|}$$

is in L^1. Then its Mellin transform

$$\Phi(s) = \int_{-\infty}^{+\infty} F(x)e^{(s-1/2)x}\,dx$$

is holomorphic in every strip $-a \leqq \sigma \leqq 1 + a$ for $0 < a < a'$. We shall assume in addition, to begin with, that $\Phi(s)$ is $o(1/(\log|t|)^2)$ uniformly in $-a \leqq \sigma \leqq 1 + a$. (These conditions will be strengthened later.)

Let us take $T > 2$. The number of zeros of $\Lambda(s)$ whose imaginary part is between T and the nearest T_m of the preceding section is $O(\log T)$, and similarly for $-T$ and the nearest T_l. The sum $\sum\Phi(\omega)$ over these zeros tends to 0 as T tends to infinity.

We shall consider the integral of $\Phi(s)d\log\Lambda(s)$ over the rectangle bounded by the lines $\sigma = -a$, $\sigma = 1 + a$, $t = T_m$, $t = T_l$. By Proposition 2, the integral taken over the horizontal lines tends to 0 as T tends to infinity, by our assumption on Φ. If we denote by $o(1)$ the additive group of functions of T tending to 0 with $1/T$, then by the formula of residues, we get the following congruences mod $o(1)$:

$$-\delta_\chi[\Phi(0) + \Phi(1)] + \sum_{-T<\gamma<T} \Phi(\omega)$$

$$\equiv \frac{1}{2\pi i}\int_{\mathrm{Rec}} \Phi(s)d\log\Lambda(s)$$

$$\equiv \frac{1}{2\pi i}\int_{1+a+iT_l}^{1+a+iT_m} \Phi(s)d\log\Lambda(s) - \frac{1}{2\pi i}\int_{-a+iT_l}^{-a+iT_m} \Phi(s)d\log\Lambda(s)$$

$$\equiv \frac{1}{2\pi i}\int_{1+a+iT_l}^{1+a+iT_m} \Phi(s)d\log\Lambda(s) - \frac{1}{2\pi i}\int_{-a+iT_l}^{-a+iT_m} \Phi(s)d\log\Lambda(1-s, \chi^{-1})$$

$$\equiv \frac{1}{2\pi i}\int_{1+a-iT}^{1+a+iT} \Phi(s)d\log\Lambda(s) + \frac{1}{2\pi i}\int_{-a+iT}^{-a-iT} \Phi(s)d\log\Lambda(1-s, \chi^{-1}).$$

In this last step, we use the estimate of Proposition 3 to insure that the integrals taken between T_m, T and T_l, $-T$ tend to 0 as T tends to infinity.

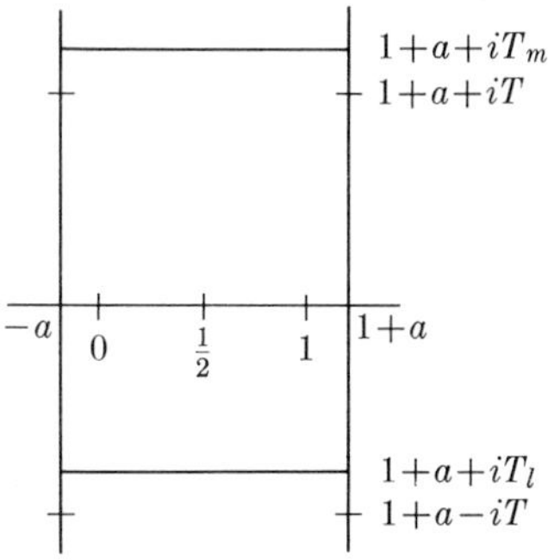

Figure 1

In order to evaluate these integrals, we shall use the product decomposition of Λ to get three types of integrals, involving the terms G_0, G_v, and L. Furthermore, we shall assume that our function F satisfies the additional conditions:

(A) F is continuous and continuously differentiable everywhere except at a finite number of points α_i, where $F(x)$ and its derivative $F'(x)$

have only a discontinuity of first kind, and such that

$$F(\alpha_i) = \tfrac{1}{2}[F(\alpha_i + 0) + F(\alpha_i - 0)].$$

(B) There is a number $b > 0$ such that $F(x)$ and $F'(x)$ are $O(e^{-(1/2+b)|x|})$ for $|x| \to \infty$.

Under these hypotheses, we see that for $0 < a' < b$ our function Φ is $O(|t|^{-1})$ uniformly in $-a' \leqq \sigma \leqq 1 + a'$ and the preceding discussion applies for $0 < a < a' < b$ and $a \leqq 1$.

The integrals on the line $1 + a$ and $-a$ will be reduced to integrals on the line $\frac{1}{2}$. Our final result will be:

Explicit formula. *Let $F(x)$ satisfy conditions* (A) *and* (B), *and let Φ be its Mellin transform. The sum $\sum\Phi(\omega)$ taken over the zeros $\omega = \beta + i\gamma$ of $L(s)$ satisfying $0 \leqq \beta \leqq 1$ and $|\gamma| < T$ tends to a limit as T tends to infinity, and this limit is*

$$\lim_{T\to\infty} \sum_{|\gamma|<T} \Phi(\omega) = \delta_\chi \int_{-\infty}^{\infty} F(x)(e^{x/2} + e^{-x/2})\,dx + 2F(0)\log A$$

$$- \sum_{\mathfrak{p},n} \frac{\log \mathbf{N}\mathfrak{p}}{\mathbf{N}\mathfrak{p}^{n/2}} [\chi(\mathfrak{p})^n F(\log \mathbf{N}\mathfrak{p}^n) + \chi(\mathfrak{p})^{-n} F(\log \mathbf{N}\mathfrak{p}^{-n})]$$

$$+ \sum_{v\in S_\infty} \frac{N_v}{2\pi} \hat{\mathfrak{q}}_v(F_v),$$

where $F_v(x) = F(x)e^{-i\varphi_v x}$ and $\hat{\mathfrak{q}}_v$ is a functional to be described in §5.

If one takes for F the function

$$F(x) = \begin{cases} 0 & \text{if } x < 0 \text{ or } x > \log y \\ e^{x/2} & \text{if } 0 < x < \log y \end{cases}$$

for some fixed number $y > 1$, then one recovers a classical formula as in Ingham, Chapter IV. We leave the exact statement to the reader. Observe that conditions (A) and (B) are obviously satisfied, and that in the sum taken over $\mathfrak{p}$, n only the terms with positive powers of $\mathfrak{p}$ will appear.

§4. *Evaluation of the sum: First part*

In our explicit formula, the term with δ_χ arises in the obvious fashion from the definition of $\Phi(0)$ and $\Phi(1)$.

For the others, we use the identity

$$d\log\Lambda = d\log G_0 + d\log L + \sum_{v\in S_\infty} d\log G_v$$

and compute our two integrals successively for the three cases.

Take first the case of G_0. We have

$$\frac{d}{ds}\log G_0(s) = \log A, \qquad \frac{d}{ds}\log G_0(1-s) = -\log A.$$

In view of the fact that we integrate a holomorphic function, we can shift both integrals to the line $\sigma = \frac{1}{2}$, and combine them into the integral

$$\frac{2\log A}{2\pi i}\int_{1/2-iT}^{1/2+iT} \Phi(s)\,ds.$$

We make the substitution $s = \frac{1}{2} + it$, $ds = idt$, and take the limit for $T \to \infty$. The Fourier inversion formula is applicable, and we find the desired expression $2F(0)\log A$ as an answer.

We take up next the case of the integrals over $d\log L$. We look first at the integral on the line $1 + a$. A trivial computation yields the value

$$\frac{-1}{2\pi}\int_{-T}^{+T} dt \sum \int_{-\infty}^{+\infty} H^{+}_{\mathfrak{p},n}(u)e^{itu}\,du,$$

where

$$H^{+}_{\mathfrak{p},n}(u) = \frac{\log \mathbf{N}\mathfrak{p}}{\mathbf{N}\mathfrak{p}^{n/2}}\chi(\mathfrak{p})^n F(u + \log \mathbf{N}\mathfrak{p}^n)e^{(1/2+a)u}.$$

If we now use the fact that there is a constant C such that

$$|F(x)| \leqq Ce^{-(1/2+b)|x|},$$

we get by a trivial estimate:

$$|H^{+}_{\mathfrak{p},n}(u)| \leqq \frac{2C\log \mathbf{N}\mathfrak{p}}{\mathbf{N}\mathfrak{p}^{n(1+a)}}.$$

This shows that our series $\sum H^{+}_{\mathfrak{p},n}(u)$ is absolutely, uniformly convergent and defines a function $H^{+}(u)$ in L^1.

A similar computation for the integral on the line $-a$, and estimate for

$$H^{-}_{\mathfrak{p},n}(u) = \frac{\log \mathbf{N}\mathfrak{p}}{\mathbf{N}\mathfrak{p}^{n/2}}\chi(\mathfrak{p})^{-n} F(u - \log \mathbf{N}\mathfrak{p}^n)e^{-(1/2+a)u}$$

yields a similar series. We put $H_{\mathfrak{p},n}(u) = H^{+}_{\mathfrak{p},n}(u) + H^{-}_{\mathfrak{p},n}(u)$. Interchanging a series and integral sign, we find that our integrals over $d\log L$ are equal to

$$\frac{-1}{2\pi}\int_{-T}^{+T} dt \int_{-\infty}^{\infty} H(u)e^{itu}\,du.$$

Since $H(u)$ is continuous and continuously differentiable except at the points $\alpha_i \pm \log \mathbf{N}\mathfrak{p}^n$ where it and its derivative have discontinuities of first kind (remember that there is only a finite number of α_i), and since $H(u)$ takes on the middle values at these discontinuities, it follows that the Fourier inversion formula applies, and hence our integral has a limit as T goes to infinity, namely $-H(0)$. This gives precisely the desired sum over $\mathfrak{p}$, n in our explicit formula.

§5. *Evaluation of the sum: Second part*

We now come to the last term.

We have to compute each integral over $d \log G_v$. We observe that G'_v/G_v has no pole in the half-plane $\sigma > 0$ and is $O(\log |t|)$ in any given strip, outside neighborhoods of its poles. Consequently, the integral taken from $1 + a - iT$ to $1 + a + iT$ is congruent to the integral taken from $\frac{1}{2} - iT$ to $\frac{1}{2} + iT$ mod $o(1)$. By the same type of argument, flipping s into $1 - s$, we can replace the integral on the line $-a$ by a similar integral on the line $\frac{1}{2}$. Thus our integrals become:

$$\frac{1}{2\pi i}\int_{1/2-iT}^{1/2+iT} \Phi(s)[d \log G_v(s, \chi) - d \log G_v(1 - s, \chi^{-1})]. \tag{1}$$

Writing down explicitly the definitions of G_v, we find that our integral is equal to

$$\frac{N_v/2}{2\pi i}\int_{1/2-iT}^{1/2+iT} \Phi(s)\left[\Gamma'/\Gamma\left(\frac{N_v(s + i\varphi_v) + |m_v|}{2}\right)\right.$$
$$\left. + \Gamma'/\Gamma\left(\frac{N_v(1 - s - i\varphi_v) + |m_v|}{2}\right)\right] ds,$$

and making a change of variables, letting $s = \frac{1}{2} + it - i\varphi_v$, with $ds = idt$, we get

$$\frac{N_v/2}{2\pi}\int_{-T}^{+T} \Phi(\tfrac{1}{2} + it - i\varphi_v)[\Gamma'/\Gamma(z) + \Gamma'/\Gamma(\bar{z})]\, dt, \tag{2}$$

where $z = \frac{1}{2}(N_v(\frac{1}{2} + it) + |m_v|)$.

Let

$$\psi_v(t) = \Phi(\tfrac{1}{2} + it - i\varphi_v)$$

and

$$F_v(x) = F(x)e^{-i\varphi_v x}.$$

Then, using the usual change of variables, we get

$$\psi_v(t) = \int_{-\infty}^{+\infty} F_v(x)e^{itx}\,dx,$$

and the function F_v satisfies conditions (A) and (B).

We define the function

$$\text{Ч}_v(t) = \operatorname{Re}\Gamma'/\Gamma\left(\frac{N_v(\frac{1}{2}+it)+|m_v|}{2}\right).$$

We can then rewrite our last integral (2) in the form

$$(3) \qquad \frac{N_v}{2\pi}\int_{-T}^{T} \psi_v(t)\text{Ч}_v(t)\,dt.$$

Since $\psi_v(t)$ is $O(1/|t|)$ for $|t| \to \infty$, it is in $\mathfrak{L}_2$. But from Stirling's formula,

$$\text{Ч}_v(t) = \log|t| + g_v(t),$$

where g_v is in $\mathfrak{L}_2$. Hence we cannot apply Plancherel's formula directly, nor take the integral from $-\infty$ to $+\infty$ without a specific convergence proof, and a justification of a generalized Plancherel formula to the special situation facing us.

We shall prove eventually that

$$\lim_{T\to\infty}\int_{-T}^{T} \psi_v(t)\text{Ч}_v(t)\,dt$$

exists. For this, we need some considerations of functional analysis.

For the sequel, we agree that

$$\int_{-\infty}^{\infty} = \lim_{T\to\infty}\int_{-T}^{+T}.$$

We shall also refer to Schwartz's book *Theorie des Distributions* by the symbol TD.

We consider the linear space of functions which are bounded, continuous, and satisfy a Lipshitz condition uniformly on every compact subset of the real line. Such functions will be called BCL.

The linear space generated by these functions and characteristic functions of intervals which do not have 0 as endpoint will be called the space of functions which are *almost* BCL. Such functions are then always continuous at 0.

On the space of almost BCL functions, we define a functional W by the limit:

$$W(\beta) = \lim_{\lambda \to \infty} \left[\int_{-\infty}^{\infty} \frac{1 - e^{-\lambda|x|}}{|e^{x/2} - e^{-x/2}|} \beta(x)\, dx - 2\beta(0) \log \lambda \right].$$

Of course, we must prove:

Lemma 3. *On the space of almost BCL functions, the preceding limit exists.*

Proof. In a neighborhood of 0, the denominator

$$|e^{x/2} - e^{-x/2}|$$

behaves like $|x|$ (mod x^2). It will then suffice to prove our assertion when we replace this denominator by $|x|$ and β by a function which tends rapidly to 0 at infinity.

Using linearity, consider first the case of a characteristic function. If the origin does not lie in its interval, then the limit clearly exists. If the origin lies in the interval, then we are led to consider an integral of type

$$\varphi(\lambda) = \int_0^b \frac{(1 - e^{-\lambda x})}{x}\, dx, \qquad b > 0, \quad \lambda \geqq 1.$$

We can differentiate under the integral sign, and taking $b = 1$ for simplicity, we get

$$\varphi'(\lambda) = \frac{1}{\lambda} - \frac{e^{-\lambda}}{\lambda}.$$

Hence $\varphi(\lambda) = \log \lambda +$ an integral which converges for $\lambda \to \infty$. From this it is clear that the term $2\beta(0) \log \lambda$ will cancel, and leave an integral whose limit exists as $\lambda \to \infty$.

Next, suppose that β is BCL and tends rapidly to 0 at infinity. Decomposing β into its odd and even parts, and subtracting a characteristic function we may assume that β is even and $\beta(0) = 0$. In that case, $\beta(x)/|x|$ is bounded in some neighborhood of the origin, and hence the integral

$$\int_{-\infty}^{\infty} (1 - e^{-\lambda|x|}) \frac{\beta(x)}{|x|}\, dx$$

has a limit as $\lambda \to \infty$. The term involving $2\beta(0) \log \lambda$ is 0, and so our assertion is proved in that case.

Let β be a BCL function. If we write

$$\beta(x) = \beta(x) - \beta(0) + \beta(0),$$

we obtain by linearity

$$W(\beta) = \beta(0)W(1) + \int_{-\infty}^{+\infty} \frac{\beta(x) - \beta(0)}{|e^{x/2} - e^{-x/2}|}\, dx.$$

There is no convergence problem about this last integral, and thus we find:

Lemma 4. *If β is a BCL function, then*

$$|W(\beta)| \leqq C(|\beta| + \mathrm{lip}_1\, \beta),$$

where C is a fixed constant, and $\mathrm{lip}_1\, \beta$ *is a Lipshitz constant on some compact interval containing* 0.

The above lemma allows us to prove a continuity property for our functional W, namely:

Lemma 5. *Let $\{\beta_n\}$ be a sequence of BCL functions, converging to a BCL function β. Assume also that the functions $\{\beta_n\}$ are uniformly bounded, that the convergence is uniform on every compact set, and that the Lipshitz constants* $\mathrm{lip}\, \beta_n$ *are bounded on every compact set. Then $W(\beta_n)$ converges to $W(\beta)$.*

Proof. We write for each n,

$$\beta_n(x) = \beta_n(x) - \beta_n(0) + \beta_n(0).$$

Then $\beta_n(0)$ converges to $\beta(0)$. This reduces the proof to considering the sum of the integrals

$$\int \frac{\beta_n(x) - \beta_n(0)}{|e^{x/2} - e^{-x/2}|}\, dx$$

over intervals

$$A \leqq |x|$$
$$\epsilon \leqq |x| \leqq A$$
$$|x| \leqq \epsilon$$

taking $\epsilon > 0$ small and A large. For A large, the exponential function in the denominator makes the integral small. For ϵ small, the last integral has a small value in view of the uniform bound for the Lipshitz constants. The integral in the middle range is then close to the corresponding integral for $\beta(x) - \beta(0)$. Thus our lemma is clear.

Let β be as before. If y is any number, we denote by β_y the function given by $\beta_y(x) = \beta(x + y)$. Then by what we said above, the function $W(\beta_y)$ is continuous (as a function of y).

Let $\{\rho_n\}$ be a sequence of regularizing functions, i.e. infinitely differentiable $\geqq 0$, with compact support shrinking to 0, and whose integral is equal to 1. We can form the convolution $\beta * \rho_n$, and it is easily verified that the sequence of functions $\{\beta * \rho_n\}$ converges to β in the sense of the additional assumptions of Lemma 5 for this convergence.

For any function β, we denote by β^- the function

$$\beta^-(y) = \beta(-y).$$

Then we obtain:

Lemma 6. *Let $\{\rho_n\}$ be a regularizing family as above. Then the functions $W((\beta * \rho_n)^-{}_x)$ converge to $W(\beta^-{}_x)$ uniformly on every compact set.*

From this we conclude:

Lemma 7. *The functional W is a distribution. Let β be a BCL function. The convolution of W with T_β (the distribution represented by β) is represented by the function whose value at x is $W(\beta^-{}_x)$. Symbolically,*

$$(W * T_\beta)(x) = W(\beta^-{}_x).$$

This function is continuous.

Proof. If T is a distribution, which is represented outside some compact set by a function tending exponentially to 0 at infinity, and α is a C^∞-function which is bounded, then by the theory of distributions, one knows that

$$T * T_\alpha$$

is represented by the function $T(\alpha^-{}_x)$, which has a meaning in this case. We can apply this result to the functions $\beta * \rho_n$, and hence our lemma follows. [Cf. TD, Theorem XI of Chapter VI, §4 and formula (VI, 1; 2).]

We shall now prove the analogue of Lemma 7 for almost BCL functions.

Lemma 8. *Let χ be a characteristic function of an interval which does not have 0 as its endpoints. Then the distribution $W * T_\chi$ is represented by a C^∞-function locally at every point other than the endpoints of the interval, and its value at such a point x is the value $W(\chi^-{}_x)$.*

Proof. This follows from the general properties of convolutions of distributions, e.g. TD, Chapter VI, Theorem III of §3 and Theorem XI of §4.

Corollary. *Let F be a function which is almost BCL, and is continuous at 0. Then the distribution $W * T_F$ is represented by a C^∞-function locally at every point other than the points of discontinuity of F, and the value of* *this function at* 0 *is*

$$W(F^-).$$

We now come to more specific considerations concerning the gamma function.

From its Weierstrass product, one gets (in every book on the gamma function)

$$\Gamma'/\Gamma(z) = -\frac{1}{z} - \gamma + \sum_{n=1}^{\infty}\left[\frac{1}{n} - \frac{1}{n+z}\right].$$

Substituting $z = \frac{1}{2} + it$ and taking the real part, together with the limit

$$\gamma = \lim_{M\to\infty}\left(1 + \cdots + \frac{1}{M} - \log M\right)$$

we obtain at once

$$\begin{aligned} \text{Ч}(t) &= \lim_{M\to\infty}\left[\log M - \sum_{n=0}^{M}\frac{n+\frac{1}{2}}{(n+\frac{1}{2})^2+t^2}\right] \\ &= \lim_{M\to\infty} \text{Ч}_M(t), \end{aligned}$$

denoting by Ч_M the function inside the brackets.

Lemma 9. *The convergence of this limit is uniform on every compact set. Furthermore*

$$|\text{Ч}_M(t)| \leqq C \log|t|$$

for some constant C *independent of* M, *and say* $|t| \geqq 2$.

Proof. The first assertion is clear. As to the second, observe that the sum in the expression for Ч_M is bounded from below by

$$\frac{n+\frac{1}{2}}{(n+\frac{1}{2})^2+t^2} \leqq \frac{1}{n+\frac{1}{2}}.$$

Say $t > 0$. For $M \leqq t$ the expression for Ч_M is bounded by $\log M \leqq \log t$. For $M \geqq t$, we observe:

$$\sum_{n=0}^{M} \geqq \sum_{n=t}^{M} \geqq \log M - \log t - \text{constant},$$

which gives us again what we want.

For the rest of this section, we agree to normalize the Fourier transform as follows. For suitable functions f, we define

$$\hat{f}(t) = \int_{-\infty}^{+\infty} f(x)e^{-itx}\,dx.$$

We also denote by $\langle\ ,\ \rangle$ the integral of the product of the two functions appearing in the blank space of this scalar product, whenever the integral makes sense. Then formally (for a restricted class of functions f, g), the **Plancherel formula** asserts that

$$\langle \hat{f}^{-}, g\rangle = \langle f, \hat{g}\rangle.$$

(The Fourier inversion formula would read

$$\hat{\hat{f}} = 2\pi f^{-}.)$$

By **Fourier transform** we shall mean $\hat{f}$ in the above sense, from now on. The Fourier transform of a function

$$\frac{a}{a^2 + t^2}$$

can be found easily by integrating over a semicircle (upper or lower according as $x < 0$ or $x > 0$). Hence if we write

$$\text{Ч}_M = \log M + g_M,$$

then we find

$$\hat{g}_M(x) = -\pi\,\frac{(1 - e^{-M|x|})}{|e^{x/2} - e^{-x/2}|}\,.$$

In the sense of distributions, the Fourier transform of the constant function 1 is

$$\hat{1} = 2\pi\delta,$$

where δ is the functional $\delta(f) = f(0)$. From these considerations, we obtain:

Lemma 10. *As a distribution,*

$$\hat{T}_{\text{Ч}} = \hat{\text{Ч}} = -\pi W.$$

Proof. The boundedness condition of Lemma 9 insures that the limit of the Fourier transforms is the Fourier transform of the limit. (Use TD, Example 3 of Chapter VII, §7.)

Our goal is to prove:

Proposition 4. *Let F be a function satisfying properties* (A) *and* (B). *Let*

$$\psi = \hat{F}^{-}.$$

Then $\langle \psi, \text{Ч} \rangle$ exists, and

$$\langle \psi, \text{Ч} \rangle = \lim_{M \to \infty} \langle F, \hat{\text{Ч}}_M \rangle,$$

or by what we have just seen, it is equal to $-\pi W(F)$.

Proof. Writing F as a sum of an even function and an odd function, i.e.

$$F(x) = \frac{F(x) + F(-x)}{2} + \frac{F(x) - F(-x)}{2},$$

has the same effect on the Fourier transform. Thus it suffices to prove our proposition for even and odd functions separately. But $\text{Ч}(t)$ is even. Thus for odd functions F, the integral $\langle \psi, \text{Ч} \rangle$ is 0. The limit on the right is also equal to 0 (each term being 0) and so our assertion is trivial.

We may therefore assume from now on that F is even. In particular, F is continuous at the origin.

We shall now prove the assertion of Proposition 4 for a more general type of function. Namely, we assume that F satisfies the following conditions:

(i) F is almost BCL, and is even.

(ii) F is in $\mathcal{L}_2$, it is differentiable except at its points of discontinuity, and its derivative is in $\mathcal{L}_2$.

Any even function satisfying conditions (A) and (B) also satisfies conditions (i) and (ii).

Lemma 11. *Denoting as usual by T_f the distribution represented by a function f, we have*

$$\hat{T}_{\psi\text{Ч}} = \hat{T}_{\text{Ч}} * T_F.$$

Proof. This follows from the theory of distributions, and hypotheses (i) and (ii), because W decreases rapidly and T_f is tempered (*TD*, Theorem XV of Chapter VII, §8).

We have seen in Lemmas 7 and 8 that $W * T_F$ is represented by a continuous function outside of the points where F is not continuous.

Writing $F = \beta + \sum \chi_i$ as a sum of a function β which is BCL, and characteristic functions of intervals, and using condition (ii), we can conclude that ψ has an expression:

$$\psi(t) = \sum_{\nu} c_{\nu} \frac{\sin a_{\nu} t}{t} + \frac{h(t)}{t},$$

where c_{ν}, a_{ν} are constants, $\pm a_{\nu} \neq 0$, and h is in $\mathcal{L}_2$.

Since the product of two functions in $\mathcal{L}_2$ is in $\mathcal{L}_1$, we conclude that

$$\psi(t)\text{Ч}(t) = \sum_{\nu} c_{\nu} \frac{\sin a_{\nu} t}{t} \log |t| + k(t)$$

where $k(t)$ is in $\mathcal{L}_1$.

Each function

$$\frac{\sin a_{\nu} t}{t} \log |t|$$

(say for $t > 0$) oscillates as t tends to infinity. From this we conclude that the limit

$$\lim_{T \to \infty} \int_{-T}^{+T} \psi(t)\text{Ч}(t)\, dt$$

exists. (This has the same convergence as an alternating series whose terms decrease to 0 monotonically.)

We can compute the Fourier transform of $\psi\text{Ч}$ (as a function) by the integral

$$\int_{-\infty}^{+\infty} \psi(t)\text{Ч}(t) e^{-itx}\, dt,$$

applying the integral separately to $k(t)$ and to each term

$$\sin a_{\nu} t \, \frac{\log |t|}{t},$$

provided $x \neq \pm a_{\nu}$ for any ν (because under this hypothesis, the convergence is uniform in a neighborhood of x). Thus this Fourier transform is a continuous function, defined outside the points a_{ν}.

The function $\psi\text{Ч}$ also represents a distribution $T_{\psi\text{Ч}}$ whose Fourier transform (as a distribution) is given by Lemma 11. We also have:

Lemma 12. *Let f be the function $\psi\text{Ч}$. Except at $\pm a_{\nu}$, $\hat{T}_f$ is represented by the continuous function given by the integral*

$$\int_{-\infty}^{+\infty} f(t) e^{-itx}\, dt.$$

Proof. Let A be a compact interval, $-T \leqq t \leqq T$, and let f_A be the function f multiplied by the characteristic function of A. Our statement is true if we replace f by f_A. Hence T_{f_A} approaches T_f as a tempered distribution, and consequently, $\hat{T}_{f_A}$ approaches $\hat{T}_f$ also as a tempered distribution, hence as a distribution locally at each $x \neq \pm a_\nu$. But the integral expressing $\hat{T}_{f_A}$ converges to

$$\int_{-\infty}^{+\infty} f(t)e^{-itx}\,dt$$

uniformly (hence as a distribution) on every compact set not containing the $\pm a_\nu$. Hence $\hat{T}_f$ is represented by this integral in the desired range.

Now the two distributions $\hat{T}_{\psi Ч}$ and $\hat{T}_Ч * \hat{T}_F$ are continuous functions in the complement of a finite number of points, given by integrals, and are equal as distributions (Lemma 11). Hence these continuous functions are equal almost everywhere, and hence everywhere. In particular, they are equal at 0. Using the Corollary of Lemma 8, we conclude the proof of Proposition 4.

The arguments which have been carried out above for the function $Ч(t)$ could just as well be carried out for $Ч_v$, carrying throughout the parameters N_v, $|m_v|$. For this purpose, we define the functional

$$W_v(\beta) = \lim_{\lambda\to\infty}\left[\int_{-\infty}^{\infty}(1 - e^{-\lambda|x|})K_v(x)\beta(x)\,dx - 2\beta(0)\log\lambda\right],$$

where $K_v(x)$ is the function given by the formulas:

$$K_v(x) = \frac{e^{(\frac{1}{2}-|m_v|)|x|}}{|e^x - e^{-x}|} \qquad \text{if } N_v = 1$$

$$K_v(x) = \frac{e^{-\frac{1}{2}|m_v x|}}{|e^{x/2} - e^{-x/2}|} \qquad \text{if } N_v = 2.$$

The same type of computation that gave us the Fourier transform of $Ч(t)$ gives us the Fourier transform of $Ч_v$, and one obtains:

Lemma 13. *The Fourier transform of $Ч_v$ is given by*

$$\hat{Ч}_v = -\frac{2\pi}{N_v}W_v.$$

Putting everything together, we obtain:

Proposition 5. *The last sum in the explicit formula is equal to*

$$\sum_{v\in S_\infty}\frac{N_v}{2\pi}\hat{Ч}_v(F_v) = -\sum_{v\in S_\infty}W_v(F_v).$$

Bibliography

[1] E. Artin, *Algebraic numbers and algebraic functions,* Lecture notes by I. Adamson, Gordon and Breach, New York, 1967.

[2] ———, *Theory of algebraic numbers,* Notes by G. Wurges, translated by G. Striker, Göttingen, 1956.

[3] E. Artin and J. Tate, *Class Field Theory,* Benjamin, New York, 1967.

[4] Z. Borevich and I. Shafarevich, *Number Theory,* Academic Press, New York, 1966.

[5] N. Bourbaki, *Commutative Algebra,* Hermann, Paris, 1962.

[6] R. Brauer, "On the zeta-functions of algebraic number fields II," *Am. J. Math.* **72** (1950), 739–746.

[7] J. W. Cassels and A. Frohlich, *Algebraic Number Theory,* Proceedings of the Brighton Conference, Academic Press, New York, 1968.

[8] H. Hasse, "Bericht uber Neuere Untersuchungen und Probleme aus der Theorie der algebraischen Zahlkorper," *Jahresbericht D. Math. Ver.*, 1926, 1927, and 1930.

[9] H. Hasse, *Vorlesungen uber Klassenkorpertheorie,* Marburg notes, reprinted by Physica Verlag, 1967.

[10] D. Hilbert, "Die Theorie der algebraischen Zahlkörper," *Jahresbericht D. Math. Ver.* **4** (1897), 175–546.

[11] E. Landau, *Einfuhrung in die elementare und analytische Theorie der algebraischen Zahlen und der ideale,* Chelsea, New York, 1949.

[12] J. P. Serre, *Corps Locaux,* Hermann, Paris, 1963.

[13] J. Tate, *Fourier analysis in number fields and Hecke's zeta function,* Thesis, Princeton, 1950, also appears in [7].

[14] A. Weil, *Sur les "formules explicites" de la théorie des nombres premiers,* Comm. Séminaire Math. Université de Lund (dédié a M. Riesz) (1952) pp. 252–265.

[15] A. Weil, *Basic Number Theory,* Springer Verlag, New York, 1968.

Index

ABCDE79876543210